Praise

"Portia writes with the cynical and biting humor...

The basic gist goes like this: regular, healthy, normal people (read: non-lawyers) don't realize what a dysfunctional mess the legal system is, how much it is going to negatively disrupt their life, and how little they are ever going to get out of it.

It's like gambling ... but no fun, way more expensive, and somehow less morally worthwhile for society.

Lawyers, however, are intimately aware of how worthless the system is, and thus will not use it to pursue you if you...even if you don't pay them.

It's kinda eye opening.

If you're a civilian who's about to encounter any form of "civil" litigation in the near future...it makes a pretty winning case for why you shouldn't." AMAZON Reader Number 13

"...an engaging narrative style that, at times, almost humanizes lawyers." AMAZON Reader Number 12

"... brought back memories and ... made me laugh and feel your pain." AMAZON Reader Number 14

"I hope that none of my clients ever read this book"

ALSO BY PORTIA PORTER

Beaver vs. Beaver (Family Court, book 1)

Alienation of Affections (Family Court, book 2)

CAN YOU STIFF YOUR DIVORCE LAWYER?

TALES OF HOW CUNNING CLIENTS CAN GET FREE LEGAL WORK, AS TOLD BY AN EXPERIENCED DIVORCE ATTORNEY

PORTIA PORTER

CHEETAH PRESS

Published in the United States by Cheetah Press
Jacket art by Jean-Honoré Fragonard
Logo art by DolphyDolphiana
CHEETAH PRESS™ and the portrayal of two cheetahs with a book
are trademarks of Cheetah Press

Library of Congress Registration Number TXu 1-995-455
Porter, Portia
Can You Stiff a Divorce Lawyer? (Tales of How Cunning Clients
Can Get Free Legal Work, as Told by an Experienced Divorce Attorney)
visit www.porterbooks.com for updates
ISBN   13 978-0-9975555-2-3
e-book ISBN 978-0-9975555-0-9

Manufactured in the United Stated of America
10 9 8 7 6 5 4 3 2
First Edition 2016

For Valentina

Table of Contents

A Note From Portia

THIS BOOK IS INSPIRED by people who stiff divorce lawyers.

It was written by a divorce lawyer who learned what is in these pages through painful experience. Really!

For folks who might think about stiffing their lawyer, this book lays out the hows and the whys, the dos and the don'ts, and the many traps to avoid. To avoid what? Answer: to avoid inadvertently screwing up your own case while trying to cheat your lawyer. There are stories in the book about masterfully skilled stiffers who, without causing any unintended consequential damage, succeed in bilking their lawyers out of amazing quantities of free legal services. And then there are stories of less adroit stiffers, who not only barely get anything done for themselves, but also do grievous legal harm to themselves and to innocent others. Some of these folks ignorantly and unintentionally trigger more collateral damage than a dirty bomb.

I fervently hope, dear reader, that you belong to that select, conscientious subset of the human race that would never ever nourish the slightest intent to bilk a lawyer. Even if, as you have now learned, a lawyer *can* be stiffed. Although you might not imagine yourself ever to be using any unscrupulous stiffing wiles, this book treats you to hopefully amusing—and, and many instances, probably quite surprising—lessons about How Things Really Work in the world of divorce lawyers and the people who try to cheat them. So, how did this book come to be?

My agent was puzzled.

"Stiffing?" said the Agent. "Why, that's like stealing. Who'd want to read about people stealing from their own lawyers?" asked the Agent.

"People who do not want to pay their lawyers," I countered. "So, almost *everybody*?"

"But that just confuses the reader. Who's your hero, and who's your villain? What are you, a divorce Robin Hood?!"

"You see," I said, "It's like a gas station heist. Suppose you're tending to a gas station, and . . .."

He abruptly terminated the Skype session, changed his

status to "busy," then "on medical leave," then to "no such user."

MY friends who are not lawyers couldn't understand.

"Wait just a minute! You are still a divorce lawyer, aren't you? Telling people how to stiff *yourself*? You tell people where you keep your spare house key too? That a joke?"

"You do not understand," I said, "It's a safety matter. Imagine you own a gas station, and one day . . .."

That got them talking about owning gas stations, which got them distracted from thinking about stiffing lawyers.

MY friends who *are* divorce lawyers, though, did not get distracted at all. They erupted in outrage at my proposal to betray the location of vulnerable chinks in the bill-payment armor of our profession:

"We ought to report you to the State Bar for aiding and abetting fraud," threatened my friends who are lawyers.

"It's interference with the contracts, what you are doing. You want the profession to suffer for your private amusement!"

"Listen to me," I said, "Have you read 'Getting to Yes,' in law school . . ." but they did not want to get to anything.

"You are betraying our professional guild!" complained my divorce lawyer peers, "It's an ethics breach! It's treachery! We are writing you up!"

Divorce lawyers can be a hard-headed (as well as hard-hearted) bunch.

It seemed my professional peers were seriously determined to report me, even though they at least dimly realized that what I proposed was neither unethical nor illegal. Maybe my mother was right, and my divorce lawyer friends are not, in the end, really my friends.

My mother, always dependable, said: "No, I get it. It's like . . . imagine you are minding a gas station and three masked teenagers come in and try to rob you for the thirty bucks that's in the register."

"Exactly," I said.

"And then they get all spooked and shoot the rusty rifle they dug up somewhere and smash two thousand dollars-worth of glass, and one of them shoots another in the leg, and then they all end up behind bars."

"Yep," I said. "Sort of like Donny."

"I remember Donny," said my mother. ". . . And you feel bad for these no-goodniks because they are like kids and do not know what they were doing."

I was not sure if she was still with the metaphor or actually talking about Donny. In any event, I was glad that I did not have to resort to the hopelessly careworn example of the hapless bull in the china shop.

"Right on," I said. "Donny. I wrote about him. But it's upsetting to the Union."

"Write it anyway!" she said. "People are going to stiff divorce lawyers either way; always have. This might at least guide them to do less damage to themselves? . . . Tell the Union to like it or lump it!"

Well, dear reader, although the lawyers' guild will have to lump it, I avidly hope that you *like* it.

Part One

Chapter One

Five Reasons Not To Panic

IN THESE PAGES, I am going to open your eyes to how to stiff a lawyer successfully.

Yes, a lawyer.

Doubtless to the eternal displeasure of my legal colleagues, I will tell you the tricks, all illustrated by stories based on my own experience as a divorce lawyer. You may not want to stiff your lawyer, but many people do. In any event, I daresay that you will find what follows to be both surprising and amusing. When you have no experience of stiffing lawyers, it is easy to worry about trivial matters and unlikely complications.

"This is a lawyer, after all," you might think to yourself.

"If I stiff a trained and licensed lawyer, what's to stop my legal beagle from suing me for unpaid fees and getting them? With collection costs. And penalties. And what do you call that punitive thing—triple damages?"

Do not let your imagination run amok, entertaining visions of bankruptcy court and debtor's prison. None of it will happen. Worrying about such unlikely outcomes only distracts from your real problems.

What *real problems*? We'll get to that in later pages of this book. But first, let's talk about stiffing lawyers.

Contrary to what many people think, getting away with unpaid legal bills is a relatively simple process, especially once you manage to run up the tab. At that point, nine times out of ten, the only escape plan you will need is to sit back and watch your lawyer quietly quit, never to be heard from again.

Nevertheless, it is wise to take some common-sense precautions. As a rule of thumb, do not commit crimes, such as making extortionate threats. Do not be so gratuitously obnoxious as to make your lawyer a passionate personal enemy. And do not force your lawyer to choose between economic disaster and pursuing you like the hounds of Hell. Don't write bad checks: it's a criminal offense and the local prosecutor will lock you up and demand that you cough up the money as restitution.

Don't inflame matters by boasting about your successful rip-off on Facebook or Twitter. Also, don't boast about that expensive cruise you are taking instead of paying your bills.

Lastly—and this may seem like an obvious point, except that so many of my clients insist on missing the point—don't push your lawyer into personal bankruptcy.

For instance, under no circumstances should you follow this over-the-top scenario:

First, persuade a lawyer to give you exclusive representation, promising to pay once you win.

Second, monopolize lawyers' time for two years.

Third, win a humongous chunk of cash; and,

Finally, refuse to pay because "you need the money more," now that you "are moving on with life."

This is a dangerous plan because it potentially forces your lawyer to choose between going out of business and suing you. Even for a lawyer, choosing the costs and hazards of courtroom warfare over certain personal financial ruin is a no-brainer. As I will explain below, the lawyer's potential bankruptcy is practically the only thing that will likely motivate a lawyer to pursue you relentlessly.

Definitely don't do all of the above and then rub it in by writing to the Dr. Phil show, telling him how badly you suffered and how your incredibly wonderful lawyer helped reunite you and your husband.

Similarly, don't take an oath before a judge swearing that you can—and will—pay your attorney, only to immediately turn around and stiff your attorney for big bucks. Judges who have just been lied to and dissed are far more powerful foes than attorneys.

These all seem like pretty basic rules, and it is hard to think that somebody would even do any of these crazy things. The only reason I even bring it up is because real people make all these blunders. Every one of the bad ideas on this list I've gotten from my own clients. And even among these deadbeat geniuses, I only sued one. In that case, it was the deadbeat's letters to Dr. Phil that put me over the top. The jury read about my incredible wonderfulness as related to Dr. Phil and the verdict was unanimous: the client should pay her fabulous lawyer. Stay away from writing letters to Dr. Phil; they may come back to haunt you.

So long as you are reasonably polite and somewhat sensible about the whole thing, your lawyer will likely leave you and your unpaid fees alone. I'm about to tell you why.

Does that mean you should go skipping out on your legal fees with carefree abandon except for, maybe, some pangs of conscience?

No, it does not.

Because the moment your lawyer stumbles away into the sunset starts the *real problems* I mentioned earlier: you are now without a lawyer. You are, in the jargon of the legal trade, unrepresented—and therefore reeking of vulnerability as if you were wearing a "Kick Me" sign. As soon as your spouse's lawyer gets wise to your lonely situation, the balance of your litigation will shift. That's when you will come the closest to feeling like a spy getting burned in the middle of an off-shore sting operation against a murderous warlord—there's no answer from the handler and none of your cunning technological gadgets works. Later chapters deal at length with this predicament, but we deal with the easy part first.

Portia Porter

Phew!

WHY LAWYERS RARELY SUE DEADBEAT CLIENTS

ANYONE WHO HAS TRIED to skip out on a doctor's bill knows that it's a non-starter.

Hospitals will unleash a hideous hell of ill-tempered, ill-mannered, insomniac bill collectors to inundate every waking hour of the offender's life. Mercilessly, they'll interrupt dinners, weddings, business meeting and funerals. They'll fill mailboxes with threats, and will not rest until the offender caves in—or until the offender's wages are garnished, credit is ruined, and blood pressure rises to dangerous levels.

Those who have no experience skipping on legal bills fear that lawyers will respond in the same vein as the doctors, unleashing collection agencies and lawsuits. After all, suing is what lawyers do for a living, or so goes the logic. Lawyers will be way worse than the doctors, right?

But never fear. Lawyers are not that way at all. Lawyers are so much more submissive to being stiffed.

Nine out of ten times, the stiffed lawyer will sigh, mumble a few obscenities, throw the unpaid bill into the already mountainous pile of other uncollectible and shuffle on to the next assignment.

One out of ten may show a little spunk by sending a polite email around Christmas, reminding that you were naughty. The email will point out that the invoice is eight months overdue and ask firmly for a payment—at least some payment. When most clients plain ignore the plea for payment, the matter usually just fades. No bill collectors, no mean letters. Well, possibly this slightly exaggerates the kindliness of the aggrieved lawyer's reaction—but not by much!

If you stiffed your lawyer, you need not even bother crossing to the other side of the street to avoid a confrontation. It will only take a few weeks for your image to fade from the hapless attorney's memory—you will just merge into a vast faceless crowd. Your non-payment was just another little bump in a constantly bumpy road. For once, you should celebrate being a total Nobody, too unimportant to trigger the grinding gears of bill collection.

"But what about the rich and powerful lawyers?" you may ask. "Won't they have lawyers' lawyers primed and ready to sue at a drop of a hat?" The answer is: no. Do not worry about the rich and powerful either. All lawyers—rich or barely scraping by, specializing in lowly divorces or in the Wall Street Journal front page mergers, connected on the Hill, and even those historically significant—are in pretty much the same boat here. You'll soon understand why.

Stiffing lawyers is nothing new. Even Thomas Jefferson couldn't manage to collect on his bills when he had his own law practice. Jefferson's biographer noted that Jefferson nearly starved because his clients refused to pay even modest legal fees. The clients devoutly promised to pay their debts, then proceeded to stiff the President-to-be.

Describing Jefferson's financial experience as a practicing lawyer, his biographer observed that

"... if his debtors had been forthcoming, [Jefferson] would have earned a modest living. But his debtors disappointed him, and if any earnings remained after he had paid his expenses, they were a meager reward for his labor." [Dewey]

Disappointed by his ineptitude in legal bill collections, Jefferson quit his law practice and applied his talents to an easier task—getting himself elected the Leader of the United States of America.

You may think that the future president of the United States failed with client bill collections because he was at the time a puny one-man operation, but that's not the reason either. Consider the example provided by Sullivan & Cromwell, the powerful law firm that has been in business since 1879 and has become a household name. Why is this firm considered such an eminent powerhouse?

Well, this 137-year-old mega-firm shaped not only the

law and the business, but even the geography of the Americas. Without the firm's founding partner, Mr. Cromwell, Americans would never have built the Panama Canal. Cromwell organized a revolution in Colombia, influencing in the process two United States Presidents in a row—all just to win a case for one of his clients. Presently, the firm employs roughly 800 lawyers in 12 offices in 9 countries and reports a revenue over a billion dollars. The firm's clients include Microsoft and Goldman Sachs. The firm's alumni include a former US Secretary of State and Director of the CIA.

Even among the brash New York lawyers, being on the interesting end of a demand letter sporting S&C's blue raised letters of 125 Broad return address sends chills through the veins of any litigator, as his trembling hands tear into the elegantly blue-inked envelope of Doom. S&C surely has sufficient money and hordes of fresh blood available to collect its fees. Technically, the Firm operates with the efficiency and resources of a Death Star. I say all this so you fully appreciate the significance of the Firm's approach to bill collections. A client of Sullivan and Cromwell that expresses its disappointment with an invoice, is met with this retort:

"If you don't think this is fair, pay whatever you think is fair, but then please get another firm to handle the rest of the matter for you. Don't ask us to do anything more for you." [Lisagor at 288]

As demands go, "Pay whatever you think is fair but don't come back" is hardly Darth Vader threat territory. Can you believe that such a powerful firm could be such a pussycat when it comes to collecting fees?

And this is the law firm that rejects more business than it accepts and that only accepts a new client if the partner can justify its business in a "two-page single-spaced letter" with a "total of nine subjects" of which the main criterion is wealth. (Or at least that's the rumor on the Street.) [Lisagor at 283-84]

The bottom line here?

As the policy of this powerful and prestigious law firm illustrates, only a fool of a lawyer sues non-paying clients. (In keeping with the old saying "It takes one to know one," I should know because I've done it.)

To be sure, lawyers do not write off bad debts because they have some perversely masochistic need to do free work. Like most normal people, lawyers do not enjoy forsaking vacations, worrying about late rent, working through the weekends and ignoring the needs of their families, all to save the client some playing money. Lawyers write off legal fees for one reason only: lawyers' eyes are uniquely open to the sobering reality that any litigation is a costly and dangerous road that, at best, often leads to a dead end. Unlike many other professions, lawyers are intimately familiar with the business of justice. They can tally the cost in advance. In their expert judgment, walking away is cheaper and more prudent almost every time.

If you're a lawyer, suing your clients for unpaid fees is not just a bad idea—it is a disastrous one, and who better than a lawyer can foresee the potential Parade of Horribles triggered by resort to the legal process? A lawsuit against a client will strain the lawyer's finances, foment complaints that threaten the lawyer's license to work and maybe create enough stress to cost a marriage. It will be an experience not far behind an operable cancer or getting hit by a very slowly moving vehicle. Only a reckless dunce sues his own clients. As we'll see in a minute, there is hardly any profit in such a lawsuit, either, even when the collection suit is technically successful.

Let's explore five reasons why suing a client is such a disastrous idea—even in case of a lawyer who eventually wins the lawsuit.

Imagine a lawyer whose work for the client is beyond reproach—above and beyond the call of duty. Every phone call answered same day, every page submitted to the court discussed with the client, every deadline made ahead of time. (OK, I did say "imagine" such a lawyer!) The client's only reason for non-payment is that money is better spent on the client's own wish list (client's vacation, snazzy new car, better-looking boobs, etcetera) than on the greedy lawyer. But even such a uniquely flawless lawyer would be a fool to sue the selfish deadbeat client.

THE MONEY

LAWSUITS ARE VERY, VERY EXPENSIVE. A lawyer who wishes to sue his client for unpaid fees will have to hire another lawyer to handle that lawsuit. "He who represents himself has a fool for a client."

Attorneys' fees for the full-blown lawsuit—from researching whether the law is sufficiently on your side to even allow starting the lawsuit, to the final closing argument before a jury—can easily run tens or even hundreds of thousands of dollars. Worse, the fees are dauntingly unpredictable. The range of fees itself is so large that trying to estimate the cost is almost as useless as just reading tea leaves. Spending $5,000 for attorney's fees to sue a client for unpaid attorney's fees is not out of the question and $180,000 is also completely possible. Or, in a high-stakes, bitterly litigated case, it could get up to $300,000 or more. There is no way to predict with any confidence because suing a deadbeat client opens up, not a can of worms, but a can of snakes. You will know what the lawsuit costs you only when it's over and done with.

And that's just the lawyer's fees.

But lawyer's fees are not the only expense. An attorney suing a client for fees would have to shell out money for what's known as "costs": the transcriber costs, copying costs, filing costs, subpoena costs, mediator costs, and the cost of coffee beans for those late nights that stretch into the mornings. These costs do not seem like they'd be much at first, but they can add up to many thousands of dollars.

But wait, as the pitchmen say on TV, "there's more!"

Inevitably, the client who stiffed the lawyer will respond to a suit for unpaid fees with a counter-claim lawsuit, claiming that the lawyer did a bad job and therefore doesn't deserve any payment. For strategic effect, the client might even demand a refund of what little was paid already. You may be thinking that you'd never file such a baseless counter-claim—but most clients actually do, and lawyers have come to expect it. Most clients will boldly counter-claim that their attorney was incompetent, whether the job in fact was good, excellent or outstanding.

With the lawyer suing the client and the client counter-suing the lawyer, now you have got two lawsuits combined in one. What that means for the lawyer is that all money outlays are inflated, maybe doubled. Fortunately, the lawyer's professional insurance kicks in to fight off the client's claims. But it's not all free. The immediate price of invoking the professional insurance is the deductible. That's usually in the range of $2,500 to $10,000.

But, perhaps more importantly, there's also a down-the-road cost. Just as an accident prone driver will see his insurance premiums hiked, so also will a lawsuit-prone lawyer wind up with more and more expensive premium for his professional insurance coverage.

All told, the fees and costs of a fee-collection suit may wind up topping what an average lawyer makes in a whole year. That is the worst case scenario, of course, but there's no guarantee that the worst will not happen.

But wait, there's even more. There may very well be an appeal after the trial is over. An appeal would add yet another eighteen months of fighting with all the corresponding fees and costs, before the stiffing client pays a penny. And after that, there is a (slimmer) chance of an appeal to even higher court.

And remember, we have not even started talking here about what happens if the jury does not find for the lawyer, as they might. Lawyers are not popular with the public. Then there are the cases when the jury finds for the lawyer, but the obstinate client still does not pay. There will follow a costly and perhaps fruitless process to collect the lawyer's favorable court judgment.

To an outsider, lawyers may seem like unstinting, undeterrable warriors, but they do have their limits. Most lawyers much prefer making a buck by fixing up stuff rather

14

than losing money in bitter personal battles. You know the old saying about not "throwing good money after the bad?" When you are a lawyer, hiring another lawyer to fight an ex-client is only rarely worth the expense.

One question may come to mind: if you are a lawyer yourself, why hire another lawyer at all? Why not make it a do-it-yourself project and save on those mad legal fees? One answer is, of course, that doing all the legal work necessary to properly sue former clients takes time away from the lawyer's working hours which, in turn, could be better spent making money on fresh, paying cases. Also, many lawyers have paper-shuffler practices and may not even be comfortable standing up in a courtroom with possibly an experienced and formidable trial lawyer on the opposing side. (Analogously, a urologist wouldn't feel very comfortable about entering a baby-delivering contest with a board-certified obstetrician as the competition.)

And that is not all. If a client strikes back with a grievance to the State Bar (we'll talk more about the grievance process later in the book), the unlucky lawyer would be wise to hire a separate lawyer yet who is skilled in dealing with this particularly prickly set of problems.

And that is not all, either. If the grievance progresses beyond the initial stage of "investigation," to an actual proceeding, the Bar may tax the accused lawyer with a substantial "administrative fee" for the process. The amount varies but, for instance, in North Carolina, the accused lawyer must pay to the Bar $1,500 *a day* for each day he is being tried for his alleged ethical violation. (Although the lawyer can reduce this outlay to a mere $750 by "pleading guilty" and accepting whatever punishment he is offered.) [North Carolina Assessment]

In short, collection against a non-paying client can be a very costly affair.

THE TIME

AND THEN THERE IS THE COST of lost time.

Even if the stiffed lawyer hires another lawyer to sue the former client, that does not mean the collection effort will take care of itself and the check will just show up in the mail one day, like a royalty.

Lawsuits have an insidious way of taking over one's life.

Hours will disappear in depositions, document exchanges and endless requests for information.

Litigation has a way of taking up time. It takes over thoughts, over conversations at family dinners and chats with friends. It distracts at work.

Plus, there will be no chance of getting away from the lawsuit: it constantly demands attention. Count on spending at least two hours a week in a light week, twenty in heavier weeks, and, eventually, every waking moment as the trial date draws near. Of course, it will keep you busy the whole day, every day in trial. From start to finish, the ordeal of a collection lawsuit will last 12-18 months. And then there might be the unwanted encore of an appeal—maybe another eighteen months on top of the earlier court proceeding.

CAN'T TAKE A WIN TO THE BANK

NOW LET'S SUPPOSE that the collection lawsuit yields an "as good as it gets" result for the lawyer. Fast-forward to the happy day.

The jury of Client's peers has finally spoken: the Client owes the money and must pay. The members of the jury were polled, one by one, after the foreman delivered their verdict. All twelve, one by one, rose up to repeat:

"Yes this was my verdict. Yes, this is still my verdict."

All twelve stood by their decision, shiny, unwavering, proud.

In a crushing defeat to every deadbeat client in America, the jury denounced chicanery and voted to reward the Lawyer's hard work. The Client must pay. The Lawyer won.

That was more than a verdict. It was a true testament to Truth, Justice, and The Great American Way.

After three months of stern letter demands ignored by the Client, five months spent in mandatory mediation which was thrice rescheduled and twice continued for the Client's busy schedule, after eighteen months of depositions, requests for admissions, multiple motions for summary judgment, and after four days of trial, the Lawyer is at last vindicated. The hard work and the hard stance had finally paid off. It is time to collect the due.

The faint jingle of gold could be heard in the air as the last juror trickled out of the box, satisfied with the discharge of his democratic duty. The Lawyer hugged the stenographer and cried jubilant tears.

Then the Lawyer watched the Ex-Client slink out of the courtroom, and the Lawyer's team packed twelve sets of heavy trial exhibits back into sturdy banker's boxes, preparing for the heavy roll out of the courthouse. The team's hearts were light, though. A party ensued, and the victorious Lawyer fell asleep after midnight, clutching onto his phone, so as not to miss the call confirming delivery of the long-awaited payment.

But the mornings rolled by, and, with the passing days, no call and no mail from the Ex-Client.

As the calendar pages turned, the jingle of expected money grew fainter. Finally, it became dismayingly clear: there would be no call. There would be no letter. There would be no voluntary payment. The Lawyer would have to extract the judgment by force, by yet another costly and uncertain process.

There is, indeed, a process to collect on a judgment. However, the Lawyer would not be allowed to start collecting right away. There is a waiting time before collections attempts are allowed to begin, a few more weeks of wait. Finally, those waiting weeks dragged to their end as well, and Lawyer filled out yet more paperwork at the courthouse, signed yet more forms, and made more payments of court-related fees. And finally, the sheriff was dispatched to collect.

You're kidding, right? Collect what exactly?

The victorious Lawyer was not the only one anticipating this day of reckoning. The quick-witted Ex-Client was put into high alert many moons ago, when the whole collection circus began. In the meantime, Ex-Client did not give a wink's rest to his resourceful and devious brain in search of ways to obviate the problem, to insulate his resources from any judgment.

By the time the sheriff's department was dispatched to collect, the banks that used to house chunks of Ex-Client's cash and stocks and bonds were barer than the shelves of the grocery stores before a hurricane. The sheriff flashed his badge in all five banks and discovered an overdrawn checking account and three money markets totaling twelve dollars and some lonesome pennies. After three days of honest effort, the sheriff returned with nothing. Well, not exactly nothing at all: what he had for the Lawyer was the Sheriff Department's own bill for faithful service, to add to the pile of bills for this Sue-Your-Client Operation.

Can You Stiff You Divorce Lawyer?

After the bland failure of the sheriff's collection efforts, the duped Lawyer ponied up for a private investigator. His name was Richard, but everybody called him Dick. Dick's ad in ABA Journal Classified section read:

> *Assets located.*
> *Anywhere in the world.*
> *Work Fast.*

Dick did work quickly. The Lawyer only had to wait three hours for Dick's first assessment:

"Ingenious fellow, that Client of yours," assessed Dick.

"Ex-Client," corrected the Lawyer.

"Astute and ingenious," repeated Dick. "And must've been busier than St. Nicolas on Christmas Eve."

"I'm sure I don't know what you mean, but no matter. Just go out and locate some money, please," shrugged the Lawyer and pressed into the Investigator's grip a list of Client's tangible assets, saved from three years ago, before the day when Lawyer and Client parted ways. Automobiles, jewelry, real estate, the lot.

The list of Client's resources was impressive—certainly long enough to pay off the Client's debt to his Lawyer many times over. But even more impressive was Client's ingenuity. Twenty-four hours later, Dick prepared his very short report.

There was nothing left.

Dick could've sworn it all had vanished.

Nothing in nature vanishes completely, of course, but the items on the list were, indeed, not easy to find.

The Client's real estate—all transferred to a niece twice removed who headed a corporate housing company headquartered in Montana. The niece herself had changed her name three times—twice on account of unhappy marriages, and once for personal reasons.

The county bonds—cashed out.

The jewelry—mingled inextricably into the older sister's jewelry box.

The house sold, and Client's new address a rental, albeit a high-priced rental with high ceiling and sea-salt pools.

Nothing to collect there.

Even the high-end Mercedes went absent—donated to a local charity for use with inner city youth program—thus yielding a deduction on Ex-Client's past income tax return.

To sum up, three years of fighting might have gotten Lawyer a judgment, but that was just a piece of paper. There was no cash in it yet. And maybe there never would be.

The stark truth about civil litigation is that fighting a crooked defendant is much more expensive than fighting an honest defendant. The law works fairly well against the honest people, but collecting from a deadbeat is uncertain and expensive.

You might be thinking: but all that asset hiding can't possibly be legal, there must be a law against it. And you are sort of right: the law of fraudulent transfer covers all these clever tricks. Of course, the law of fraudulent transfers does not enforce itself. Lawyer would have to sue his Ex-Client again, this time for fraudulent transfer, and start all over with the attorney's fees and transcriber fees, and subpoena fees and—this part's new—investigator's fees. Somebody has to find all those hidden assets, and that investigative job calls for tricky skills which the Lawyer's Code of Ethics does not entirely condone.

In a year or two that second suit will be over, and, if everything goes well for the Lawyer, his Ex-Client may even be ordered to something extra as so-called "punitive" damages. But, then again, lawsuits are unpredictable. It just might happen that the Ex-Client will prove that he had transferred some, or even all, of his property for some perfectly good reasons. In that case, the Lawyer gets nothing, or at least less than the judgment ostensibly granted.

Maybe you are reading this and one thought comes to mind: what does that have to do with you? You are certainly not brazen enough to hide your assets in devious arrangements, to transfer your house to a straw man and to commit bare-faced fraud.

And that's not an unreasonable point. Plenty of people who stiff their lawyers draw a line at also defrauding the courts. But then again, plenty of people don't draw that line. You know and I know that your particularly upstanding moral character would lead you to pay up if you lost the lawsuit. But here's the deal: your lawyer does not know that about you. After all, you've already had the outrageous nerve to stiff your ex-advocate. So, your track record gives good reason to think you might also have the nerve to stiff the legal system too. As the saying goes, "sometimes it pays to have a bad reputation."

Make no mistake about it: I am not suggesting you commit fraud. Not at all. All I am saying is that any lawyer who sues his client is wise to consider the cost of not one, but two arduous legal processes—one to get the verdict, another to collect the fees granted in the first verdict. And even then, there's no guarantee of collecting from a client who is stubborn, resourceful, and unscrupulous.

But even that is not all. For a lawyer suing the ex-client, the troubles do not stop with spending time and money and getting nothing in return. As I shall explain, the troubles go much deeper.

THE DEADBEATS' UNLIKELY ALLIES

SOME FOLKS just like to get something for nothing.

Dine and dash, chew and screw, skip on rent. It's human nature, at least for some humans. Whether it's a two-buck glass of beer or two hundred thousand-buck legal services, there just will always be people who want something for nothing and skip on their bills.

It's a fact of life.

Every successful industry has a plan to deal with it.

Lawyers have discovered that the best plan is this: run in the other direction from the pothole-ridden, dead end path of litigation. You are now well on the way to understanding why but the best is yet to come.

A fact of life is the one we just talked about: just about

every time a lawyer sues for unpaid invoices, the ex-client who had skipped on the bill reacts by suing the lawyer right back, for supposedly inept performance. The lawyer's suit for unpaid fees and the client's counter-suit for lawyer malpractice go hand in hand, like sunrise and sunset, or yin and yang, like a game of tennis.

Hollywood courtroom dramas touch very little on the dark world of unpaid legal fees, and there's nary an HBO drama that would zoom in on the plots and twists of a battle between a conniving client and his naive lawyer just striving to get paid. There's simply no good TV in naïve lawyers. What entertainment producer would cast naïve lawyers as the Good Guy heroes?

Because of the resulting gap in popular education, the public does not realize just how frequently tried the tactic of bringing a counter-suit against the lawyer really is. Far from being a brilliantly new twist about a rare happening, a story about a lawyer being sued is, to other lawyers, a tale that is actually about as shop-worn as "boy meets girl."

In my world, when one hears that a lawyer sued his client, one automatically asks "is there a counter-claim for malpractice *yet*?"

Two things are widely known in the legal industry about the counter-suits brought by the deadbeat clients.

First, everybody in the industry expects a suit like that.

Second, everybody expects a suit like that to be nine parts outright falsehood and one part gross exaggeration.

The repeat players of the legal industry—from judges to courtroom bailiffs—have seen these counter-suits played out time and time again. They know the score by heart. The client stiffed the unfortunate lawyer and, not wanting to pay the bill, is now strong-arming the lawyer (and the lawyer's insurance) with lies and threats. The judge, the court reporter, the lawyer, the lawyer's insurance company, even the janitor who is passing through to change out the water bottles, are all certain of that. On the other hand, if the case goes to a jury trial, the inexperienced jurors are not clued in on the nature of the game and may believe heaven-only-knows-what.

If you are the one who cheated your lawyer and are now doing the strong-arming, take heart—your lawyer is not inspiring anybody's sympathy, not even from his professional colleagues. To other attorneys, the lawyer is a fool who ought to have known enough to stay away from a hornets' nest, but marched into it anyway. Everyone with half a brain expects the bogus suit for a "bad job" to follow the legitimate suit for unpaid fees. It's like ebb and tide, like the sun rises in the morning and sets in the evening. And even though the client's bogus law suit may never succeed in the end, that bit does not much matter from the financial standpoint: there's still a cost. Fighting off a bogus suit still costs the kinds of time and money that we have already discussed.

You may be thinking: but wait a minute, aren't lawyers insured for that sort of thing? We already learned about a few drawbacks to relying on this insurance but, once the client sues, shouldn't the insurance take over litigating that fight at no further cost to the attorney?

It is tempting to say that this thinking is half-right, except that it's actually dead wrong. But we are onto something critically important here: the Insurance Company's Influence when it comes to suing clients for unpaid fees.

It is certainly true that every time a lawyer gets sued, the insurance company becomes a player. Paradoxically, this makes lawyer's insurance companies the biggest advocates of the stiffing ex-clients.

What? Insurance Companies are a friend of the stiffers?

Yes, that's exactly right. That's the way it works out in The Real World.

You see, the professional liability insurance premiums get paid regardless of whether the insured lawyer can collect from the clients. It's the same principle as your car insurance, for example. Does the car insurance company care how much you get paid at work? Of course not! Your car insurance is paid every year whether you just got fired or received a bonus. Same deal with professional liability insurance for lawyers—the premiums get collected every year regardless of whether the lawyer gets paid by his clients or gets stiffed. And guess what: if the lawyer does not need any defense, these annual insurance premiums are pure profit for the insurance company.

So what happens when a lawyer gets stiffed?

Basically, there are two ways the lawyer could go: sue the client and try to collect—or just walk away.

If the lawyer walks away, the client is unlikely to retaliate with a bogus malpractice suit. Unless the lawyer really screwed the pooch, the client who stiffed him simply disappears. That means a clear win for the insurance company: its annual premium is paid, but it does not have to lift a finger in the lawyer's defense.

On the other hand, if the lawyer adopts an inflexible stance and doggedly sues the client for unpaid fees, the bogus retaliatory "malpractice" lawsuit is almost a certainty. That means a clear loss for the insurance company: it has to pay for the lawyer's defense or, even worse, his liability as may (even wrongly) be found by a jury.

So, try and see it from the insurance company's point of view now.

If the lawyer eats his bill, it's all around good news for the insurance company. The lawyer may be out of a fee, but the insurance company gets to pocket its premiums and go back to smoking cigars and sailing its leased yachts. But if the lawyer fights the client—courageous and righteous stance though it is for the lawyer—that mulishness translates into all around bad situation for the insurance company. The thing is, this fight has some upside for the lawyer because he might get paid at least something. But for the lawyer's insurance company, there is no upside at all: even if the client eventually is made to see the error of his deadbeat ways and pays up, that is great news for the lawyer but the insurance company does not get anything extra.

For all the insurance folk care, unscrupulous clients can never pay a cent, so long as they do not sue and the insurance company is not forced to defend.

In short, the interests of the lawyer and his insurance

company diverge here. The lawyer cares that he gets paid, the insurance company does not. If the insurance company had insured the lawyer against the financial ruin, it would have cared whether the client paid. But instead, it only insures against legal malpractice—real or imagined by clients. So long as nobody screams "malpractice," the insurance does not give a hoot about anything else. Sad and cynical, but pretty much the way the world works.

Before we move on, let me answer an obvious question: what does it matter if insurance company disapproves of a fight? Why would a lawyer care about what the insurance company frowns upon or encourages?

What you need to know here is that insurance company have tremendous influence on the way most conscientious lawyers conduct their business.

But why?

There are several reasons. Some are financial. Other reasons are, believe it or not, of an emotional sort.

One thing you might not have realized about lawyers is that they do not have many people to turn to when they are truly in trouble. I am not talking about those small unpleas-antnesses when a client does not pay bills. Those are not real troubles. Those are little disappointments on the job. I am talking about big-time troubles: missing a deadline or a new regulation of the court, blowing a tire and getting late to the start of trial only to discover that the judge had dismissed the client's case, getting attacked by a vicious computer virus that wipes out an appellate brief two hours before the court's upload deadline. That sort of potentially career-ending trouble. (You will not be surprised, I trust, if I tell you that even the best of lawyers sooner or later make some worrisome misstep.)

Where can lawyers turn in that case?

Colleagues?

Even the ones who are not competitive backstabbers are often required by the rules of professional ethics to report all trouble to the State Bar. Non-reporters risk being cited for ethical violation themselves. Of course, a good friend will likely not rat, but why put a friend in this precarious position?

The State Bar?

Although the job of each state Bar nominally is to guide and keep its lawyers out of trouble, in actuality, the Bars are bureaucratic enforcers first and foremost, with somewhat arbitrary and unpredictable enforcing habits. The more lawyers are punished by the Bar's enforcing hand, the louder the Bar pats itself on the back for keeping the profession clean. So, no lawyer in his right mind would tempt Fate by willingly inviting Bar bureaucrats to poke their noses into his problematic private affairs.

Friends?

Perhaps. Assuming lawyers have friends not in the legal business who might help and are not weighted down by reporting obligations of their own professions. But non-lawyers are mostly useless for lawyers' troubles. They mostly would not understand the problem, much less know what to do about it.

In short, there are simply not a lot of people who could help a lawyer with a quandary about what is arguably a professional fault.

Except that there are the insurance company lawyers. If you are a lawyer and you have a spot of trouble, you can call your insurance company any time. There's a team assigned to you. These lawyers know the law and rules of ethics cold, they are under no obligation to rat you out, they are definitely not out to get you. In fact, they are very much on your side. In the land where everybody is either clueless or out for the errant lawyer's blood, the professional insurance company lawyers feel almost like true friends and trusted confidants. Well, sort of. You know the saying: "In the land of the blind, a one-eyed man is a prophet." At least the insurance company shares one basic desire with the lawyer—avoiding the malpractice lawsuit.

So what does that all mean for the client stiffing his lawyer?

Youpaye & Wheecover-Maybey LLC, the insurance company that for a few thousand dollars a year promises to keep us lawyers out of professional trouble, is where lawyers call for protection in time of dire need.

I am speaking from experience. With the possible exception of my mother, nobody returns my calls of distress so quickly and eagerly as my professional insurance company. With the exception of my mother and my dog, nobody is so earnestly concerned for my continued professional well-being as the good people of Youpaye & Wheecover-Maybey,

LLC. All the time. Because my continued freedom from malpractice suits translates as their continued financial advantage.

That is my experience, and it is typical for every lawyer: in a world full of gratuitous hatred, senseless envy, backstabbing and spite, Youpaye & Wheecover-Maybey, LLC malpractice insurance is my ever-illuminating torch, its flames ready to light my way. The folks of Youpaye & Wheecover-Maybey, LLC root dependably and expertly for the lawyer who hired it.

Think of what I am saying!

Even should a lawyer make a mistake and accidentally screw up somebody's case, Youpaye & Wheecover-Maybey, LLC still roots for that lawyer. It does *not* root for the injured party. And not for justice. Not for the truth. Not for the retribution and exposure of all responsible. When Youpaye & Wheecover-Maybey, LLC learns that one of its insured lawyers screwed up and lost millions for a client, it does not become indignant and sermonize about *protecting the public*. It does not get on a soapbox and pontificate about greed, carelessness, ethical violations and the necessity of reform that would immediately disbar every lawyer for as much as being a subject of a complaint. A professional insurance company is not in the business of stamping out injustice or upholding the morals of its clients and the white-knight image of the legal profession. That's not the insurance company's business. The courts and the State Bars and the internet vigilantes have got that well covered. A professional insurance company will not urge a lawyer who screwed up to confess and accept the appropriate level of punishment as a way to clean the soul. Instead, a professional insurance company will do its job, which is to protect its insured lawyers, no matter what. Not even every mother is that protective of her children. (Unless, of course, the insurance company finds some way to deny coverage and washes its hands of the problem altogether. But that's a different story.)

It is a truth universally accepted that the views of a person's allies and influencers are all excellent predictors of that person's own behavior. If you were a lawyer and you had a "foxhole friend" in your corner, wouldn't the friend's advice carry considerable weight—even in times of peace? I thought so. And the insurance company does not just snooze off during the quiet times. No, indeed! In the days when lawyers are not screwing up, and not contacting their carriers, Youpaye & Wheecover-Maybey, LLC invests in prophylactic treatments in the form of preventive education and supposedly sage advice.

When a lawyer stumbles, the insurance company is there to throw a soft worn padding of trite advice to break the fall. When a lawyer adjusts course by taking on work in hitherto unfamiliar areas, the insurance company hires and pays law-savvy guardian angels to pitch the news of every legal update or pitfall on the new course. The insurance company lures its insured lawyers with monthly free breakfasts and crams in a talk about the habits of clean living and espouses work ethics to rival Saint Benedict's. And at Christmas, the insurance company elves send every lawyer on the list (nice and naughty alike) the same toy—a nifty cardboard contraption with moving parts that slide up and down, clockwise and counterclockwise, and calculate statutes of limitations for dozens of offenses—so not one lawyer misses a deadline and gets sued.

That's the name of the game. That's the Youpaye & Wheecover-Maybey, LLC's motto: do not get sued. Whatever else you do or do not do, do not get sued!

As I go about my day in my little law firm, I feel grateful to the stalwart soldiers at Youpaye & Wheecover-Maybey, LLC who start and end their days standing guard to protect me from myself. And at the end of the year, we congratulate each other on one more 365-day stretch when no legal action was filed against me, and not one dollar of Youpaye & Wheecover-Maybey, LLC's money was spent for my defense. And as I write out the check for the next year's premium, we toast to our mutual success with goblets of twenty-four carat gold.

"To never needing your services," I toast.

"To doing no work and keeping all the premium payment," the insurance chimes in.

Professional insurance ("malpractice insurance" if you want to be crass) is mandatory for anybody who wants to practice law in most of the American States. But even if not mandatory, it is more than just a good idea. For a practicing lawyer, the two to five thousand dollars a year insurance premium is an investment in peace of mind. Without insurance, every misstep—real or imaginary—has the lawyer wondering whether today is the day he must sell all earthly possessions to pay for that one botched case, that one disaster. And trust me when I tell you that every thinking lawyer imagines that he made at least a few arguable missteps with every page of the calendar, and at least one of those worries seems a possible festering catastrophe.

Youpaye & Wheecover-Maybey, LLC and I have been together for ten years, and I have not once screwed up. Never did I miss a deadline, or forgot a cause of action, or sued the wrong defendant, or otherwise cost money to my client. At least not that I know of. Never in ten years did Youpaye & Wheecover-Maybey, LLC have to pay a red cent of damage to any client of mine. Does that mean I begrudge the thousands of dollars I paid to the coffers of Youpaye & Wheecover-Maybey, LLC? Not even in the least. It is worth the fee just for the peace of mind. For the dozens of times I dialed the company's lawyers just to confirm my course. For the speed with which it springs to my defense should there be a bogus suit.

So why do I tell you all this? Because I want you to grasp the significance of Youpaye & Wheecover-Maybey, LLC's opinions to every lawyer insured by that stalwart protector. In particular, the beliefs about suing my clients.

What do the insurance companies, who are, after all, among the lawyers' major influences, whisper into the lawyers' ears on the subject of suing clients? Now that you appreciate the importance of Youpaye & Wheecover-Maybey insurance company's opinions, you want to know, don't you?

And by jolly, Youpaye & Wheecover-Maybey, LLC does voice an opinion insistently and persuasively!

Suing clients comes up as a separate matter in every second newsletter. And then again at least twice a year, featured top center in the drill of "top five things that *will* get a lawyer sued."

Here it is, verbatim. If you want to gaze into your lawyer's soul, read this.

Know that these are the words your lawyer sees more often than you see a beer commercial:

> *"Whenever it's possible, avoid fee disputes.*
>
> *If you find yourself in the difficult situation of trying to recover an earned fee from a client who is unwilling to pay, it is strongly recommended that you do not file a lawsuit against the client for the amount of the unpaid bill.*
>
> *Fee disputes that are brought to court often result in a counterclaim by the client against the attorney, where the client alleges that the reason they didn't pay the bill is because the lawyer's legal services were negligent.*
>
> *You may know that the allegations of malpractice are baseless, and that the client is simply trying to gain leverage to negotiate a lesser fee, but the counterclaim is one that needs to be reported to your malpractice carrier, and the cost of your time and money defending the baseless claim need to be taken*

into account.

And this is the upshot of what is expected from the insured lawyer:

> *Be willing to negotiate the fee, as the cost of chasing an unpaid fee in court can be much greater.*"

Do you get the idea here? Avoid at all costs "the cost of chasing an unpaid fee in court." To say that Youpaye & Wheecover-Maybey, LLC dislikes the thought of lawyers suing clients is like saying that turkeys dislike Thanksgiving holiday dinner.

In fact, if Youpaye & Wheecover-Maybey, LLC has a choice between insuring drunks instead of sober and upstanding lawyers who "chase their unpaid fees in court," it is not even a competition: the drunks win hands down. You know how I know that? Because of the annual renewal application which reintroduces every lawyer to their insurance company through a hundred-plus questions. Each year, every lawyer answers the same questions: areas of practice, number of attorneys in the firm, corporate structure of the firm, size of the firm's clients and then the ever-important one:

> *Have you initiated lawsuits or arbitration procedures during the last two years to enforce the collection of unpaid fees?*

For those lawyers who mark the box 'yes,' a whole host

of additional questions awaits, culminating with the question that Youpaye & Wheecover-Maybey, LLC deems the most important one:

> *Have steps been taken to prevent fee suits in the future? Please provide details.*

Read these two quotes again. If I fess up to suing a client for fees, will it matter to Youpaye & Wheecover-Maybey, LLC that I was in the right? Does it matter whether my non-paying client was a total jerk or an opportunist? Does Youpaye & Wheecover-Maybey, LLC want to know just how much I lost in those unpaid fees? Or whether a suit for lawyer's fees was perfectly justified. If I won the lawsuit? Of course not! None of these questions matter in the slightest. There's only one question that really matters: Did I learn from my mistakes and do I promise to never sue a client again? Can I prove I'll never sue?

Meanwhile, do you know what Youpaye & Wheecover-Maybey, LLC wants to know about my weekly alcohol intake? Maybe I down a six-pack each evening, or dabble with crack?

Here are a few questions the malpractice insurance *does not* ask its insured lawyers:

> *Do you drink?*
> *If yes, do you black out?*
> *If you black out, do you black out legal statutes and caselaw, or just the facts of life?*
> *Your life or your clients?*

Do you get sober by daylight?
Do you dry out for your court appearances?
If not, have the judges started commenting on it?
Do you drink at lunch?
If yes, do you take your lunch between the court sessions or right at the counsel's desk?
Would you submit to a random drug test?

If Youpaye & Wheecover-Maybey, LLC cared to know, it would not have been out of its character to pry a little: the annual renewal application asks a dozen pages worth of questions and requires stacks of documents in proof of all the answers. It even wants to see a copy of the lawyer's letterhead and a copy of the lawyer's form contract with prospective clients. When Youpaye & Wheecover-Maybey, LLC cares about something in the lawyer's life, it is not shy about demanding every mind-blowing and excruciating detail. If it does not ask me for details of my alcohol or drug intake, there is only one reason: it does not care to know.

Plainly, the lawyers' big influencer—their insurance company—hates lawyers who sue for unpaid fees much more than the drunks, the druggies, the lazy and the uninformed. Possibly it hates lawsuits for unpaid fees even more than class action work. You get the idea, right?

Is it any wonder that the rational lawyers decide to "take a hint" and forgive the unpaid fees rather than become embroiled in a lawsuit?

By the way, if the lawyer decides to act irrationally and refuses to take that hint, Youpaye & Wheecover-Maybey,

LLC is not without resources to spell out its message.

The insurance company has many ways of expressing its disappointment and tell the lawyer like it is.

First comes a mile of paperwork to fill out, then an increase of annual insurance premium and, finally, the lawyer will get dropped and quickly discover that every other insurance company is onto him, and won't insure. After a week of hasty searches, a very shady agent will appear out of nowhere and suggest an out-of-state C-rated insurance enterprise nobody ever heard of before. The C-rated insurance will agree to take on the risk, but there will be a catch.

Several catches, actually. The premium will surge to four times the usual rate. Non-refundable. The entire annual fee upfront. The deductible will grow to the size of most people's monthly salary. And, most intriguingly, there will be a separate rider, an exclusion to the policy, naming every client whom the lawyer ever sued and who sued the lawyer back. Any litigation involving these folks will not be covered.

So what does that mean for you, the client contemplating stiffing a lawyer?

In addition to the threat to quadruple the lawyers' insurance cost, you have the power to put the lawyer personally at risk. That means that after your original bogus lawsuit is tossed out of court and you decide to bring yet another bogus lawsuit, you just might catch the hapless lawyer uncovered by his new insurance. The lawyer is now on his own to defend himself, the new insurance company is not getting involved, not defending against you, not for any toffees. You are in the rider, named personally as an exclusion. Do you, deadbeat client, understand what a great bargaining advantage you have been handed by that exclusion? The lawyer is now personally at risk for any suits filed by you!

To be sure, bringing a barrage of bogus lawsuits is inadvisable, and I suggest you restrain from doing that. It would be wrong, very wrong. But the important point is that your lawyer has no way of knowing that you will exercise restraint, and he is wise to act cautiously in the extreme.

As I said before, you might not win that bogus lawsuit of yours, but your lawyer will lose for sure. And your lawyer will be scared of you, more scared than you realized before I explained the lay of the land to you.

For a lawyer who stubbornly insists on suing his client for unpaid fees, the parade of horribles is not over yet. We talked about the colossal losses of money and time, embarrassing and costly loss of insurance coverage, but all that is child's play compared to the even scarier problems that await the lawyer.

THE GRIEVANCES

EVERY PRACTICING LAWYER IN AMERICA is a member of the lawyer's professional union colloquially known among the lawyers as "The Bar," officially known as The Alabama State Bar, or The Illinois State Bar, or, in my case, the South Duck State Bar.

By law, this Bar membership is mandatory if you want to actually practice law: a non-member cannot argue in court, cannot give legal advice, cannot sign documents in court. Getting a law school degree and passing the bar examination are all largely worthless until one applies to become a card-carrying member of the Bar, and is accepted after a thorough review of his entire life.

Once the lawyer does become its member, the Bar starts

to tax and regulate him.

As part of its regulating activities, the Bar watches over every step of the lawyers' daily work—from the exact type of bank accounts lawyers must use (lawyers can only use the banks that agree to collect all the interest on the clients' retainers and send the collected funds to the State Bar for the Bar's own use) to what lawyers name their firms (ever wondered why law firms never dare call themselves anything descriptive, like "Most Awesome Lawyers of Chicago"? It's not that no lawyer has never thought of it. It's that the Bar punishes names like that severely).

The Bar controls how lawyers get paid (in some cases, working on a percentage "contingency fee" is punishable even if that's what the client wants) and how lawyers pay their own staff (it's fine to pay the paralegals a salary, but paying a percentage is punishable). The many rules and regulations of the Bar are not unchanging either. Every month, the State Bar staff adds and alters and tweaks the rules. Dozens of new rules come out. What used to be allowed may newly become prohibited.

A lawyer who misses one of these new rules or slips up on an old rule can look forward to being pushed back in line by the Bar's disciplinary arm. This "discipline" can range from mild "admonition" ("don't do it again") to "reprimand" (a black mark that permanently damages the lawyer's professional reputation, but does not stop him from working) to "disbarment," which takes away the lawyer's right to practice law—sometimes permanently, other times for a few years, until the Bar possibly decides to forgive the lawyer.

Can You Stiff You Divorce Lawyer?

Every lawyer—honest or crooked, young or old, successful or struggling on the verge of personal bankruptcy—lives in constant terror of his State Bar. And with good reason: every lawyer's license is valid essentially at the pleasure of the Bar's bureaucrats.

I am telling you all this because the daily terror of impending Bar investigation is an overriding influence over each lawyer's every decision. It is always in the thoughts of every lawyer. So what does all that have to do with the lawyers' decision to forgive their clients' unpaid bills? Everything! It is crucial!

Remember our discussion earlier in this book about potential blow-back for a lawyer reckless enough to sue his ex-client for unpaid fees? We talked about the inevitable counter-suits that are apt to pop up and gravely upset the lawyer's day and his professional insurance carrier.

Unfortunately for the lawyer, these client's counter-suits are not the only form of retaliation, and not even the most lethal ammunition in the deadbeat client's arsenal. Statistically, most clients who get sued for their outstanding bills will also lash out and try to strong-arm their lawyers with the aid of the State Bar. It is easy to contact the Bar and complain that the lawyer violated one of the myriad of rules and regulations. Lawyers know that well, and are highly motivated by fear of a Bar investigation—even if they have done absolutely nothing wrong. Think about it as like fearing a letter from the IRS that announces an audit of your tax returns, even tax returns that you believe to have been conscientiously and correctly filed.

Incidentally, many people do not realize it, but you do not even need to be a client in order to complain about a lawyer to the Bar.

No particular connection is required.

Complaints against lawyers are welcome from anybody: a client's girlfriend, a witness in a case, a party on the other side of the lawyer's client, a judge, a neighbor, or even just a vigilante who prefers to remain anonymous to the lawyer. Anybody is welcome to complain.

Consequently, if you are, for example, a landlord trying to get an upper hand in negotiations with a tenant who just happens to be a lawyer, or if you are a contractor strong-arming a homeowner in a payment dispute, and the home-owner just happens to be a lawyer, you may just have discov-ered a pressure-point: announce that you plan to register a grievance and watch your opponent crumble. (If you are wondering whether a grievance of that sort would actually succeed, the answer is "most likely not." But that is very much not the point.)

In the decade and a half since I first got my license, I received dozens of threats to report me to the Bar. Most of them came from the lawyers on the other side and were cal-culated to manipulate me into selling out my clients. That's a routine trick, at least among divorce lawyers in Duckling-burg. But quite a few threats—and even actual complaints to the South Duck State Bar—came from people I barely knew and who surprised me by even knowing I was a lawyer.

Can You Stiff You Divorce Lawyer?

A creative use of the Bar investigation threat came when I was a newbie lawyer trying to buy my first home-office.

The house I had an eye on was conveniently located in the back of a local watering hole bistro, a great place to attract new clients. And the property had a tiny salt-water swimming pool. It was a perfect place! Being fiscally responsible, however, I low-balled the seller. The seller, mindful of the market, suggested that I take a hike.

I responded with a second bid, still too low.

Given the location of the house—what with the watering hole's garbage cans just on the other side of its backyard attracting rats and bugs, I was convinced that the seller would see my low offer as a fair one, eventually. But, as is often the case, I was wrong.

Competition came in the form of a sweet Southern couple comprised of two gay designers. They bid five thousand over me and were ready to close in a week. Or at least that's what the seller said.

"Will you be topping the bid?" the seller called to ask me. "Get it in before tomorrow."

But before I put my pen to paper, the phone rang again—it was the sweeter one of the couple. He wanted to tell me that he reported me to the Bar.

"For what?!" I screamed, forgetting for a moment both my manners and my grammar. (I was new to the game.)

"Unethically destroying our deal," came the prepared response.

Before I could retort, the sweet man got ahold of himself and walked back his announcement. There was no report to the Bar in the works *yet*, he admitted. He just got upset, he was so sorry. Then he added: "Of course, you are not really going to bid on *our* house, right? Our hearts are set on raising our children there."

I hung up and speed-dialed my professional insurance carrier layers at Youpaye & Wheecover-Maybey, LLC. Together, we parsed the Code of Professional Ethics and, at length, confirmed that nothing in the Code or opinions prevented me from making a bid on a house. My competitor had no legitimate Bar complaint.

"But can I ask you something?" murmured the insurance lawyer warmly. "Is your heart truly all that set on this particular house?"

I told him—and ever since have been telling myself—that I did not really want that house in the first place. Not the unique architecture, not the shady yard with its tiny saltwater pool, and nothing attractive about the location. Instead, I got me a rickety walk-up condo and never looked back.

By the way, notice here that the best ammunition against a lawyer is a *threat* of a State Bar complaint, *not* an actual action. That is because the accuser is without power to take back the accusation. Once the Bar does get involved, there is no taking back the complaint. Consequently, the accused lawyer stops caring about the grievance blackmail. It works the same as taking a hostage. A threat of killing the hostage works well, but once the hostage is actually dead, the hostage taker will have lost all the leverage.

BUT we are getting ahead of ourselves. To fully appreciate why lawyers are so fearful of Bar complaints, you need to appreciate the unique mechanics of the grievance process.

A complaint to the Bar about one of its lawyers is called a *grievance*, and in most places is initially handled by the State Bar's *grievance department.*

Leveling a Bar grievance against any lawyer is as easy as Daphne Moon's shepherd pie, and even more health-threatening. That is, health threatening for the lawyer on the receiving end of it, not for whoever brings the grievance. Whoever brings the grievance need fear nothing. There is no expense, no inconvenience, no backlash: the Bars made sure of that. Usually, the complainant enjoys complete civil immunity against any damages that a wrongly accused lawyer might claim.

Contacting your State Bar grievance department is a wonderfully liberating experience rivaled only, perhaps, by entering Neiman Marcus with an unlimited gift card—it is free and there are scores of wonderfully helpful bureaucrats all delightfully eager to help you. That feeling is not an illusion: grievances are a very well financed enterprise. Your grievance experience has been pre-paid from the Bar coffers, and quite generously.

For example, in 2014, the California Bar spent $62,180,735 on disciplining its lawyers. That's right: California lawyers paid over sixty-two million dollars to be punished. And it was not pocket change for the California Bar either: discipline ate up a little under 95% of the Bar's total expenses. Competence educational programs got only a little under a meager 3.5%. [2014 Independent Auditor's Report at 3] In 1995, California lawyers self-punished to the tune of $29.7 million.

What do these tens of millions of dollars mean for you? These numbers mean that complainants like yourself are the source of jobs for a teeming swarm of bureaucrats. Full time lawyers and staffers are hired, systems put in place, IT paid, computers tuned up, all to serve the anticipated flood of grievances. If you do not come and complain about your lawyer, these people will lose their salaries! That's why everybody is so helpful at the State Bar grievance team: the complainant is their valued customer! The person bringing a grievance is the bread and butter for a team of full-time professional disciplinary lawyers and support staff. If grievances dry up, the professional grievance enforcers might be out of jobs and might even be forced to actually practice law, like—who knows—shake the bushes for some divorce cases!

Your grievance is bread and butter for the State Bar paper-pushers (many with law degrees), but is also so much more than that! Your grievance is a critical peg in the machine preserving lawyers' social hierarchy nation-wide.

This may sound counter-intuitive at first, but the Legal Elite—the State Bars' top brass, the Judges and Justices of the States' High Courts—want to see as many grievances against the low-ranking lawyers as possible. The logic here goes like this: the larger the numbers of lawyers punished (or at least investigated), the cleaner the profession. And, of course, the cleaner the profession—the more glory to the upper echelon for its hard work in cleaning the profession. It is the same logic as "if the washing water is dirty, then the laundry must be clean." Since the Legal Elite is in charge of assuring the low-ranking lawyers' cleanliness, the larger the count of grievances processed, the bigger the feather in the cap of the top brass.

The grievance fad is a fairly recent development, apparently budded in the early seventies owing to the enthusiasm of the then Supreme Court Justice Tom C. Clark in tandem with the American Bar Association. The American Bar Association—the *eminence grise* of the legal industry—made sure that the fad percolated to the Bars of the States. It became politically advantageous to the State Bar bureaucrats to tote up large numbers of grievances. The larger the number of grievances processed, the more money spent on the "discipline," the cleaner the lawyers of the particular State. Lots of grievances equals spotless State Bar governance, supposedly.

So why should you care about all that? What does that mean for you?

That means that every grievance you register against your low-ranking divorce lawyer is invited, protected and cherished by the top of the lawyer's profession. Got it? Your grievance warms the cockles of the hearts of your state's Supreme Court Justices. Here's an example, directly from the mouths of the Justices of the Supreme Court of Kentucky: "We must encourage persons with complaints against attorneys... ." [Morgan]

Got a grievance? Don't be shy: Supreme Court Justices encourage you. You've got friends in the highest court in your State.

And encouragement by the powerful triumvirate of the State Supreme Court, Lawmakers and the Bar brass does not just come in the form of a meaningless politician's hug or a holiday card inscribed "Thank you for performing your civic duty, Faithful Citizen." No, it is much more substantial than that. If you are considering bringing a grievance, this troika of legal elite has got your back: they made sure that you can never get into any trouble for a grievance, no matter what your grievance says.

All grievances, whether truthful, somewhat truthful, mendacious or even malicious are immune from the law of slander, defamation, abuse of process, and the like. If you lie and slander your attorney in a grievance, he cannot sue you. Even the nastiest falsehood is immune from any legal retaliation, if properly clothed in the guise of a grievance. How does that work? Simple. In order to encourage as many grievances as possible, the Legal Elite changed the laws: the lower echelon of lawyers who get the brunt of bogus and blatantly false accusations cannot fight back. In some States, the legislature did it, in other States the Justices did it, but the end result is the same: the low ranking lawyers got stripped of all protections afforded everybody else in the country to not be defamed, slandered or harassed at work.

Obviously, if the lawyers on the receiving end of a bogus grievance could strike back with a defamation suit, every potential accuser would think twice. As the Supreme Court of Kentucky put it: "The threat of any retaliatory suit—whether it is for defamation, slander, or abuse of process—would have a chilling effect on the filing of bar complaints." [Morgan] Not to chill any potential of grievances—legitimate or bogus—the Justices and lawmakers stripped all attorneys of the right to fight back against bogus grievances.

The Justices of Kentucky coyly called this blanket immunity for the accusers an "encouragement" of "persons who might ... have some doubt as to the ... validity of the complaint." Meaning: when in doubt, bring your grievance anyway.

The Maryland Judges, back in 1888, were blunt and called this principle much more plainly: "an immunity to the evil-disposed and malignant slanderer." [Bartlett 1888]

In short, whether the accuser has his doubts, or whether the accuser is plainly an evil knob with an axe to grind, he never has to worry that the wounded lawyer might respond with a lawsuit for defamation and infliction of emotional distress, or at least abuse of process. Defame the lawyer in a grievance all you want—the people who pass the laws made sure that any false statements about the lawyer's reputation are immune!

Here's from the Justices of the Supreme Court of Appeals of West Virginia:

"It is imperative that complainants be free from the threat of themselves being sued." [Farber 1990]

For the Legal Elite, no price is too high to pay for the goal of a statistically robust grievance process, and as to the non-ranking lawyers—they suffer the consequences in order to keep their licenses. In the words of the Florida Judges: "one who elects to enjoy the status and benefits as a member

54

of the legal profession *must give up certain rights* or causes of action." [Stone]

To put it plainly, so long as your lawyer wants to keep his license, he has to let you defame him and harass him with impunity—so long as you call it "a grievance." For a lawyer, being attacked by the "evil-disposed and malignant slanderer" is simply an occupational hazard, like heat for construction workers in Arizona and cold for Alaska fisherman.

So go ahead and write that the lawyer lacks knowledge, education, ethical boundaries and expertise. Write that the lawyer billed you too much, or was aloof, or looked panicked in court, or looked at you in a prurient way. Whatever it is you dream up, it is all immune.

Are you beginning to see why lawyers are deathly afraid of your grievance to the State Bar?

———————

YOU may be thinking: suppose I lie in the grievance. What's my lawyer's harm from these tall lies? The accused lawyer will just explain that what I said was not true, and that will be that.

You are partly right: the chance that a total fabrication sticks is small. But a small chance is still a chance. Total fabrications do occasionally stick. People get wrongly convicted all the time. Not to get too dramatic about it, but even death row has its share of mistakes, and the accused on the death row get a whole lot more legal protections, at least in theory.

If a total lie sticks, the lawyer falsely charged will survive physically, of course, but his career may be dead as a doornail.

Besides, a grievance puts lawyer's entire life up for review. And there is much more to the Code of Professional Ethics than working hard for the clients and not stealing from them. Dozens of prohibitions and commandments intrude on every part of the lawyers' lives, with new rules and prohibitions coming out each month. Advertise your law firm as Smith & Associates—violation of the Code if you have no associates. Suggest to your client's husband that you will not report his fraudulent tax returns in exchange for favorable settlement for your client in divorce—violation of the Code. Suggest that the judge is biased against your client—the judge might anonymously complain that you disrespectfully violated the Code. On the other hand, close your eyes to an obvious bias of the judge and fail to make a motion to recuse him—also might be a violation of the Code. File an action that challenges an existing law—violation of the Code because lawyer should have respected the settled law. Refrain from filing an action that challenges an existing law—violation of the Code because the lawyer has an obligation to zealously explore every avenue to help the client, even if it involves challenging outdated and unconstitutional laws at times. Quite frankly, it is hard for any lawyer to be completely sure that he is not violating some twist of the Code at any given time.

THE thing is, *if* a grievance against a lawyer happens to be successful and the lawyer loses the license, this would mean total vocational ruin. It will not just cost the lawyer his current job, but the ability to practice law anywhere. This is a significant loss because every lawyer has decades' worth of effort and hundreds of thousands of dollars invested in his vocation. Before one is sworn in as a lawyer, one must invest in a college degree, the LSAT qualifying examination, three years of law school studies and exams, two or three-day long bar examination, the MPRE examination, the inanely long character assessment questionnaire which tests every address where one lived and every parking ticket received, get finger-printed and, finally, hold one's face through a short but terrifying admittance interview for the State Bar. After that, one gets sworn and the expenses are tapered but not quite finished: there are an additional couple of thousand dollars a year for Bar dues, annual mandatory Continuing Legal Education courses, hortatory specialization courses and exams, necessary books, specialized websites and subscriptions. All these investments can be laid to waste by a single letter from the State Bar. Gone will be the leased Mercedes and the proud image flaunted to the neighbors. Only the student debts would remain as the sole reminder of the better days as a practicing attorney.

However remote the chance that a bogus grievance could blossom into this devastating potential, there is still *a chance*. Naturally cautious lawyers will go far to avoid that chance. With all the time and money invested, would not you?

The consequences of a loss of license are just too dire. If the target of your grievance is a solo practitioner, his law firm will be closed, his paralegals and secretaries out on the street, contriving to find a new job with reinvented resumes that avoid any mention of the time spent in the employ of the suddenly tainted lawyer.

If the lawyer worked for a law firm, most likely he will be fired immediately. In most States, a law firm wanting to keep a disbarred lawyer, even as a mere paralegal, would have to report it to the Bar, like the firm harbored a convicted sex offender. Sometimes there is a form to fill out and present to each new client: "you will be working with a disbarred lawyer." What law firm would stand for the humiliation?! In short, if a grievance succeeds, the lawyer is destroyed: he will be looking for a completely new line of work, which would be a challenge considering that his baggage is the quarter million dollars to half a million of non-dischargeable student debt.

But even if the lawyer can prove he had done nothing wrong and the grievance fails (as most baseless grievances do) it will still impinge upon the lawyer's health, family, and sleeping patterns.

When the grievance is delivered to the targeted lawyer, he faces a few weeks of hectic work. The Grievance committee staffers love tight deadlines, and if a lawyer gets on the wrong side of the staffer in charge of the grievance, not even an eye surgery will get the accused lawyer's response deadline extended. For a few weeks, everything in the accused lawyer's life must be put on hold. While the lawyer writes his report, assembles exhibits and makes boxes full of copies, his colleagues snicker and secretaries gossip—and as the whispering swells to the volume of a thunderclap, something is likely to snap.

If bad luck comes in clusters, the stress of the bogus pending grievance will get the accused lawyer worked up to the point of losing concentration and making a real mistake in another case, which could rightly get the lawyer into an entirely new bushel of trouble.

And there's more: the stress you are empowered to deliver by filing a baseless grievance does not end when the accused lawyer finally finishes the response denying all accusations, assembles the exhibits and delivers the package to the State Bar. After the response is delivered, the looooonnng wait begins. It will last not fewer than six months; a year more likely.

The staffers in charge of processing the grievance operate on their own time. Even though the accused lawyer must respond within a few weeks, the staffers are under no such stringent deadlines. It will take them roughly a year to let the lawyer know that he's dodged the bullet. (Despite all the statistics craze, none of the State Bars disclose statistics for the time it takes to dispose of bogus grievances. Only the numbers for grievances processed, bad apples punished, and occasionally the time it took to bring the punishment are important.) A year is about what it will take, speaking from my limited experience, though. But then again, in my State of South Duck, I've seen bogus grievances stay in review for close to four years. Four years it took the South Duck Bar paper-pushers to realize the grievances were baseless or, as the letter from the Bar somewhat pompously put it, lacking in "probable cause." Four years! Think about it. For a lawyer, that means four years of wondering *every day* if today is his last day as a licensed lawyer. Imagine four Christmases, four Easters, four Summer vacations filled with the constant, nagging terror that something has gone berserk in the State Bar grievance department and the postman is on his way carrying the sad news: the lawyer is prohibited from working, starting today.

Even if the lawyer survived the pressure-cooking weeks of responding to the grievance and made no mistakes in his other files, there's still the possibility of blowing it in the following years while he is waiting for the grievance to be decided. With every knock on the door and every certified mail delivery bringing a threat of loss of professional license, the hanging Sword of Damocles is sure to inflict some wounds.

"Can I take the weekend off, or should I work till I'm more withered than a wraith to save up in case the Bar takes my license next week? Can my spouse and I have a baby, or will I be out of work tomorrow?"

This cloud of oppressive uncertainty will put a ding in the lawyer's sleep patterns, slow down his response time while driving and trigger distracted behavior at work. It will trigger crabbiness with family and friends, and inability to walk in a straight line in the shopping mall. By the time the good news arrives that the grievance is dismissed, the lawyer's life might be already in the dumper.

And that is the *best* case scenario. If you were in this

lawyer's shoes, how far would you go to avoid this "best case"?

Now comes the important bit: the probability of the grievance. Statistically, almost every client who is sued for unpaid fees, will retaliate with a grievance or at least a threat of it, even if only just to lodge a vague complaint that the unpaid fees are *unethically high*, not justified by the effort or the results. (Considered as a grievance, it seems like a non-starter, but you'd be surprised how much work this one sentence will generate for the accused lawyer, who will now have to write long essays to the State Bar rationalizing every billed dollar.)

From the alleged high fees, a grievance might move on to saying that the client's case suffered from hiring too many paralegals, or too few. Or too many secretaries, or too few. Or too many phone calls or court appearances, or too few. The grievance doesn't have to be rooted in persuasive fact. As long as the accusations pass the "straight face test" of not being facially laughable, there is created a whirlwind of stress for the accused attorney. And even if the straight face test can only be passed with the mark of D minus, the State Bar still might take up the grievance under its own flag. As we'll discuss in a few pages, the organization is unpredictable.

I know what you are thinking: you are not that kind of a person. Skipping on the bill is one thing, you say, but sneaking behind a man's back to gratuitously destroy a career by false complaints is something completely different. It is not your style. You will not stand for it. I know you are a decent person, and that is jolly decent of you to let your lawyer have a life after you are through with him.

But here's the thing: it does not matter that you are a decent person because it will not change your lawyer's concerns. *You* might not be the sort of a fellow who files a bogus grievance against your own lawyer. But your lawyer will not be motivated by an analysis of your moral character. Instead, your lawyer will be motivated by statistics and probabilities. And, like I said before, *statistically*, a client who skips on the bill will level a grievance if pressed to pay. Your lawyer has no way of glancing in your soul to discover your good intentions. (Clearly, if you are stiffing your lawyer, he had made at least one incorrect assumption about you already.) But your lawyer is smart enough to realistically assess probabilities and risk.

The fear of a bogus grievance is what makes lawyers so much more agreeable to some pretty aggressive demands from their clients. Of course, I am in no way suggesting that you actually go ahead and register a bogus grievance against a perfectly innocent lawyer. Considerations of fairness and decency aside, actually registering a grievance will work against your financial interests: the cornered lawyer might decide that there's nothing to lose and start fighting you as a matter of survival. So actually leveling a grievance is a dumb move. But, as we discussed in the chapter about bogus lawsuits: it helps to look like you are the crazy SOB who just might cause this sort of trouble if riled.

Another question that comes to mind, especially if you had a competent and conscientious lawyer, is this: "What is there even to complain about?" Or to put it differently, "If my lawyer did nothing wrong, why would he fear a complaint?" Concocting a bogus grievance is a highly individual adventure. If one rummages thoroughly enough through lawyers' work, there is always something that could be criticized with a somewhat straight face. Lawyer warm and available—complain of perceived sexual tension. Lawyer matter-of-fact like Dr. House—complain of neglect. Lawyer loud in the courtroom—complain of unethical rudeness that destroyed your chance of rapport with the judge and your spouse's counsel. Lawyer quietly dignified in the courtroom—complain he did not fight vociferously enough for you. But what makes grievances especially problematic for the accused lawyer is not so much what you complain about as how you phrase your displeasure. To illustrate this point, it helps to look at how grievances are processed in South Duck.

ALL grievances pass through the State Bar, so if one decides to level a grievance, that's the only address one needs to use. No need to let the accused lawyer know —the State Bar will handle that later.

When you are a lawyer on the receiving end of a grievance, you might get a telephone call from the Bar, but in most cases, you first learn of your predicament when the postman with a look of *schadenfreude* rings the bell and asks you to sign for a thin certified letter with the ominously familiar return address of the South Duck State Bar. Whether the grievance was penned by a former client or by a landlord muscling a rent payment for a place covered in black mold, or by a competitive lawyer at the end of the street, the news always comes by certified mail with the return address of the Bar. Never from the complaining party. There is no direct communication between the accused and accuser at that stage.

The certified letter from the South Duck State Bar comes in a size 10 envelope which is more than enough to accommodate the single page prepared and signed by a member of the Bar Grievance Team. Even if the complaining client (landlord, competition, judge, or whoever else) had delivered to the Bar thirty pages of emotional, repetitive and detailed ramblings, propped up by notebooks filled with documents, in the State of South Duck, the accused lawyer still receives just a sheet of paper. The accuser's ramblings and notebooks remain safely hidden away with the South Duck State Bar. The accused lawyer only receives what's called a *Substance of Grievance*, a synopsis which paints the accusations in broad brush with lamentable dearth of details.

At the bottom of the page the *Substance of Grievance* letter will list a few numbers and letters. These are the references to various rules or regulations of the Code of Professional Ethics: the accused lawyer is required to prove that he had not violated them.

So how does an accuser's thirty-pages-long far-reaching

plaint become a one-pager *Substance of Grievance* with references to the Code of Professional Ethics? Of course, members of the public cannot be required to prepare such a document, nor can they be expected to marshal the references to the Code of Professional Ethics. That's where the Bar steps in to help the public: somebody on its staff (and occasionally a volunteer) reads the complaint and extracts "the substance." Of course, a detail or two may get lost in the process.

I'll give you an example.

Mary Doe complains about her lawyer to the South Duck Bar. She prepares this ramble:

> *My lawyer did not cite* <u>State of South Duck v.</u>
> <u>Boon</u> *at my custody hearing. That's a violation! My cousin's lawyer got her full custody because of* <u>State of South Duck v. Boon</u>. *My lawyer is incompetent, and that's why I got no custody.*

If the Bar were to forward Mary Doe's ramble to her lawyer directly, the accused lawyer would have no trouble responding.

Here's the answer:

> <u>State v. Boon</u> *does not apply in Mary's case.*

There you go, the grievance is defeated. The accused lawyer does not need to say much more. But it gets worse for Mary Doe. Because the accused lawyers are allowed to reveal client's confidential information to the Bar to the degree needed to defend against grievances, Mary's lawyer might even go on to add:

> *Besides, the real reason Mary did not get custody was because she came to the hearing two sheets to the wind, and the sheriff smelled it on her breath when she tried to tackle her husband in the courtroom.*
>
> *P.S. State v. Boon actually works against Mary's case.*

Now Mary's amateurish grievance is truly defeated.

But fortunately for Mary and her grievance, she is not expected to go it alone against her lawyer. The South Duck State Bar comes to her rescue. Mary's original ramble stays safely locked in the staffer's desk, and Mary's ex-lawyer receives, instead, a *Substance of Grievance* letter. The Bar's one line summary does not usually get bogged down in fine point like whether or not State v. Boon applies to Mary Doe. The Bar's "*Substance*" gets straight to the core of Mary's feelings:

> *Complainant client complains the accused lawyer lacks competence in child support matters. R. 1.1, Competence.*

The lawyer is incompetent! *That's* the substance!

If the accused lawyer cannot prove his overall competence, he will be punished.

No longer an easily rebuttable minor detail which could be brushed off in one sentence, Mary's grievance has been transformed into a vague general claim that now puts the accused lawyer's whole career on trial. Not so easy to defeat Mary's grievance now, is it?

Perhaps Mary's lawyer can ultimately prove that he is competent enough, but that takes a lot more ink. Lawyer's competence begins with performance in law school, is continued through the experience of cases worked, is aided by the Continuing Legal Education classes taken, and is proved by clients' reviews and a record of wins in trials and appeals. Challenging lawyer's competence in a grievance will, at best, cost the accused lawyer a good deal of time to describe his career path, collect all the necessary proof, and create a presentable package for the Bar. That's hours or days to take away from the job and the family. Apart from sapping lawyer's time, what if the accused lawyer is actually somewhat new at the specialty? Suppose it is only the lawyer's second year as a divorce practitioner? Suppose the grievance is that the lawyer is not competent in child custody law? What's the accused lawyer to do—offer to take a quiz?

By the way, among all the grievances I personally had to defend, I cannot remember a single one *without* an accusation that I "lacked competence." For all I know, "incompetence" might just be thrown in with every Bar charge, added for even measure.

A handful of years ago, the South Duck State Bar was pondering a grievance against me. I never learned who had filed this particular one—most likely a lawyer on the other side upset by the turn of his case. It came "anonymously" and was dismissed before I could dig down to the source. In any event, the grievance complained, among many other things, of "lack of competence in divorce appeals." Which got me miffed, because I fancy myself highly competent in that small niche.

I countered by listing my educational credentials and skills, and provided spectacular client references. No budge from the Bar: it continued "investigating," or at least it did not tell me otherwise. After about two years of sinister silence, I panicked and started looking for a way to shake off the problem. I contrived to find a conspicuous way to prove my competence.

I was in luck.

Inside the time this particular grievance was pending, the South Duck State Bar sent out invitations to lecture on the very same subject in which it was investigating my competence—or lack thereof—appellate litigation. I sent out my proposal and, amazingly, it sailed through. I was offered a slot!

I'd given lectures like this before. It is a "service" to the Bar and the fellow South Duck lawyers, which is a fancy way of saying that it's an unpaid gig. All the proceeds go straight to the Bar's coffers. Frankly, I'd decided a few years ago that the hours it takes me to prepare are never worth the local fame and credit. But this time I was excited to "serve." Surely, being featured as an "expert" by the Bar itself would help shake off the accusation of "incompetency" which the Bar was investigating!

That month, the South Duck Bar's monthly CLE newsletter reached out to its list of twenty-three thousand subscribers and suggested they enrich the knowledge of appeals and divorces by listening to what I had to say for the moderate fee of $165 each, payable to the State Duck Bar.

"Surely," I thought, "once the Bar starts collecting admission fees and bestowing educational credit for my lectures, that should elevate me at least far enough to crawl out of the ditch of the incompetence!" The pardon has to come any day now, I thought.

No such luck.

Still under the black cloud of being investigated for "incompetence," I traveled to the Bar multimedia studios in Big Duckling, two hundred miles away from my house in Ducklingburg. The State Bar put me up in the capital's best five-star hotel, warmly welcomed me as the "talent of the day" in its state-of-the-art recording studios with flattering lighting and competent cameramen who sucked up to me like I mattered.

I waited for a Bar rep to come in and whisper the good news in my ear anytime now, but nobody came. Half an hour to start . . . ten minutes . . . three . . ..

The clock struck, and the pro producer snapped his fingers and pointed at my nose: the cameras started rolling, I was on the air. Maybe "they" were waiting to see if my lecture was good enough, I thought. Or maybe it was a trap? Maybe "they" were planning to find mistakes in my lecture and use them to bury me? I'd know after the lecture, I decided, and bravely smiled to the wall behind the camera.

But nothing happened after. The CLE liaison shook my

hand, gifted me three paper coasters embossed with the words South Duck State Bar and a picture of duck pecking the state flower, and I was on my way.

A week later, the video of my lecture was added to the Bar's regular catalogue to be promoted for infinity. Still no word about the grievance. Quite clearly, I was had.

The grievance stayed open for about another year after.

The reason I bring up this anecdote is to illustrate the power of a vague grievance. Even if you cannot come up with any complaint that passes the straight face test, at a minimum you can always question competence. That still packs sufficient punch to cloud your lawyer's day. Or, in my case, roughly 1,277 days. Not a bad bang for your ten-minute investment!

And you can make your grievance even more powerful.

We discussed the techniques developed by the South Duck Bar staffers to punch up the *Substance of Grievance* letters: delete the identifying details and broaden the inquiry. That's a good technique. But, in my opinion, what makes the inquiries truly impenetrable and almost unconquerable is something the Bar staffers chanced into.

It's the misleading revisions. Yes, editorial rewrites that serve to obscure the actual issues.

The original grievance filed by a deadbeat client might read:

> *My lawyer did not file the Affidavit for the 09/01/15 hearing, and that's why I did not get my kids after hearing.*

70

A clearly amateurish attempt. There are only two possible answers to this statement—the Affidavit either was filed or it wasn't. If the grievance is, indeed, bogus, the accused lawyer will simply retort:

I filed that Affidavit. Here it is. See for yourself.

Where's the frolic and adventure in that?

However, the grievance process gets much more interesting when a Bar Staffer presents the accused lawyer with this rewrite:

Complainant complains that her lawyer did not do enough for the Summer hearing. As a result, Complainant received a bad decision from the judge. This was unethical over-billing.

Instead of focusing on "the 09/01/15" event, the staffer wrote "the Summer." Now that all the details of the event in question are scrubbed and the dates are fudged, the relevant time period becomes problematic. Will the lawyer guess that "the Summer hearing" actually stands for the specific "09/01/15 hearing?" Perhaps. But what if there was also a Summer hearing in addition to the September hearing? What if that Summer hearing made the accused lawyer, with 20-20 hindsight, second-guess his work in a way that the client did not even suspect? Spurred by the perceived broad scope of the complaint, the lawyer will now reluctantly unearth and attempt to defend his own arguably imperfect performance. Score for Team Grievance!

The references to times and places and the exact alleged missteps are almost always vague in the Substance of Grievance notices. That, I think is a matter of policy designed to encourage the accused to cough up every last scrap of self-critical details. The Bar might even refuse to tell the accused lawyer who submitted the original grievance, marking it "anonymous" or, if the complainant is powerful enough, signing it "by the South Duck Bar."

Grievance staffers are busy people, with reams of grievances to process. It is hard for them to get every detail right. In those *Substances of Grievance*, child *custody* becomes child *support*, early *September* becomes *Summer*, the words *plaintiff* and *defendant* get mixed up.

What's more, there might have even been mistakes and slips of pen in the original grievance. If the accused lawyer had access to the original grievance, he might have been able to figure it out. But in the one-page summary with little context, any lapse can make a grievance as impenetrable and as dangerous as a minefield.

This one last level of misdirection can enmesh the accused in a true trap. In South Duck, the Code of Professional Conduct requires the lawyer to answer every grievance fully and completely. That means that the accused lawyer cannot just respond to a grievance with: "I don't know what you are talking about." The Code of Professional Ethics calls a flippant answer like that a "failure to cooperate with the South Duck Bar investigation." That's a serious offense in itself. No lawyer wants to step into that hot water.

So if you were to complain that the lawyer failed you at

a January 2016 hearing, and there was no such hearing, the accused lawyer will probably write back: "Perhaps the client is thinking of a January 2015 hearing, or a February 2016 hearing, or even December 2015 hearing.

As to those hearings, let me explain each and every one . . .."

What just happened? The accused lawyer just became his own investigator. Another score for Team Grievance!

———

You might ask: but why wouldn't the accused lawyer simply call the South Duck Bar staffer and ask to see the full file? Why not just read the original complaint where every detail is clearly spelled out by the unhappy client or conniving opposition or the furious judge or "friend of liberty desiring to stay anonymous," or whoever it is on the accusing end?

That would clear things up, right? Well, when I got my first complaint that was the idea I got: Just call the South Duck State Bar and get the original complaint.

Bad idea. Disastrously bad idea.

My very first complaint—the first in a long line of unhappy people grieving to the South Duck Bar—was a woman called Bea Boots. Bea had never been my client. She was a jilted ex-lover of my client Bob, a husky bartender with a zipper problem.

A few weeks before I met my client, Bea and Bob were

a striking couple, very much in love. An extravagant wedding was in the works, and Bea had mapped out detailed plans for the happily-ever-after. Then, Bob dumped her, in a spectacularly flagrant fashion. The poor woman tried to keep her man with a lawsuit, and that's when Bob hired me.

Bea versus Bob was a weak lawsuit. A breach of a promise to marry—a far-fetched heart-balm law that almost never succeeds. It was over in a few weeks, and I barely gave it another thought.

Jilted Bea licked her wounds for almost a year, then struck again, this time, against me. By then, the Bob&Bea saga was for me only a dim memory.

The first sentence of the *Substance of Grievance* read:

> *Respondent [that was me] intentionally misrepresented to the Court the content of deposition testimony of the star witness in the Bea v Bob lawsuit.*

"I never," I screamed in indignation, addressing nobody in particular. (I was alone in my condo.)

"Never in my life! And I will prove it!"

With laptop fired up and all my phones disconnected, I was ready to type up a storm of proof when I realized the problem. I had no idea what the complaint was all about.

All I remembered about Bea was that she was sad and tall and bony and flat, and careened to one side when she walked, pulling down the gentle foam of ruffles she pinned on in lieu of breasts, all of which made her look like a somewhat lopsided Amazon.

Astonishingly, all eight of her bridesmaids were petite curvy energetic young things, sporting brilliant complexions, made even brighter by the warm-hue bridesmaids dresses of shiny pink silk, which the Amazon simple-mindedly let them wear. Nature took its course at the rehearsal dinner when one of the junior maids got caught with the groom. Regrettably, both not only refused to apologize and forget the whole thing but, instead, decided to giggle and run off in a quickly hailed Uber.

The Amazon soon sued my client Bob, and for reasons nobody could completely figure out, insisted that all eight of her bridesmaids attended the closed mediated settlement session.

"I need witnesses," she insisted.

That was a strange request because there are no witnesses in mediation. That's a basic tenet of mediations: no witnesses. But it is also a basic tenet that anything a jilted ex-bride wants, she gets. So long as it helps the mediation. And so the bridesmaids were summoned. Amazon commanded that they all wear their pink bridesmaids' dresses, "for authenticity."

The torrent of pink bridal glory took over the beige floors of the law firm where we all assembled to mediate, all eight giggling and gossiping and demanding that the overworked secretary bring skim milk for their decaf coffees. We let them into the conference room, and they rushed in like a gossipy maelstrom, all talking at the same time. Then they suddenly all hiccupped and froze: Amazon walked in.

One by one, Amazon called upon each bridesmaid to

walk to the chair in the middle and "tell him how he made me feel, for the record." There was, of course, no *record*. Mediation is the exactly opposite of the record. Everything said in mediation is supposed to stay a secret. But there was no real use in arguing.

Seven of the bridesmaids sat down and chirped that husky Bob broke poor Amazon's heart. The eighth, for some reason, kept repeating: "spo-o-sal privilege." The spectacle was highly irregular, but nobody really cared because twenty-five minutes later everything was done and settled. Amazon burst out crying and declared that she "did not want nothing from *him* no more." Bob sighed and swore mildly and said he'd pay for both lawyers. And that was that.

Bob and Bea's story was a sad one, but I was young and uncaring, and Amazon's heartbreak to me was nothing but an easy case with a smallish fee, immediately forgotten. That is, forgotten until the postman delivered the "*Substance of Grievance*" which was, per usual, two paragraphs of a single-spaced text plus a list of Code section numbers. The list of rules of ethics I allegedly violated was so long that it spilled to the second page.

According to the referenced sections of the Code, I was a cheat, a liar and a fraud. Allegedly.

Which I was totally prepared to disprove, except for . . . I reread the first sentence again:

". . . misrepresented to the Court the content of deposition testimony of the star witness."

What "deposition"?
There were no depositions!

76

What "star witness"?
There were no witnesses!
And no court!!!

After about twenty minutes of searching my memory and five hours of searching every box of my old files, a question came to mind:

What if Amazon had gone crazy?

Then it dawned on me: Amazon did not even write the page I was trying to decipher. I should just ask for Amazon's original writing. That should clear things up!

That's when I called the staffer who signed the letter at the South Duck State Bar, a Mrs. Laticia Jones of the Grievance team.

"Your grievance number GR-8201666 here," I said with all the cheerfulness I could muster "it says here..."

"Hold please," interrupted Mrs. Laticia Jones of the Grievance team and hung up.

That was my clue to get lost, but I did not get it.

I redialed.

"It's me again, your GR-8201666," I said. "Got disconnected?"

Mrs. Jones tapped the computer key, locating my file.

"You Portia Porter?"

"That's me. I wanted . . ."

"You got fifteen days to respond," interjected Mrs. Jones.

"That's not what . . ."

"I can give you five extra days," Mrs. Jones stifled a bout of squeamishness.

"Thank you, Mrs. Jones," I was oblivious to her squeamishness. "But that's not what I . . ."

"Due on the 25th. That's your last extension, have a good day now," shook me off Mrs. Jones with ironic salutation.

"Please don't hang up," I interrupted with firmness easily parsed to imply: your salary is paid by my dues, don't you dare hang up!

This time, she did not click off, and I jumped in with my agenda of getting the grievance in the original.

"Would you mind sending me Ms. Bea Boots's original grievance?"

Mrs. Jones gasped:

"You want what?!"

I persisted:

"You did not include the original grievance. I am entitled to see it, right?"

Had I said that I proposed to drive over to Big Duckling, march into Mrs. Jones's office and make photocopies of the contents of her entire desk, I would not have caused her as much shock.

"You are not allowed to see that! I can't do thaaaat, Ms. Porter. That's a legal document, we don't give that out," she almost choked.

I kept on:

"Why not? I'm the accused here!"

Mrs. Jones regained her composure and returned to the script: "You need to provide *full and fair disclosure of all the facts and circumstances pertaining to your misconduct, Ms.*

Porter... ahem... alleged misconduct."

"I want to, very much," I was getting defensive. "It's just that..."

"We cannot disclose the original complaints. That would impede you from providing *full and fair disclosure of all the facts*..."

"But that page of nonsense," I raised my voice and was speaking over her, "that rewrite you sent me, it's just senseless."

"*Substance of Grievance* was prepared to assist you with your full and fair disclosure, Ms. Porter . . ."

"But . . ."

"It was prepared by me," inserted Mrs. Jones.

Crap! She personally penned that gibberish!

There was still time to hang up and pray the whole business gets forgotten.

"Look," I said instead of doing the sensible thing and running for the woods, "just *look* at the first sentence! About the *star witness* . . ."

"If you did not misrepresent the witnesses, provide a written response by the 25th. Anything else?"

"Yes," I was quick. "There *were no witnesses!*"

"Just a minute . . ." Mrs. Jones tapped her keyboard again, "Ms. Bea states that there were eight witnesses."

"Eight?!"

"Eight witnesses were presented."

"Eight? Eight? Where? Who? You mean the bridesmaids?" I was rambling now, defeated.

"That's your decision if you do not want to disclose the

eight witnesses, but let me make you aware that you are required to provide full and fair disclosure of all the facts and circumstances pertaining..."

"Got it. Full and fair. Got it the first five times."

"I am not going to flag you for those witnesses you just misrepresented to me on the phone, but I have to flag you for attempting to get the confidential information."

"Confidential what?! I cannot see the grievance against me? Why the heck not?"

"Full and fair disclosure, Ms. Porter."

It started to dawn on me how the grievance process works in South Duck: they were not going to tell me what Amazon's gripe was until I confessed everything imaginable. "Full and fair disclosure of all facts and circumstances" meant guessing what Amazon was thinking, and woe was the lawyer who forgot a possibly incriminating detail: punishment for failure to confess could be harsher than punishment for the original misdeed. Brilliantly devious!

What Ms. Jones was so inarticulately telling me was that my snooping around to see what the Bar did or did not know already about my alleged transgressions was subverting the Bar's process and, hence, was considered proof of my guilty conscience.

An accused lawyer was expected to gather every smallest detail that could have possibly be seen as a violation. Then the accused was allowed to explain that it wasn't a violation at all. A big job for the accused, but the South Duck Bar sets no page limit for grievance responses. Write your own War & Peace if you must.

_____

If you like watching the law-and-order-type shows, you might be thinking by now: but what about the right to not testify against yourself? And the "innocent until proven guilty," and the "right to face your accuser"? What happened to those inalienable rights? Doesn't the American Constitution guarantee these rights to every single American?

The short answer is, NO. Our Constitution does not guarantee those rights to everybody all the time. In particular, these rights do not belong to lawyers in the first stage of grievance investigations. Not in South Duck, anyway.

Most Americans incorrectly assume that *every* American citizen is *always* protected from testifying against himself, always has the right to face his accuser, and is innocent until proven guilty. It is common to think of these protections as basic American rights.

But they aren't. These familiar protections—the 5th Amendment and the 6th Amendment and the whole "burden of proof is on the accuser" idea—are decidedly not basic rights of every American at all times. These protections are just the rights of criminals in the *criminal* process.

So, if a lawyer were to get charged with murdering somebody, he'd have these protections. But not a lawyer accused of violations of the Code of Professional Ethics.

In fact, the first thing the lawyer learns after tearing into the Envelope of Horror from the South Duck State Bar is that the prosecutors of South Duck made very little effort to prove the lawyer's guilt: it's up to the accused lawyer to prove his innocence.

Please hear me well: I am not talking about some break in the process. The Bar staffers are not bad cops ignoring good laws.

When a South Duck Bar staffer refuses to give the accused lawyer details of the accusation, or threatens additional punishment for "refusal to cooperate" (code for refusal to self-incriminate), or sets impossible deadlines, all this *is* the established process, at least during the investigation stage. The staffer has not gone rogue. The staffer is simply implementing the investigation techniques approved by the profession which puts "protection of the public above protection of the lawyer's reputation or livelihood." [Levin at 82]

As I strained to figure out what Amazon could possibly have written in the secretive original grievance, one thing was becoming clear: the 6th Amendment rights to be informed of the nature and cause of the accusation did not apply to the South Duck Bar investigations.

In a criminal investigation, a chap suspected of theft or rape or even murder is told exactly who's the victim, when and where the crime took place, *and what the prosecution has on him.*

"You've got nothing on me and I am not talking to you" is a perfectly valid approach if one's talking to the police detectives. The 6th Amendment has guaranteed it. But when you are a South Duck lawyer facing a grievance, your only bet for professional survival is to tell the whole story.

Or else.

"There were eight bridesmaids in Ms. Boots's wedding party," I started my long and intricately detailed response.

I do not want you to think that the South Duck State Bar can get all the way to censuring and disbarring lawyers without ever having to disclose what the accusation was all about and prove the lawyers' guilt. Only the first part of the grievance process—the "investigation"—works that way. Once the investigation is completed, and once the accused lawyer has given the compulsory disclosures, the grievance process gets a little harder for the State Bar than just saying "abracadabra, you are censured." But those later stages are long ways away—months or even years. First, the lawyer has to get through the investigation stage, and while that goes on, even the most toothless grievances are likely to wreak havoc in your lawyer's life, especially if phrased in a properly vague way.

Maybe your State Bar does not so helpfully perform Substance of Grievance rewrites, veiling grievances into enigmas of vagueness, broadness and incorrectly rendered dates, times and subjects. In that case, you must help yourself. It is quite simple. Here are a few delightfully enigmatic grievances I've seen over the years:

> *My lawyer gave me bad advice. So I got a bad decision from the Judge.*

In any regular, run-of-the mill case, your Judge will be making lots of decisions— some more favorable than others. And there are lots of pieces of advice a lawyer gives the client: "dress conservatively," "you do not have to produce this document," "we should hire a private investigator," "sit up in court."

Faced with a complaint like this, your lawyer will have to second-guess everything he ever said to you. Best case scenario for the lawyer—it will take a lifetime of work to prepare a written report explaining why every single piece of his advice was stellar.

My lawyer has done unnecessary work in the Fall.

I see this sort of complaint in two types of situations. One is where there was nothing going on in the Fall—and so the lawyer has to describe all the work done in the Summer and the Winter, just in case. The other is when there was more than one Fall involved. If your case went on for several years, your lawyer will have to respond detailing the whys and wherefores of all the work done in the Fall of 2013, and 2012 and 2011 . . . and, just for even measure, in the Summer and the Winter of these years. And the lawyer will face the same problems we talked about in the previous sections. Best case scenario—it will take forever to finish the response. Worst case—some work may indeed have not been strictly necessary, especially in 20-20 hindsight. For instance, preparing for a deposition that got cancelled. Not necessary in hindsight.

Submission was not prepared on time.

Which submission was "not on time"? Never give a hint!

If you have a large-volume case, this type of a complaint has a potential to devastate your lawyer. The lawyer will be forced to inventory every single submission. Given the multitude of changes in divorce litigation deadlines and inevitable disputes between the lawyers about when things are due, your lawyer is almost guaranteed to drown in recreating the confusing history.

There is simply no one-line way for any lawyer to answer grievances complaining of "insufficient work," "untimely submissions," "unethical remarks," or "displeasure of the Judge." Besides, who can rebut a plaint like that with certainty? Heck, in retrospect, even Clarence Darrow would have to admit that some of his advice could have been better, or was unnecessary, or caused judicial displeasure.

Responding to vague and general accusations is always a daunting task. Plus, the harder the case, the more work was done, the longer it takes a lawyer to respond. And if there was something the lawyer chose not to do on your behalf, he'll name it, explain it, and detail why he elected not to do it. Now the lawyer is playing both parts: the accusation and the explanation.

Intrigue abounds!

Can You Stiff You Divorce Lawyer?

WHAT we learned so far is that the grievance process empowers you to effortlessly and with impunity cause your lawyer lots of trouble and anguish, and that you can do it even if your lawyer had done nothing to cause a complaint.

That's good news for you, but wouldn't experienced lawyers eventually get immune to these grievance stunts? After all, if the lawyer had done nothing wrong, what harm could a bogus grievance cause him? *What's the worst that can happen?*

And that's a fair question: surely no lawyer ever gets disbarred for "unnecessary work," or running three minutes late for a deposition, for example? Or do they?

The answer may come as a surprise.

The first thing you notice if you flip through a copy of a typical (they differ somewhat by state) lawyers' Code of Professional Conduct is that there is no sentencing section in the Code. The book is just a very thick catalogue of what is prohibited to lawyers, but there are no gradations for the listed prohibitions. That feels odd. Surely, not every offense is punishable by the professional death sentence, disbarment! A few of the offenses have to be just minor transgressions. But the Code does not say.

Culturally, we expect every prohibited act to fall into a predetermined range of punishment: that's the Western way. Think of your own everyday transgression possibilities. Parking in a tow-away zone, littering on a highway, running a red light. You know that you are not supposed to do these things. And you know the worst thing likely to happen. You'll pay a few bucks of a fine. You will not go to jail for life if you park in the wrong zone, that's a certainty.

Murder your spouse, on the other hand, and you very well might expect to spend considerable time behind bars. No surprise there, either.

We are accustomed to having a good idea of the size of our comeuppance relative to the size of our transgressions. That is because our lawmakers dedicate gobs of time and energy to grids, lists, guidelines and laws that strive to make sure that punishment fits the crime. There are grids for "felonies" and "misdemeanors" and "tickets" and "fines." We can be fairly certain that a murder will not trigger just a fine and that spitting on a sidewalk will not be prosecuted as a felony. We have written sentencing laws that create at least some semblance of reasonable expectation about penalties. And on those rare occasions when the system fails and punishment turns out to be disproportionate to the crime, we as a society are outraged and work to solve the perceived injustice. Punishment must be commensurate to the crime. That's the American way.

Except when it comes to American lawyers.

A lawyer accused of violating one of the numerous prohibitions in the Code of Professional Conduct cannot point to any grid that lays out "what's the worst that's gonna happen." There is no grid in the Code. The punishment lurks each time in the uncertain hands of the men and women of the lawyers' State Bar enforcement apparatus.

For example, if a client decides to register a grievance complaining that her divorce lawyer tried to make a pass at her, what's the worst the accused lawyer has to fear? Is it a private talking to? Public reprimand? Suspension from practice? Disbarment? Recently, the North Carolina State Bar disbarred a lawyer called Stanley for sex with a client. Around the same time, another North Carolina lawyer called Wallace only suffered a two-year suspension with permission to re-apply in six months. So Stanley was out of the lawyering business for good, but Wallace might return in half a year. In 2003, another North Carolina lawyer called Arthur also had sex with his client. Arthur's practice did not miss a beat. Arthur was punished with a "reprimand," a little black smudge on his reputation that did nothing to halt his professional practice. So, there is no reliable basis for predicting the consequences of a grievance—except that there's always a chance of what is in effect the professional death penalty. The disciplining arm of the Bar moves in unpredictable ways, and there is rampant suspicion that those unpredictable ways are heavily influenced by "who you are and who you know."

Not that this uncertainty of punishment is any news to the legal industry: plenty of authoritative commentators have been complaining about the "disparity of punishment" for decades.

In 1998, an authoritative commentator lamented that the lawyers all over the nation were sanctioned "unevenly." "Fairness" of sanctions should be studied and improved, he postulated. [Levin] State commentators from Alaska to Washington agreed and echoed, publishing research under emphatic titles like "Adding Chaos to Confusion in Washington Legal Ethics." [Goldman; Woods]

A decade and a half later, Dr. Stephen Gillers localized a very similar lament featuring uneven and unpredictable punishments doled out to New York lawyers. [Gillers 2014] Professor Gillers's work operates under an unquestioned assumption that those instances when punishments for identical transgressions are doled out unevenly are nothing but system errors, an undesirable situation that calls for a change. And that is a common sense expectation based on how Americans evaluate their punishment system—the more predictable and even-handed, the better.

But not every State agrees even in theory that predictability of punishment and punishing proportionally for the similar transgressions is a goal. The North Carolina Supreme Court, for instance, expressly refuses to consider the relevancy of dissimilar punishments for similar offenses. Each case of attorney violation in North Carolina is reviewed anew and punished without comparing it to the cases before. What this means is that a North Carolina lawyer who gets punished more harshly than has been customary for decades is not allowed to argue that there was a long line of his colleagues who were not punished nearly as harshly. Such an argument is considered irrelevant, and the North Carolina Supreme Court "expressly disapproves of any reference" to other cases. [Talford] [Small]

What does all that mean for clients? For North Carolina lawyers, it attaches even greater terror to the threat of a grievance because lawyers of that state cannot console themselves with the fact that "nobody ever got disbarred for this."

Their State *expressly disapproves* reliance on what sanction is customary. Nobody may have been ever punished for waiting to return a phone call for 48 hours instead of returning it within the customary 24, but that does not guarantee that a North Carolina lawyer cannot be thusly penalized to some wildly unexpected extent.

Such sheer randomness and potential arbitrariness is what any lawyer fears the most. A client might not have any reason for a grievance, but the grievance process itself is so filled with uncertainty that no thinking lawyer should ever risk getting entangled in such professional jeopardy, not for any mere fee.

THE OUTLIERS

A RATIONAL LAWYER WON'T SUE a client for unpaid fees.

There are too many reasons not to do it: the royal loss of time and waste of money, the shame of being counter-sued, or subjected to the dreaded State Bar grievance process, the fear of yelp reviews that anonymously proclaim the stiffed lawyer the "unethical misfit of the year." This Parade of Horribles is what a lawyer gets to embrace if he sues for the unpaid fees. A rational lawyer can see plain as day that any emotional or financial upside is uncertain and insignificant compared to the lawyer's expected losses.

But not all lawyers act rationally all the time. Some are

not smart enough to think ahead. Some do not know everything that you just learned from reading this book. Some are just stubborn. And there remain a few with a blinkered belief in the infallibility of the American justice system. Those few sue because they believe that they are *in the right*, and, therefore, *should win*. Some are also fools who believe that public annihilation of a client might deter future clients from skipping on their bills. (That last one's a crock, as they will soon discover. The more likely deterrence it will accomplish is dissuading future potential clients from hiring them. Who wants to deal with an ill-tempered, litigation-happy irrational lawyer?)

Whatever the reasons, lawsuits against deadbeat clients do happen from time to time.

So what do you do if you one of these over-optimistic fools gives you trouble? An obvious answer is: invest in curative education. Buy your lawyer a copy of this book, and helpfully forward to your lawyer the pages in this chapter. Add one fifty-dollar check marked "In Satisfaction of All Amounts Due" and a personal note urging acceptance of the fifty bucks in full payment of all you owe. Unless your lawyer is one of those weirdo crazy litigious bastards—the sort that will sue his mother just because he happened to pass the courthouse with twenty minutes to spare—he just might reluctantly send you a release.

Of course, an even better plan is this: Stay away from the lawyer crazies. Stick with lawyers who are smart enough to allow themselves—albeit grumpily and with poorly suppressed anger—to do the rational thing and leave alone their clients who do not pay.

One final word of caution: your state's Code of Professional Conduct probably makes it a violation for a lawyer to contractually condition any benefit in exchange for the client's promise to not bring a grievance.

This means you cannot say outright: "If you write off the last $10,000 I owe; I will not tell the Bar you helped me lie to the judge."

No, no; that kind of crass *quid pro quo* offer is actually what the Law might consider the crime of blackmail, of extortion.

A subtler way to get across that point and still maintain plausible deniability is to say, for instance: "Hey, counsel, I am having pangs of guilt about that false testimony we cooked up together . . . But maybe I am overreacting . . . Maybe I just need a vacation . . . But, sadly, I have no money after paying all your bills . . . By the way, you sent me a bill for $10,000. Could you cut me some slack here?"

Chapter Two

Can You Stiff A Lawyer?

NOW THAT YOUR FEAR OF CONSEQUENCES is assuaged let's talk the mechanics. Exactly how does one do it, how does one stiff a lawyer, what are the steps? The lawyer might not pursue a deadbeat client for unpaid fees, but how to get to that point? Won't the lawyer be smart enough to take precautions against being stiffed?

Let's cut to the chase.

The basic principles of stiffing your lawyer are easy:

First, entice the lawyer to work on credit;

Second, do number (1) as long as you possibly can, and then

Third, ditch the bill.

At its core, the art of stiffing lawyers is a simple dine and dash—the same principle as stiffing a restaurateur. Order, chew, swallow, and run.

Of course, this advice is akin to saying that the key to successful stock trading is to "buy low sell high"; it begs more questions than it answers.

Just how do you run up the tab at a legal establishment without getting thrown out like an unwelcome pub regular given the boot by a vigilant barkeep? How do you even get any legal work at all on credit?

The secret is in knowing that there are several chinks in the lawyers' armor. Gaming the system starts with understanding how the system works and studying its vulnerabilities.

The major vulnerability of every litigator is this: the day when the client ceases to pay is **not** the day when the litigator can quit representing the client in court.

If the case is already in court, the lawyer cannot just quit any day that he decides to. Of course, it does not mean indefinite servitude: lawyers can (mostly) get out of working for a non-paying client. But sometimes it can take weeks or months.

And now for the most important part: during that time when the lawyer is trying to get out of the non-paying client's service, the lawyer is nevertheless obligated by the rules governing his profession to continue to work diligently, and to give it the lawyer's best professional effort—despite the fact that the client does not pay.

That is the little-known (to clients!) chink in the armor, the vulnerability of the system, which clients can explore and exploit. Amazing, isn't it?

The "For the Geeks" blurb in the next section below details the steps that a lawyer is required to take in order to get out (withdraw, as the term has it) from representing a non-paying client. However, the exact steps are not important for now. What's important—the takeaway for this chapter—is that, for a lawyer who wants to quit representing a non-paying client, there are hoops to jump through, and that the jumping takes time, and that during all of this time, the unpaid lawyer must continue working zealously. So guess what? Make the most of hoop-jumping time and run up the tab while the lawyer is helpless to quit!

Easy enough? Of course, not. It begs so many questions. And not just the already identified issue of *"how you run up a tab?"* Even more puzzling, how does one even *start* a tab with a lawyer? It is no secret that most divorce lawyers want money upfront.

So what do you do?

In this chapter, we follow the adventures of stiffing expert Lucky Lynda, whose story exemplifies the top tricks of success at lawyer-stiffing. We then review the top mistakes which hopeful stiffers make and the best ways to avoid these blunders.

For the Geeks

Here is a very important thing to know: once a "representation" agreement has been made, and so long as there are any active court proceedings, a litigator cannot just stop working for his client without first getting permission. That is true even if the attorney has eminently good justification for wanting to bail out. Permission to leave (or as it is called in the industry, to *withdraw* from the representation) can come in only two ways. One source of permission is, as you might expect, the client. It many times happens, however, that it is not in the client's best interests to willingly set the attorney free. When the client refuses to agree, the attorney must engage in a formal judicial process in order to get a judge to agree to the withdrawal.

For permission from the judge, the following steps must be taken.

First, the lawyer must prepare and file a written *motion* explaining what is the justification for leaving (for instance, if the client is not paying, that normally is a good enough reason).

Second, the lawyer must deliver his Motion to Withdraw to the client and to the opposing counsel, and give each of them some time, usually *about a week,* to respond.

Third, a courtroom hearing is held where the lawyer will ask for permission from the judge to drop the client and the other interested parties may speak up pro or con if they wish.

Usually, the judge does give the requested permission.

What drags out this process is the need to schedule a hearing. Although, in theory, the judge could hear the matter within about a week, this is not what happens in practice. Often, the first available date for the withdrawal hearing is not for a few weeks, or even a couple of months. During that time, the lawyer has an obligation to continue working "zeal-ously" for the client—paid or not.

This is the obligation that provides potent ammunition for savvy clients who know how to take advantage of it.

LUCKY LYNDA HIRES A LAWYER

LYNDA ADAMS, (a multimillionaire's wife, but otherwise a woman of no perceptible independent substance) earned her place in the annals of the Ducklingburg local courthouse rumor-mill as the Serial Mulcting Queen.

Lynda's reign over Ducklingburg lawyers ran roughly for eight years. Yes, eight!

She sponged off the local legal talent for so long and with such brazen abandon that being her dodo was becoming a rite of passage for the ripening members of the local Bar. Around year three of her divorce process, the rumors of Lynda's mastery had reached the status of a local legend, shared in hoarse whispers among legal secretaries. At year eight, the semi-secret society of Lynda's former lawyers would need three mid-sized plastic tables to seat down together shame-facedly for whatever solace could be gained by sharing their regrets.

The sum total of unrequited invoices, which these attorneys had presented to Lynda over the years of pushing her case along before the glacially-moving divorce judge, exceeded that particular divorce judge's annual salary at least ten-fold. (The economics of divorce litigation being what they are, it is hard to resist the conclusion that there must be a way to persuade those judges in some manner that is more cost-effective than paying lawyers. But that is an another day's story.)

Lynda duped the town's lawyers for eight years. Eight generations of law students received their diplomas, sat for the Bar exam, and took oaths, ready to provide Lynda with her new pick of chump lawyers.

All that while, Mrs. Lynda Adams was still the talk of the town. Her husband's wealth was only rivaled by the notoriety of his charity themed productions and his bewildering gambling wins (Rick played cards and, somehow, never lost). Both the charities and the gambling caused media frenzy each time the Adams name was mentioned. Rick Adams's star brightly radiated its reflected halo around Lynda. In turn, each lawyer whom the lucky woman deigned to draw into her orbit, was brightly irradiated with Lynda's moonlight halo, acquiring instantly the coveted status of Ducklingburg C-list celebrity.

Five times during the Adams's divorce process, the Ducklingburg Herald featured Lynda's new lawyer. On The

Herald's page six, the next new mark's honest face was shining with expectant smiles of impending riches. None of those lawyers stayed smiley for long.

I would love to tell you that in these eight years our local lawyers got organized, created a *Lynda support hotline,* or at least forged a cautionary website with her picture in mugshot format and, in flashing neon lights, dire warnings of her foxy financial snares. I would love to tell you that no lawyer could possibly be as gullible as Lynda's.

I really, really would love to be able to say that. But when I set out to write this book, I resolved to never exaggerate the divorce lawyers' ability to cooperate with each other or their smarts and talents, and so I here too stick resolutely to the shameful truth. The truth is that Lynda only stopped defrauding the local lawyers because she no longer had any use for them. After eight years of heated litigation, her divorce was finished, and she no more had a use for a lawyer than a woman has use for a midwife after the baby is already born.

I would likewise have liked to tell you that Lynda succeeded because she had preyed on the weak or the young—lawyers too decrepit to see the fraud or suffering from a bad disciplinary record, or challenged by too ardent a recourse to seeking wisdom in a whiskey bottle. But that wasn't it either. Lynda's victims were strong, healthy specimens, all of whom should have known better than to trust her.

Membership in Lynda's Dodos' Club extended to many of the town's fat cat lawyers. They, each of them, knew how to collect big bucks from a client. Yes, Lynda's lawyers were no wilting violets when it came to getting paid by their regular clients. Still, they were no match for Lynda.

LYNDA'S first lawyer worked ten months before he came to terms with the sad truth: Lynda would never, never, never pay. The Ducklingburg legal community judged the first guy harshly: mocked him, gloated, called him "slow on the uptake."

Ten months *is* a long time for unpaid bills to pile up. He should have woken up sooner. He should not have taken Linda at her word. His simple-mindedness shamed the profession. Even men in much simpler and much happier professions—like lawn or pool care—would have tumbled to the true situation and escaped long before ten months. A lawyer who displayed the lack of wit required even by these simple professions was a disgrace. "Dumber than my pool guy," the lawyers snickered.

"WHY did he stay on so long?" I asked bluntly, but feigning disinterest.

I had gotten myself invited to the *Jackal's Wednesdays*, a weekly lunch of a semi-secret society of a few lesser lawyers of Ducklingburg.

Can You Stiff You Divorce Lawyer?

Divorce lawyers, like any other social unit, have a hierarchy. There are Lions who rule the jungle, and also the less important inhabitants: Wolves, Panthers, Bears and, of course, the Jackals—opportunistic omnivores who scavenge the scraps.

None of the Wednesday Jackals would be strong enough to take on Lynda's case, but they scavenged the best gossip. Lions were a tight-lipped gang, proudly guarding their secret defeats and deficiencies. I'd tried for months to get invited to the Lion's Brunches . . . In vain. Lions did not speak to the outsiders, and that was final.

The Jackals were not all that welcoming to strangers either.

In theory, the Jackals had an open table policy—anybody could pull up a tray and join in; they'd never met a lawyer they could not embrace. They even welcomed a few non-lawyer strays, so long as the strays agreed to worship in silence. Of course, all the lawyers they'd met before me were born in the three-hundred-mile vicinity of Ducklingburg and, thus, were potential members by birthright. My outlander birth might provoke a re-thinking of the heretofore "all comers" policy, I feared. Not leaving things to chance, I contrived to weasel in by invitation.

Oddly enough, my prospective source of an "in" to the Jackal's table was an artist, a pet portraitist I'd met at the mall where he had his own booth. The day we met, Pet Art was immortalizing a cantankerous King Charles spaniel, serenely applying ochre to the canvas above the hind left paw. The Artist smiled kindly at his canine model, who growled and jumped and snarled elaborate threats and canine obscenities which anybody fluent in Dog would be perplexed to discover in such a purebred's vocabulary.

"Rescue?" I ventured, reaching to pet the cantankerous creature, who immediately leaped to take a healthy bite out of my hand, but missed on purpose and slammed his tiny jaws with a threatening snap.

"Picked up some bad language in the pound," agreed the Artist.

Pet Art was a kind, resolutely bliss-minded man. First thing he said after I answered his "what do you do?" query was: "My friends are lawyers! You should come to lunch on Wednesday!" I jumped at the chance.

The thought that not *all* lawyers welcomed *all other* lawyers had never crossed his guileless mind, not even after he had made my introductions to the group. At least for this one time, his sunny view prevailed. I got a seat at the sacrosanct table with the Jackals and went straight for the gossip.

I'd heard some rumbles about *The Adams Divorce*, but never held my ear to the ground. Most of Lynda's Dupes came and went before my arrival in Ducklingburg, and their fate and struggles were nothing more than a vague fable, a folk story featuring simpletons. Until today. Today, their fate was a diagnostic in an urgent matter.

"Why did he stay? Lynda Adams's first lawyer?" I asked, again striving to sound casual.

Of course the Jackals knew the answer:

"Kevin? He just couldn't believe it, is why," they jeered.

"What do you mean?"

"He made so much money for her," drawled the Jackal's leader, an out-of-work ex-judge who still cherished the dream of getting back his judicial bench to which he had failed to be reelected. The "Judge," as he still titled himself, started a new campaign each election cycle. but never made it past the primaries. The off-election months were spent "networking."

KEVIN KOOK, Lynda's first lawyer, was no simpleton.

It was just that he was doing such a swell job, and Lynda had so much money, that it was impossible to believe that some of an ocean of money would not trickle back in response to the flood of Kevin's invoices. He was winning big in the divorce process. Or, rather, Lynda was winning, Kevin not so much.

Ten months may be a long time to let an account go, but is not so long a time to grasp the death of a dream.

Every divorce lawyer dreams of "The Case." The fame, the money, the change in the arc of his hum-drum life as a bottom-dweller in the local legal community. Landing "The Case" is what separates celebrity divorce lawyers from the hole-in-the-wall, run-of-the-mill, "affordable divorce" market niche.

Ten months before he finally came to terms with his situation, Kevin was jubilantly certain that he'd finally landed

The Case. Because of the magnitude and complexity of marital assets involved, Lynda's bill for ten months would be at least three hundred thousand dollars' worth of legal services. No cost-effective measures needed to be spared and the billable hour meter would get a mighty workout. But mere money was not all that mattered. There was also the dream of a glowing future: Divorces like hers were how celebrity lawyers were made. Kevin was sure he'd come out of the Adams divorce as a celebrated divorce genius. And he was not just a dreamer; he was willing to work his butt off to make the dream come true.

Kevin moved his entire team to The Adams Divorce Taskforce and fired up the offense against Rick Adams. He started predictably and conservatively by suing Rick for alimony, the monthly payments for Lynda's living expenses, which claims were expected and richly deserved. Such expected opening shots hardly bothered the opposition legal team at all.

Not stopping with the expected, however, Lynda's crafty counsel added the flourish of a heart-balm tort: he sued the true culprit of the marital crackup—Rick's girlfriend of the year, reasoning that the collapse of Lynda's marriage had to be that strumpet's fault.

"That bawd inserted herself into your life and stole what's rightful' yours," he explained the law to Lynda. "The Judge'll make her pay. We lawyers call it *alienation of affections*. To protect the honest women from them stealthy home-wreckers. That should make 'em heads spin!"

Kevin was quite right, too. The heads did spin.

Though dead and gone in all except for a handful of American States, the law of alienation of affections is still kicking in the Ducklingburg State Courts. What's even better, our local courts are still no strangers to suits for "criminal conversation."

"Criminal?" frowned Lynda.

". . . conversation, criminal conversation. It's when you sue 'er for screwing your husband," came the laconic response. Kevin added that little claim as well, and filed the Complaint: "Lynda Adams vs. The Mistress."

As Kevin had predicted, that deft twist sent both Lynda' husband and The Mistress for a spin. While the enemy's camp panicked and the fearful Mistress made her man's life hell, Lynda's lawyer poked into the vast and byzantine business structures forged by Lynda's husband. Availing himself of the seemingly high ability-to-pay client, Kevin left no base untouched in the litigation. His team did not get to rest either. Kevin deputed his best lieutenants to several neighboring States and even a couple of unfriendly foreign countries where they spied on companies and subsidiaries unknown even to the IRS.

The resulting success was conspicuous. The sordid Mistress abruptly stopped her overweening rounds on the golf green across from Lynda's estate (Lynda's bedroom terrace opened to the view of the third hole). Instead, the Mistress was firmly trapped in her own lawyers' offices, struggling to escape from the chilling clutch of Lynda's alienation of affections lawsuit. The Mistress had reason to fear: the most recent suit for alienation of affections in Ducklingburg court had slammed the affection-stealing paramour with an $8,000,000 damages judgment. The criminal conversation, the screwing bit, would not cost as much as the home-wrecking bit, but was sure to cause intense embarrassment. Once the Mistress's legal counsel had warned her of the grim precedents, her extremities trembled so violently that Lynda's ex-husband dared not ask for any fun anymore.

On the other front of the attack, Mr. Rick Adams quickly found himself ordered to pay alimony for Lynda's *necessities*, which came to roughly $800,000 a year.

Kevin was triumphant, and justifiably smug. He bathed in a flood of self-satisfaction, a job well done. The Adams divorce was, most certainly, The Case. Lynda pressed his hand in hers and held it, thanking him. She was touched . . . She was indebted . . . She would never forget, and would tell all her friends . . ..

Still, there was no payment.

Considering the sparkling success of his efforts on behalf of Lynda, it was unfathomable to think that no commensurate fee would come the lawyer's way. But no matter how improbable, the truth eventually had to be acknowledged: Lynda was blissfully ignoring each and every one of his amply-justified bills for services rendered. Lynda would never pay.

It was time for Kevin to get out.

Because he already made his litigation appearance, Kevin had to stand before the judge and ask permission to drop off Lynda's case. That's when Kevin's shameful predicament became embarrassingly public: ten months with no pay! The courtroom filled with snickering professional competitors and some in the back seats sneered out-loud and called Kevin a gullible loser.

A few of them should have held their tongues.

IF Lynda had merely rested on her laurels after her first lawyer had chucked her, her accomplishment still would have been very significant. A ten months stretch of tricking Kevin into paying salaries to his associates, assistants, secretaries, runners, and all stripes of suppliers—that was quite a coup. Lynda had demonstrated an artful touch, a real expertise in the stiffing game.

But who could imagine that she would repeat this endeavor again and yet again, five times in total, tricking and successfully sponging work off five of the better divorce lawyers of our city? Why, that was unprecedented, and, indeed, was hitherto believed impossible. That is, impossible until Lynda showed how it could be done. Then it was believed that Lynda was the only one who could pull off such a trick.

Lynda did show the Ducklingburg legal elite what's what.

To inveigle not one, but five separate law firms, one after another, and to put each one to work without getting paid—that required pure genius. To do that trick in a small community of divorce lawyers where the lawyers who were this evening's laughingstock for toiling free for Lucky Lynda

110

were the very same ones who just finished laughed heartily at Lynda's victim of the day before—that truly smacked of sorcery. Without a doubt, Lynda Boyd Adams (that was full legal name of the legend, the name she gave in a smooth buttery voice when she finally got to the witness stand in her divorce court) had superabundant skills.

If Lynda would have used her skills in another, conventionally productive arena, she would have no doubt acquired for herself a Wiki page surpassing in its lengths and impact that of Ed Snowden.

In the eight years that the courthouse took to grind through her case, Lucky Lynda had eventually hoaxed five lawyers. Incredibly, there were even a pair of overlaps when two different firms helped Lynda, each ignorant of the other and each proud to have her as a client and hopeful to be paid. Each of the five chumps whom she had consecutively hoaxed, stayed deceived for about ten months, at the end of which term Lynda fell from their grace, and was bounced down like Eve rejected from the orchard.

Unlike Eve, however, Lynda's descent was quickly cushioned by plopping straight into the soft lap of a fresh patsy with a law degree. Looking back, the whole thing was incredible. It was like the whole local divorce lawyer's section was blindly lining up to serve Lynda's legal cause—and to do it gratis.

Her first lawyer was played for a fool, and so was her second. But at least it was understandable that they took the case.

There was no excuse for lawyer number three even to

take the case, to start a tab for Lynda. By then, it was a received wisdom on the street that Lucky Lynda did not pay
her lawyers. Lawyer number three clearly was not paying attention. Did he not know the score? Or did he, as litigators
often do, think he was better than the ones that went before
him? History did not pay the guy enough mind to preserve
any record of why he had such unjustifiedly hopeful expectation, but it did preserve the final score: the fellow got
stiffed, just like the two before him.

I betcha that you're by now anxious to know a little bit
more about what wiles Lynda used on these lawyers, right?
Well, I have "the inside story" on one of those hapless attorneys and can therefore probably satisfy your curiosity as well
as give you a few laughs. And, speaking of laughing, I reckon
that the courthouse community rolled on the floor and peed
themselves when Lynda signed her lawyer number four.

That was me, Porter Law. My little firm.

WHAT gave Lynda such an irresistible allure was the
ease with which she *could have paid* for whatever efforts were
expanded on her behalf.

The Adams wealth was not in the billionaire league, of
course, but it was solid and, more importantly, it was well
documented, liquid and ostentatious. Lynda's jewelry collection alone appraised at over five million dollars. (That was
the Rick's appraisal. Lynda maintained the whole lot was a

112

mere three million and a half.)

At our first session together, Lynda dragged in a banker's box stacked with catalogues of her jewelry collection appraisals. Thick glossy loose-leafs of amateurishly lit photographs of the items put one in mind of a cheap restaurant menu with pictures and prices. The prices were hardly cheap, though. The top three pieces on the bling menu were also pinned conspicuously to Lynda's chest. Two from the third page jingled on her wrists. By conservative count, what she was wearing for this routine introductory meeting added up to half a million. If she were to drop a single jeweled pin, that would pay her legal fees for a month. It just was so darn *easy* for her to pay that it seemed inconceivable to think she would choose to lose yet another lawyer over non-payment of her bills.

"You are my last-est hope, Portia," sighed Lucky Lynda, reading my mind. "I cannot lose another lawyer. Will you agree to take my case? What do I need to do? What do you need in order to take me?"

Her words seemed desperate, but her voice was full, warm, and ... definitely happy. Her face, with no trace of nervousness or sadness, was only puzzled and pensive, as though she was working out her maids' schedule for the month, and found that she was one maid short. She did not ask if she could call me by my first name. She just did, and it resonated with warmth, not patronizing familiarity.

But her hands told a different story. To a body language expert, her hands betrayed distress which her face and voice had ably concealed. With her left hand, well dressed in iridescent stones, she twisted and pulled on her waist-long necklace of dark-orange garnets held together (according to the catalogue she brought) by granulated 22 carat gold. The garnets' deep, blood-hued lights washed an exotic warm aura around her face, and with each twist of her short, well-tended fingers, the diamonds on her wrist flashed rainbows of intensely surreal colors. Her whole ensemble coalesced into a scintillant halo, her face glowing effulgently in a kaleidoscope of red, orange, purple, and greenish sparks.

The gems she wore were not the sort of trinkets that entertain the fancy of an average housewife. They were not the type of baubles that can be spotted under a glass display at the mall, easily retrieved from behind the glass by an apathetic attendant with a practiced skill of intuiting the exact object at which the quavering finger of a penurious would-be beauty pointed.

No, Lynda's jewels were not the sort that languish under glass, for all mall-goers to gawk at and nervously ask to touch. Hers were the specially crafted jewels whose readiness was announced with a ring to her husband's office phone, and which were then artfully presented for inspection by Mr. and Mrs. Adams in a jeweler's secure back room. Approved and fitted, the jewels were finally delivered personally by the proud jeweler to the Adams residence. Yes, Lynda's gems were the real deal.

The diamondiferous creature flashed, glistered, sparkled scintillated before my wondering eyes. Each of her nervous twists and twitches revealed a new hue or facet of the gems, sending sun bunnies jumping around my walls, my ceiling, and my own face, filling the room with the reflected light of real wealth. I just basked. I'd never before been face-to-face with such bejeweled affluence.

Yes, a body language expert, trained in deception discovery techniques might have identified Lynda's twitches as the classic resort of self-pacifiers, typical ticks of distress, imprints of fear and doubt. But a body language expert might've missed the mark. Those ticks and twitches deliberately, "with malice aforethought" woke up Lynda's ostentatious wealth and craftily fostered the subconscious suggestion that Lynda was good for the money. The jewels were her demonstrable credentials of special status, like the spread of a peacock's feathers. Without saying as much, Lynda was strutting a display of her iridescent collateral, her indisputable ability-to-pay.

As near as I could tell, Lynda's *modus operandi* with her string of lawyers was to hitch the mark with promises of her abundantly advertised wealth, then pay with more promises, and more promises yet—until she at long last ran out of credit. I did not want to judge my fellow lawyers, but I knew I was smarter than that. I'd want some security upfront. Something very tangible.

True to form, Lynda promised to pay, and in a form designed to allay my fears.

"It is not an empty promise," she said continuing to read my mind, "I will guarantee it. I am selling a cottage. You get cash from the proceeds."

She tapped the pristinely clean screen on her phone, inviting me to see the "cottage." Indeed, the realtor's website flashed "sale pending" under the listing she had selected—a cozy but jolly well situated house. The landscape on the photos looked as though it had been fastidiously maintained by an invisible team of arbor artists who made certain that the irises, the azaleas and the wild rose-bushes, all backed by tastefully shaped hollies, bloomed in harmony and in proper sequence. A happy listing; nay, a splendid one.

"I have the papers to show you," she ducked into her purse and pulled out a perfectly neat stack: the contract of sale and the paperwork for the impending closing. The day to close was set for next Thursday. The address matched. All the terms looked to be in order.

The settlement statement spreadsheet was stapled to the contract: her closing lawyers worked fast. I turned to the last page to see the promised "proceeds" I was supposedly getting as my payment source, and could not withhold a smile. The bottom line of the settlement statement looked just as bright and tidy as the house's landscape. The proceeds of the sale— diminished by the outstanding taxes, liens and some unpaid suppliers' bills—came to roughly two million dollars and some change, a sum more than sufficient to cover whatever legal bills I could generate that year, or even in the next five years or whatever.

Waiting for my betraying face to return to sober normal, I flipped through the list of those little liens and taxes, just to stall. I did not want to look too eager, so I looked down, hoping she could not read the greed in my telltale face.

The first half a dozen bills and liens in queue to be paid off the top in this house sale were roughly what you'd expect in a large, somewhat sloppily run household. A few thousand dollars in unpaid local taxes. The usual last minute bills:

the electrician,

window cleaner times four,

driveway cleaner times two,

the locksmith,

electric gate repair,

the same locksmith again. Mr. and Mrs. Adams must've kept the fellow busy locking out each other; then could not decide who should foot the bill.

All that was unremarkable stuff. Then I flipped a page and gasped and forgot all about my face. The tail end of the unpaid bills listing read:

> *Jane Holodny, maid, $1200 * 18 months*
> *Tim Holodny, garden, $1700 *18 months*
> *Jack Blick, garden, $2000 * 18 months.*

Did I read it right?

Could that possibly be true?

Lynda's own staff worked for her without pay, for a year and a half? Could that be right? Why would these people—presumably not rich—keep working? Why not get up and quit?

To heck with my telltale face, I was now gasping for words.

"The staff's salaries?" was all I finally managed to croak. Sometimes I impress even myself with my eloquence.

I started again to explain the query, but Lynda understood perfectly.

She leaned in and for the first time since we met, Lynda's eyes flooded with copious tears.

"Those poor people," she sobbed softly, "they want to take care of me, they are like family." Then the dam burst.

Lynda had been even-keel, even cheerful, speaking about her own life, but the woeful treatment of her servants was too much. It was her husband's fault. She spoke about the court battles to obligate Mr. Adams for the servants' keep, and of his dark, cold indifference. A tear stuck to the bottom of her nose and glistened like a tiny star. Then her eyes glinted with resolve: "You must make Rick pay them. You can help Jane and Jack. And others!" If she was wearing makeup, crying did not hurt it. She was calm and brave like a little queen.

Her greedy husband defied his obligation to pay the maids and the gardeners. Not a penny beyond what was court-ordered and for Lynda's necessities. It was disgusting. I vowed to make the heartless cad pay.

With that decided, my mind wandered again, back to my own staff. If we accepted Lynda's case, that called for an all hands on deck mobilization—and the hands had to be paid. I could not put my people in the shoes of Jane Holodny, who was still waiting for Lynda's family to send her the past-due paychecks. Reading my mind again, Lynda leaned down to her purse, and solemnly produced a cream-colored personal stationary on which the Letters L and A intertwined in a happy hug. With a firm hand, she titled the note: "Directive to my Home Office."

> *June 7, 2014*
>
> *Dear William Johnson,*
> *RE: Sale of cottage on 1727 Rosehip Street*
> *All proceeds from the cottage sale must be paid*
> *out to my lawyer, Portia Porter, for my bills.*
> *Will you see to that yourself?*
> *Lynda Adams*

I watched her sign and date the directive in a firm, beautiful hand.

Under normal circumstances, with a regular client, that note was the closest thing to money-in-the-bank. But it was Lynda, and she had her reputation.

I hesitated.

When first we discussed the policies of my law firm, I had announced to Lynda my Unbreakable Rule: *no client is accepted without a retainer upfront.*

A *substantial* retainer in her case. Enough to tide over the whole crew until we are released by the judge, even if she never pays another bill again. Lynda was offering a lot of money, more than I even expected. But it was not exactly upfront. It still would technically break my rule.

Lynda sensed my hesitation. She tensed, like Kipling's Bagheera, readying for a pounce. We looked at each other, and I felt a little like a bull—strong but slow—staring into the eyes of a poised hunter panther.

"Today is Tuesday?" I said tentatively.

She was offering "all proceeds," the two million and change as the collateral. That was plenty to guarantee the fees, much more than I ever would have asked. And it was more than that. Getting paid by Lynda meant more than just a huge pile of money. It was hooking the White Killer Whale. It would bring every Ducklingburg lawyer to their knees in jealous envy and awe. Even without money, being Lynda's lawyer meant front page coverage in the Herald, the sort of fame guaranteed to bring flocks of paying wannabe celebrities, all those intent on keeping up with the Adamses.

Besides, her jewelry alone was enough to guarantee my fees. Maybe she had reformed. Perhaps I could even persuade her to use the rest of the cottage proceeds to pay those lawyers she'd stiffed before me. That would make me a heroine in the legal community. Perhaps there'd be an invite to the Legal Lions brunches . . ..

The dream of worldly riches and local glory infiltrated my face, wearing down the sternness of my stare at the sleek black panther.

"I'll write a check," purred Lynda, "to tide it over until Tuesday. Will twenty-five thousand be enough?"

That seemed legit. Now she was not leaving herself any way to wiggle out of the payment . . . My stare struggled, and I knew I *blinked*.

I blinked and Lynda leaped: "But you must promise me one thing."

At that precise moment, the fight was lost. My jugular was cut, but, foolishly, I noticed not.

"What do you want?" I returned bluntly, still under the illusion that I had the better part of the stare-down.

"I just absolutely need peace of mind. Let's sign our contract now, so you *are* my lawyer."

Like Panther Bagheera, her voice was sweeter than wild honey dripping from a tree and her fur softer than down.

She almost purred: "I just cannot be without a lawyer anymore."

She reached out to take my hand in hers, her jewels shimmering as she moved. Ever-so-sweetly, she went on: "I cannot be alone, Portia. Not for even one more day. The whole of Ducklingburg, they're all under Rick's thumb, nobody has the courage to defend me, none of the other lawyers. You are not *afraid* to take me on as a client, are you?" she murmured softly.

I was tempted to mention that there were other reasons she had hard time finding a lawyer in Ducklingburg, but it seemed like gratuitous rudeness. Lynda was already tearing a check out of her checkbook. It was a well-battered, regularly used checkbook, with a real address in the top left corner and a twelve hundred something serial number on the check. The check checked out.

To my eye, Lynda appeared finally to be reformed. A long divorce battle will do it for you. It'll make you see who your friends are, and value of staying true to one's word.

WE signed our contract and talked for a few hours after that. We clicked, Lynda and I. We saw eye to eye on her divorce strategy. She was straightforward, honest and sensible. She was grateful for my help when I impressively untangled a few legal technicalities that bothered her, and that her prior lawyers could not explain to her satisfaction. She was forthcoming with answers to my questions. She did not sugarcoat her role in the break-up and did not demonize her ex-husband.

I looked down at her hands. Lynda no longer twitched or twisted. The nervous jingling vanished. Every precious stone on her body was peacefully in place. Every diamond and jewel now shone calmly in unison with the others, proudly framing her figure in a steady glow that quietly but firmly guaranteed our deal.

JUST before parting, Lynda had one more favor to ask of me.

"Name it," I said.

"It's about my check," admitted Lynda.

I should have known! All I could manage was: "What?!"

She was just wondering: could her check stay under a paperweight until Monday? Her banker would for sure move the funds into the account to cover the $25,000 retainer.

"Today's Tuesday," I deja vued again.

"There's probably enough in the bank to cover the check anyway," said Lynda pensively. "You could try it... but..."

She just wanted to make absolutely sure. So just until Monday? Banking business loathes haste—at least when the money is being transferred *out* of the bank. So maybe her caution was reasonable?

Leaving, she leaned in for a hug, and whispered: "I am so happy you are my lawyer now. I know you will fix all the mess in no time at all. Thank you for trusting in me!"

The hug caught me by surprise. I have a rule about hugs with the clients: I don't. There are complex professional and psychological reasons for preferring a firm handshake, and I could go into lengthy blabber about professional responsibility, preserving the leader's distance, and the need for an authority figure. All these are decent reasons, but none of them is *the* reason. The real reason I do not hug my clients is not something one would want to tell a client. It's really for personal comfort: my clients are unhappy people. The simple truth of the matter is that clients' hugs are a cesspool of fear and desperation that conjures up a bad odor in the nostrils of my admittedly over-active imagination. Divorcing people emit an emotional stink! It's not that I am squeamish, I am not. It's a bigger problem. The whiff of fear and distress will infiltrate and nest inside one's nose, take hours to dissipate, all the while subverting the brain's logical thought, chasing the brain down with a primordial command to curl into flight or spring into a fight. There are simply not enough hours in the day to recuperate from the emotional miasma.

A girl who works for a living must build up defenses—or nothing will ever get done! So that's why there's the office rule. The clients stink, so stay away.

But not Lynda!

Lynda's hug conjured up the early morning in a rose garden, the burst of smell at the precise moment when the cold stream of sprinklers propels up thousands of ice-cold drops to hit three hundred closed rose petals—and startled and smiley, the roses wake up. And was there not also a bright twist of a late-night jasmine aroma in Lynda's hug, the smell that lightens the dip of the evening descending into the night? Lynda's scent was just as sparkling as her bejeweled halo.

Lynda smelled *happy*.

CATCH THE MOUSE, KEEP THE CHEESE

LUCKY LYNDA WAS TALENTED at the difficult task of trapping lawyers without putting up a penny upfront.

Sure, she paid for the *first consultations*—it would be foolish to show her true colors the first hour she met a lawyer. And besides, what was a few hundred dollars? Peanuts compared to the total representation fees!

Sure, she *promised* to pay.

Sure, she spun a solid story, and just as importantly, she had excellent *props*.

In my case, there was her $25,000 check that looked and felt completely genuine, seemingly good as gold. Also, a contract for sale of a magical cottage with gardeners and maids

whose salaries and names were listed on a professionally prepared spreadsheet and, for even more verisimilitude, were all
long past due: who would dream up an unpaid maid?? That
had to be the truth.

And sure, in a somewhat fairy-tale-ish twist, there was
an autographed directive that gave me *all* the proceeds of sale
of the Magical Cottage. The directive listed as its executive a
gentleman called William Johnson, a name more so plain va-
nilla that it might have been more fitting for a witness protection participant.

Absolutely all of the sale proceeds. The very grandness
and superabundance should have tipped me off.

It is not that the sale proceeds would necessarily exceed
her legal bills, in the end. Cases like hers, requiring experts,
and travel, and multiple lawyers tended to drag on for years,
often requiring forays to appellate courts. A couple million
dollars was not an outrageous sum, if one wanted to prepay
the full cost of the case that would be hotly litigated with "full
mobilization of the troops" in my small firm. But that Lynda
would really *prepay* anything... well, that was truly the stuff
of dreams.

IN the bright light of the morning, I hit the hard bottom
line: I woke up as Lynda's lawyer, with all the obligations,
duties, worries, and the work requirement which the title
carried. My task list spanned from finding corporate tax

counsel to outfitting three new laptops for three new gofers I had to yet hire. Also, there was the contempt motion against Lynda which Mr. Adams had apparently been long pressing, and which now was figuratively coming to a boil, scheduled for a court hearing on Thursday of the next week. There was even a need for an expert graphologist who might attest to the authenticity of some handwritten evidence and disputed signatures.

Meanwhile, Lynda had not yet parted with a single additional penny of hard cash beyond the couple hundred dollars paid at our yesterday's meeting—a drop in a bucket compared to the cost of expanding my team to work her case.

The morning broke at 7:20 with a fifty-page fax spilling out of the machine all over my kitchen floor. Before I had the time to set into a panic, both my cell phone and my landline gave rings in stereo, and when I cautiously pecked my google-phone message delivery, emails bearing Lynda's name on the subject line came popping up like hungry fleas—questioning, demanding, threatening, reminding of a "scheduled date," copying me on a letter to a judge about some apparently urgent matters that I had no idea could even exist.

By 8:10 A.M. the day after Lynda came to see me, Lynda's case was in full throttle. It took over my little firm so completely that everybody wondered what it was we did here before. The tornado of activity blew the lids off everything including our heads. There was no time to do or think or question. Putting out Lynda-related fires was all we could manage to do. There wasn't even time for a pee break. Most definitely, there was no time to squeeze Lynda for additional money.

Still, it occurred to me that I may have badly underestimated Lucky Lynda, and overestimated my intelligence.

A prudent lawyer remembers that starting work without pre-pay paves the way to troubles. Still, like all the overly trusting souls before me, I became Lynda's lawyer and jumped into doing her biddings with zero actual cash to show for it. I was not smarter than those credulous lawyers before me. As it turned out, I was not even minimally prudent. Lynda had artfully dangled her hook and I had swallowed it crook, liar, and stinker.

How did she do it? What can you learn from Lynda's story?

At its core, successful stiffing—like any magic—hinges on distraction and misdirection. Distracting a lawyer from taking client's money upfront is a task not unlike luring a mouse into an empty mousetrap: it can be done, but it is more of an art than a science. Lucky Lynda was a maestro, a genius, a Leonardo DaVinci of lawyer-stiffing. She also had the benefit of appearing fairytale rich. But clients who are nowhere near as wealthy or talented can—and have—reproduced her technique. Even a passable aptitude and lots of hard work can copy the Old Masters and produce passable performance.

The first thing one learns from studying the way of Lynda is her showy pretense of apparent eagerness. To say that Lynda came across as willing, ready, and able to pay would be an understatement. She was happy to pay her lawyers, or so she said. Happy, honored, even enthusiastic. Lawyers do not work for free: she totally got that. She never once hinted that there was even a possibility that she might require work and not pay for it. That willingness-to-pay seemed so natural in her. She understood the value of the lawyers' services and would not presume to cheapen it.

But take good notice of the number one mistake which clients less canny than Lynda make: astonishingly, the clients flat out send warning signals that alert their potential future lawyers of a possible plan to stiff. You, on the other hand, now know enough to imitate the wiles of Lynda. So, stop right here and prove it to me.

Or, rather, prove it to yourself.

HONESTY IS NOT THE BEST POLICY

COMPLETE AND UNVARNISHED HONESTY is often not the best policy in a close relationship. In a client-lawyer relationship, a client might suffer no harm from being brutally honest about a great many things. Lawyers are not judgmental about the faults and foibles of their clients and, indeed, can often do a better job if they know a client's faults. But it is a mistake to be honest about one thing: the client's looming inability to pay. Clients think that being honest is a good policy. They think they are "building rapport."

"I am going to be honest with you, Ms. Porter," a client would say, "I do not have that much money."

In actuality, that is not being honest. That is simply an

announcement that the would-be client is wasting the unfortunate lawyer's time. Yes, there is such a thing as being way too honest with your lawyer.

———

HER name was Desdemona and she was entirely honest. That tripped her up.

Also, her timing was piss-poor. She called me in the morning, on the second Tuesday of the month, a day when the South Duck Court of Appeals releases a batch of its decisions to the public, when our High Court judges, in their wisdom, renovate the legal landscape, inch by inch. Or at least it seems that way to attorneys in appellate practice. In any event, the first and second Tuesday of each month is when it all happens. Those morning are sacred to my brand of lawyers.

I had an appeal in the works, and so we huddled around the computer to wait for the new Appellate Court's opinions to surface: my eccentric office manager and the Boy Friday crew of two fresh college drop-outs, all of us trying to act nonchalant. I was compulsively hitting the "refresh" button for the Court's webpage. There was a case in the pipeline before mine. The decision would change the landscape on my own pending appeal. It was a life-and-death difference. Well, to the extent there is life-and-death difference in divorce law, which is actually questionable for anybody with a healthy perspective. But we did not have a healthy perspective. We were divorce law obsessives for whom healthy perspective was overwhelmed by neurotic professional interest. So, we were staring at the blank, unresponsive screen, waiting, watching the cursor blink.

Desdemona's call rudely intruded. Inopportune timing if there ever were one: she could not have done worse interrupting a funeral procession of one of those Appellate judges. In fact, that might have been a better day. But Desdemona did not select a propitious moment for her call. She chose the sacrosanct time when the Judges revealed their opinions.

I should not have picked up the phone, but I did.

"Do you do divorces?" queried a quavering voice.

I fessed up that I did.

"You are the lawyer?"

I fessed up to that too.

"You're a woman, right?"

I felt a trap there, but before I could go into evasive mode, her slightly emboldened falsetto went on, increasing in speed as her story developed.

"You are a woman, right. You will understand. My husband kicked me out," she said, and I was pretty sure I heard a soft sob.

"May I ask your name," I interjected, but she had no interest in revealing her own name.

"He will not call back, I have no money, I live in the car!" now there definitely was a sob.

"I really need your name," I repeated, for lack of anything warmer to say.

"And he gives me silent treatment; that's the worse part, the silent treatment. And we do have money, but he froze all the accounts, because the judge is conspiring with my ex-husband, and my lawyer refuses to do anything until I pay him."

"*Until you pay him!*" I could almost hear a door slamming in my brain.

WAS she listening to herself?

Stop for a second. Pause the tape!

This woman is already *not paying* one lawyer, and what does she do? She calls a fresh lawyer. Fair enough. But then, before she even meets me, she rats herself out for the deadbeat that she is. There really is such a thing as being too upfront and honest. If Lynda is an archetype technique, then Desdemona is the anti-Lynda who epitomizes the opposite end of the spectrum.

Have you ever contemplated making a phone call like Desdemona's? Maybe you would not dream of it. Maybe these phone calls are made by people who are all much dumber than you are. You are, after all, reading this book: you must already have some good sense, and are having more of it poured into your head page by page.

But the fact is, I really do get at least five calls remarkably like this with a frequency you might find amazing. People who want to be my clients are announcing themselves as broke. Think through this for a second. Would you call a wedding planner to tell them "I have no money, but can you please start planning the festivities today?" Of course not! The planner would hang up on you! And that's what I did to Desdemona, gritting my teeth at the waste-of-time interruption in my day.

MY office manager jumped up from her post at the computer screen, pantomiming like our whole block was on fire. But it was good news: The High Court of South Duck had smiled upon us in its latest outpouring of wisdom. It was a day to drink champagne, update my blog, call all the frenemies in the appellate practice community. Score on for the Good Guys. Now the office was in mellow spirits, but not nearly mellow enough to take on Desdemona. She already blew it. She was, in a word, too honest about a Very Important Thing.

"What did they want, by the way," asked the manager, gesturing towards the abandoned phone.

"Free work," I said, summarizing the call succinctly.

"No chance," came the predictable response.

Some clients just cannot help themselves, they just want to be so bloody honest! I have no idea why.

THINK BEFORE YOU SPEAK

IF YOU TRIED TO STIFF a divorce lawyer and failed, you only have yourself to blame.

Divorce lawyers make exceptionally easy marks. They are gullible because they are always in need. In need of more clients, in need of more money, in need of validation. People in need are a fertile playing field for scammers—that's common knowledge. Consider the State lottery schemes, widely pejoratively known as the "tax on the stupid and the poor." Rockefeller family members do not buy lottery tickets, nor does Warren Buffet. But poor people do. A lot. Lottery is a multi-billion-dollar industry.

You may be thinking: but lawyers are not poor or stupid. Lawyers are rich and arrogant! Lawyers make filthy piles of money!

You are partly right: some lawyers do make piles of money—but only a very few of them are in the divorce business. It is true that there is money to be made in the law, but one must pick a winning business model, and divorce law is simply not the easiest path to prosperity in the legal profession.

Generally, there are only two profitable schemes in the law: corporate or volume.

Corporate "white shoe" law firms make money the way the money is made in Nordstrom's fur department—by charging exorbitantly high fees off a handful of carefully selected, obscenely rich clients who expect exceptional services. Everything about this model is exceptional, just like Nordstrom's or Tiffany's. Prices—exceptional. Quality—exceptional. Security—exceptional. Client service—beyond exceptional. You can call firms like Sullivan&Cromwell at 3:30 A.M. New York time and find a tax partner eager to assist with such arcane points as tax-free spin-offs of a cash-rich subsidiary.

Lawyers who join the firms operating on this elite business model have inhumanly high work ethics and scarily high IQs. These lawyers work upwards of eighty hours a week and by their fifth year of practice get to a salary of a quarter million. Eventually, they get to a handful of millions, if they are very lucky and work even harder. The American Bar Association Journal reported in 2016 that an hourly fee that some clients pay for the BigLaw partners approached $1,500. Clients are willing to pay $1,475 for each hour of work for top lawyers at Proskauer Rose; $1,450 an hour for Ropes & Gray; $1,425 an hour for Skadden Arps. Believe it or not, the test of the marketplace says that they are worth every dollar that they earn, just like stars in the NFL or NBA.

On the other hand, a lawyer does not even need to have an especially high IQ to make good money. For a lawyer with bigger gonads than brains, *class actions* are the ticket. This sort of lawyer sues the pharmaceutical giants, conniving mortgage companies or polluting industrial plants. Amassing many thousands of clients into a large volume class action is an entirely different business model. It is not as taxing on the brain, it requires minimal client interaction, and there is relatively little actual legal work. There's a lot of legwork instead. For a retail analogy, think Walmart and Dollar Store. Hardly any client service. Class action law attracts lawyers with exceptionally large risk tolerance. When successful, class action lawyers may make billions, with a B. When unsuccessful, they may make nothing at all.

Those two models of the legal business are profitable. They are what is responsible for the popular image of rich lawyers.

But then there is divorce law. Clients here demand—nay, expect—an exceptionally high level of personal attention and exceptional service. They are not the sort of customers that can be happy when waved off to the back of the store with a general direction like "it's somewhere on isle three, or maybe six." Divorcing people are the type of customers that require VIP service: you take them by the hand, and sit them down in a plush chair, bring the merchandize to them, help them try it on, and assure that the fit does not make them look fat. A good divorce law firm model is, in terms of customer service, definitely more Nordstrom than Walmart.

On the other hand, most of divorce cases are regular people who want to pay regular prices. "Champagne tastes on a beer budget." Very few divorcing people are willing and able to pay $1,500 an hour for their lawyers—so prices-wise, divorce law is much more Walmart than Nordstrom.

There is no actual store chain that mirrors the divorce law business model, for the simple reason that a retail store like that would go out of business not long after it opened its doors.

If you imagine a Walmart-priced place with Nordstrom-level merchandise and service and only 30 shoppers-per-day capacity, you'd come close.

To put it gently, among legal practice areas, divorce law is a mutt that inherits every breed's most undesirable qualities.

When Katten Muchin & Zavis, a Chicago-based multistate legal giant swallowed a tiny North Carolina law firm which dabbled in real estate and divorce, the Chicago behemoth kept the little Southern firm's corporate lawyers, but (after a short but respectable time had passed) fired every single divorce lawyer on staff, even the ones that were "partners." Some of these lawyers were good, but none of them were profitable on the big-firm scale.

Divorce fees simply can never get high enough to rationalize the use of uptown skyscraper space. In a firm of over 500 lawyers in thirteen offices in every legal area imaginable—from antitrust, appeals, and aviation, to zoning and white collar, and everything in between from copyright to construction, divorce specialty practice is not a viable option. Think about it: the managing partners of KMZ found a way to squeeze nearly half a billion in profits from just about every area of the law. But not divorce. There was simply no respectable money to be made in divorce, no matter how hard they tried.

A divorce lawyer looking to make a buck is like a woman "of a certain age" in search of romance, compelled to always be on the lookout and never too particular. Divorce lawyers are forever hustling, forever chasing new clients. An average divorce lawyer is forced to welcome almost every client who expresses an interest (and can pay). He needs *you*, a new client, more than you need *him*. Heck, a lot of divorce lawyers actually pay some shady internet outlets for "leads" to get new clients.

So now you know: when you come though the divorce lawyer's doors, you are an asset.

Hold your head high!

Now what?

Now do not blow it.

As a general rule, when a heist fails, the root of its ruin traces to the perp's character deficiency more than to any security systems that the target of the crime had a foresight to put in place.

This rule holds equally fast when the heist in question is stiffing a lawyer. So what do you need to avoid burning your mission? Here's the script.

Do not give your lawyer reason to suspect that you plan to stiff him!

Divorce lawyers are pretty slow, but even this lackadaisical lot will dump you if you forewarn them in the first few minutes of the meeting that you have no intention (or ability!) to pay. This sounds so incredibly obvious, that I would not mention it (OK, *harp* on it) except for this: almost everybody who comes through my doors starts out by telling me that they, quite plainly, are likely to chisel me. This is amateurish and, frankly, a little offensive in terms of what the client implies about the value of my services and the depth of my gullibility. Nevertheless, it happens a lot. Why do people do it? Why would anybody tell their mark that the con is underway?

Even though I cannot prove it, I have a theory.

The problem is, in my opinion, that clients have no clue how they come across to lawyers. What clients think they are saying and what they are actually saying are vastly different things. Or at least what the lawyer hears is different from what clients think they are saying.

There are many ways in which these aspiring chiselers put lawyers on alert.

Some declare the plan quite plainly:

"I need a lawyer but I have no money," confesses a girl, even as she sinks with languid grace into the armchair across from the lawyer's desk. She has been in the lawyer's office for two minutes flat, just barely past the first introductions. The hands had been pumped, the fake smiles forced, the lawyer asked her to get comfortable in the seat, and as the would-be client settled herself in the chair, she declared... "*I have no money!*"

Does she not hear what she is saying??

This prospective client has just exposed herself as a non-paying customer. Does she not realize it? From the lawyer's point of view, this "no money" confession should be the girl's cue to head for the exit. And yet, somehow, she is still comfortably reclined in the office, whispering on: "My husband has not given me a penny since he left... I have nowhere to turn to... it is killing me! You ought to make him pay! I need your help, please . . ." She dabs her nose with the ever-present paper tissue, and sniffles out in the direction of the lawyer:

"I *need* your *help*."

Cue in the longing look, which the lawyer parses as "It's your turn to work for me since my hubby quit! So buckle up!"

If the same girl had found herself making this exact plea in a restaurant—she'd be slinking out of the bathroom window just about now. But not at the law office. Something about the comforting confidentiality of the law office makes her feel it's OK to boldly declare her impeding heist.

To be sure, not every prospective client just comes right out and declares that there is no money. The same message is, at other times, delivered less bluntly. Indeed, there are as many ways in which the clients fess up as there were plots in Scheherazade's tales.

"I'll be honest," another girl murmurs in a cadence implying a juicy secret, "You know I *can't* pay you *just now*." She pauses to make sure that she has the lawyer's full attention and moves in closer, looking straight into the lawyer's eye "but do not worry, you will get every penny."

How? When? With what money? She does not say.

Then there is one more classic approach: the waterworks. A lot of women will simply start crying. And keep crying. And keep at it. And cry every time legal fees are mentioned, and refuse to let up until the lawyer drops the entire subject of money, base and offending that it is.

Then there is the appeal to the heart, especially if the lawyer has a family.

"Do it for my children . . . sob . . . you have daughters too . . . sob . . . you understand," the girl nods at the lawyer's desk where the proud photographic display of the lawyer's progeny is presented in varying stages of maturity.

The girl is quite right: the lawyer *does* have daughters— a demanding sort in never-ending need of braces, shoes, scuba diving equipment and private school tuitions. The lawyer is also still repaying tuition debts which accumulated over the four years of college plus three years in law school.

A graduate of Campbell University Law School will have paid $115,935 in tuition by the end of the three-year law school program. (If you are wondering "what's Campbell University?", the answer is "Exactly! That's the point of my example.") A graduate of Brooklyn Law School will have paid $145,248 in three years. Since law schools do not accept applicants without a college degree, the lawyer whom the girl

has just importuned for free work had also paid (or borrowed) funds for college tuition, which, according to the
College Board reports, has amounted to between $93,640
(public schools) and $185,088 (private schools). And this is
the tab if the lawyer chose a "moderately priced school,"
whatever that may mean right after a sentence containing
numbers large enough to buy a house for four.

Yes, you read that right: by a very conservative estimate,
a divorce lawyer has invested at least a quarter of a million
dollars. But that's not all. A divorce lawyer has also spent
seven years total in college and law school, foregoing full-
time employment (read eating Ramen noodles and living in
moldy apartments). He did all that with the rosy dream of
striking it rich when—oh happy day! —he passes all exams
and finally can call himself a Lawyer, an Attorney at Law. In
further pursuit of the dream, he then rented an office, bought
a suit, shined his shoes, pressed his shirt, and turned up with
a wide smile to meet the prospective client who struck an elegant pose on his rented furniture and made him this query:

"I do not have money now, but I really need your help,
please?"

The issue here is that of differing expectations.

To the client in need, "please help me" means just that,
an SOS: "I deserve better than staying in this horrible dead-
end marriage. Somebody has to save me."

But what the lawyer hears is something different: "I plan
to steal your time and energy and money and pay you nothing. Because that's what you deserve. To service me. Because
I deserve it."

You see how we have an expectation difference here?

Now that you have considered the sheer expense of getting that law license, you might better understand the reason that after seven years of school and with over a quarter-million-dollar debt demanding pay-off, lawyers often resist an invitation to work for free.

Am I suggesting that you must feel sorry for your divorce lawyers and prepare to pay every penny of their fees? Of course not! You deserve justice, and the lawyer can be lured into delivering said justice at a seriously discounted price. If that's your goal, then maybe it's why you chose to delve into the secrets revealed in this book. But for the love of apples, don't just bluntly spit it out! Don't tell the lawyer your exploitation plan. It's a conversation that will get you nowhere.

Like this:

Rose Bloom (a handsome well-dressed woman on her second divorce): All I said was: I can't pay *just now*. I will pay *every penny*.

Lawyer Tom (late twenties): When?

Rose: Just as soon as I can.

Lawyer Tom: How do I know you'll pay?

Rose: Oh, give me a break. I have always been good for the money; we've never stiffed the help.

Lawyer Tom: You tried that line at Starbucks?

Rose: That's different!

Lawyer Tom: How? Because their baristas are less gullible than our barristers?

You get the point. Announcing openly that you want

free work will just get you a strong pushback.

"I do not work for free," Lawyer Tom will counter, and that will be that.

But don't lawyers have a duty to work for free when people have no money? you might wonder.

The answer is: No; not this *private* lawyer, not on this *divorce* case.

Sure, there are *organizations* which, greased by benevolent endowments, provide some free legal services to the poor, but you mostly have to be food-stamp-level indigent in order to qualify. And the legal problems that qualify are often of the sort that might land someone in jail. At best, you might get free help in a child support dispute. But never just to divide marital property.

This may appear egregiously unjust, and you might think you deserve better. But the truth is that, to my knowledge, no person or government has ever endowed a legal service group in aid of a middle-class housewife on a war path against her crook of a husband who is plainly cheating the woman out of the richly deserved two hundred thousand dollar 401K. Or a Honda. Or even a double-wide. And, if anything, the prospect of free legal assistance is even dimmer if the gender is reversed, where the husband is the party in need.

Here in America, there are entities that subsidize lawyers who defend non-paying tenants. We give out free legal help to (alleged) thieves, murderers and drug dealers, just so long as they are sufficiently "low income." But charitable minds engender no enthusiasm for the notion that, for the greater strength of American justice, a middle-class house-wife must get a free lawyer to help her get a fair shake at di-vision of marital property, or a middle-class husband can get help securing a few hours a week with his children. (Child support, by the way, is a different story. Low income claim-ants might get help suing a deadbeat parent for child sup-port. Can I warn one more time that income must be very low?)

By the way, "free" public defenders, the Legal Aid law-yers and other free helpers do not actually sustain themselves on the moral high generated by aiding their righteous cause. Sure, figuratively riding white horses to work creates emo-tional benefits, but what's even more attractive to young law-yers is staying out of clutches of those nasty debt-collection agencies. Those student debts are non-dischargeable, and somebody has to pay them eventually. Programs that pro-vide student loan forgiveness are frequently what attract law-yers to work for entities such as Legal Aid. So "free" lawyers are not really working for free. They are working off their loans.

In contrast, many private divorce lawyers rely on noth-ing else but the hope that the client will pay enough to sus-tain the dream of one day being free of the specter of student-loan debts. Private lawyers need your money to service their own debts, to feed themselves and their families, or just to nourish their notion of leading *la dolce vita*. If you want a lawyer to take your case, your ultimate success depends on sustaining the illusion that you'll pay.

And so we come to the central point of this chapter:

I implore you, do not say these words: "I have no money," or "I cannot pay just now" or "Do it for my children." Turn off the waterworks when the money is discussed.

For years, I was flummoxed by otherwise bright women who'd blatantly and even repeatedly reveal their intent to, in effect, steal from me. At the risk of pissing off the feminists: men are not ever as bold about it.

Why? The same girl would not tell a restaurateur she'd chew-and-screw. Shuffling the deck of cards for a crooked deal, no person would announce the impending swindle to the other players. Nor would the prospect of being a deadbeat ever be advertised in a clothing store, in a jewelry shop, or a hotel. But would-be clients do just that at the lawyer's office. Clearly, there is something about the legal profession that impels this bizarrely nervy honesty: women, who are neither poor nor dense plainly *demand* free work from a lawyer. Yes, legal services are expensive, but these same customers would never dream of demanding freebies from the purveyors of any other high-priced product line. It would be unimaginable for any of my non-paying clients to importune a cashier at expensive gourmet food emporium about her state of momentary penury. "I have no money today, dear. My husband, that rat-bastard, took it all, so I can't pay right now, but will you run me a tab for some champagne and oysters to wash away the grief? And what's the special on the sandwiches, hon?"

Heck, none of these folks would even dream of asking the Starbucks guy for a free cup of coffee, and that's under ten dollars, even with tip and tax. But asking a lawyer for ten thousand dollars of free work somehow seems a good conversation starter.

Why?! This had puzzled me for years until a client of mine, a lovely girl called Bella finally helped me crack that nut.

————————

BELLA and I were both in our mid-thirties when we met. She considered me a buddy because we were of the same age, although the age was where the similarities ended. Bella took pride in being a native Ducklingburger. She stretched her vowels, referred to "all of y'all," told loving jokes about Southern Women, and could easily use the art of cosmetics to paint an entirely new face over her own.

At age twenty-six, Bella had landed a perfect husband, a denizen of Ducklingburg nobility. A year before we met, Bella would avoid being in the same a room with a gal like me—a tumbleweed with no attribute of roots and not enough sense to cover up my face with an artful enhancement of what Nature gave me. We met when Bella suffered a little setback in what heretofore had been a charmed life: she came to see me as a self-proclaimed victim of an "unjust divorce," and she needed an advocate to defend her from the adverse consequences. Deep down, Bella was a cheerful and honest girl, with an open heart. Once she got to know me, she took a shine to me and tried to help with what she deemed my little personal flaws and idiosyncrasies. One day, she opened up about her reflection on *my* life philosophy.

"Thank God," she said "that there are people like you, Portia."

Bella was only lightly religious. We do live in the Bible Belt, though, and she felt obliged to give at least perfunctory credit to Creator of people like me.

"What do you mean?" I asked, fishing for a compliment and, indeed, fully expecting one. After all, she was grateful for people like me, right?

"People like you, who just *love* to work-work-work." She emphasized love with a child-like coquettish sigh, the way one would talk about loving puppies or pistachio ice-cream.

"What do you mean?" I repeated, concerned with a dawning realization that there was no compliment, after all.

"You just do not *love* anything else, just your work." She stopped to think and sighed sincerely: "Bless your heart."

Then, glancing askance to my ringless fingers that ended with unpolished nails, Bella opened up: "*I* could never do that much work, there is so much more in *my* life. But, thank God, *you* love working so much."

When Bella eventually stiffed me for the better part of my bill and refused to pay because "she really *needed* the money," it finally clicked for me: the genteel beauty did not stiff me to be mean. She honestly could not imagine what I'd do with the money. To her, money was her lifeline, a bridge to the goal of happiness and beauty. The hair, the clothes, the nails, the skin, the shoes, it was all extremely expensive. Did I mention the shoes, the many, many shoes?

149

Instead, my life's purpose was work alone, and I was sufficiently rewarded already. Didn't I get to work on her glamorous case? Didn't I get to revel in the satisfaction of a win? Didn't I get to boast on my website about that win? No matter how loudly I protested entitlement to fees earned in working on her behalf, all that she saw in me was a freak, purposed by the benevolent forces of Nature's providence to deliver *her* happiness.

When I eventually sued her for the unpaid three years' worth of work, she genuinely cried on the witness stand each time the money was mentioned.

"Didn't my services yield you at least one hundred sixty thousand dollars annually in alimony alone?" I narrated for the benefit of the jury.

"But he wrongly divorced me! That was what he *owed*," Bella teared up.

The jury's foreman was a redneck who worked hard for his modest living. He did not even buy into the alimony idea at all, much less for this wealthy young woman who obviously had done little to win these (in his view, undeserved) riches. The jury reasoned that Bella had to pay somebody, somehow. Their verdict was in my favor: Bella would be ordered to pay every penny of my fees.

But wait a minute, did not I just finish telling you that rational lawyers never sue clients for unpaid fees? I did. I also told you to not monopolize a lawyer's office for three years and then refuse to pay. Be considerate, don't push your lawyer into certain bankruptcy. Although I explained why suing a client is a bad choice, one always must ask "As compared to what?" Suing Bella was indeed a bad alternative, but the alternative of certain bankruptcy was even worse. By pushing me to the brink of financial ruin, Bella had, ironically, fallen afoul of her own great success in suckering me.

To be fair, Bella's obstinate refusal to pay my hardearned money was not entirely her fault. Her refusal to pay was dictated by her cultural programming. Like most Americans, Bella was idealistic. She believed in her cause—the middle-income housewife's right to be taken care of by her husband. That was a good, just cause, and here in America we always can rely on somebody to help a just cause.

Do not sneer. In our heart of hearts, we all believe that, even if only a little. Our TV shows are filled to the brims with top-notch private professional labor working tirelessly for the little guy in trouble. Surgeons and diagnosticians, private detectives, burnt spies, fixers, even a team of highly skilled criminals who provide "leverage," and, yes, lawyers—all of these privately financed professionals are eager to help the deserving cause that cannot afford to pay. At least that's how it is on TV.

Think of your favorite show that stars a professional— a lawyer, a doctor, a spy, a private investigator, a reformed thief. Got one in mind? Now consider this fellow's accounting. What's his balance sheet? Can he stay out of bankruptcy at least till the end of the show's season? Occasionally, the answer is unclear, but most of the time, it is a plain as day. Most of them are a clear fiscal disaster in the making. But do we call out the show producers on that lack of verisimilitude? Of course not. We suspend our disbelief for seasons on end!

Why? Because it does not matter one bit. Not only is that not what the show is about, but it is also not what our heroes are about. We simply do not think of professional services as a business or our heroes motivated mainly by money.

Remember *Burn Notice*, a spy show that ran on the USA network for seven seasons? Here's the actual logline from IMDb: "A spy recently disavowed by the U.S. government uses his special ops training to help others in trouble."

Raise your hand if you read the logline and the first thing that comes to mind is:

"Who's paying this spy to "help?" What's an hourly rate for those with 'special ops training?' Or even what about the spy equipment—who's paying for it?!"

What? I don't see your hand being raised? Of course that crass, profit-oriented consideration does not spring to mind! The former spy, no longer sponsored by the government, helping out deserving causes—what else could the poor sap want out of life? Surely not just an hourly rate?!

In case you missed all seven seasons of the show, here's the financial background: Michael Westen, a former spy, got fired from his government job. As part of his exit, the government froze all his bank accounts. He has no funding. To make a buck, Michael and a few of his closest friends help out civilians in need of spy-grade jobs. Michael's fee is mentioned in some episodes. Sometimes it is a couple thousand bucks. There are times when he helps out an old lady and it seems to him that even charging his expenses is wrong.

But why this shrinking from the notion that one must earn a living in order to make a living?

After grueling years (decades?) of training, intense personal sacrifice and constantly putting his life in danger, fictional spy Michael Westen has evolved into a highly skilled professional, admittedly the best in the industry and a worldwide legend. And yet, his work for the "little guy" is often done nearly for free, *so long as the little guy has a good cause.* And Michael is not just selling his skills and risking his life. He is also performing jobs that have large costs. There's the cost of the ammo, the arsenal of illegal explosives and guns, the clever home-made spy gadgets, the race car damage repairs, and surely there must be medical bills for all the cracked ribs and the burns and the concussions and the gunshots. Plus, the cost of the signature Armani suits which constantly get bloodied, burned, torn and punctured by shots. And then there are costs of rebuilding everything the bad guys burn down, blow up and chop into little pieces—from his mother's house to his own loft apartment. Once you make a quick mental addition of the cost of supplies and damage repair, you do not need an accounting degree to see that this freelancing spy is never out of the red. His business is a fiscal impossibility. It's not really a business, it is a Don Quixote, Ltd.

But are we, the audience, ever bothered by the flagrant unfairness of Michael's compensation for his good deeds? Not in the slightest. Are there furious viewers writing to the networks to demand that the little people who supposedly are Michael's clients stop taking advantage of Michael and pay him what he's worth? Not likely!

But why? Why is this spy expected to work for free? It's

not because the fellow is fictional and can't actually starve. That's not it. In other contexts, fictional characters have all sorts of problems that have the audience worried sick. Fictional characters suffer from poverty and gunshot wounds just like me and thee. It's not the fictional status that is at play here, it's the fact that Michael is a professional dedicated to the assurance that Justice will prevail no matter what. It is our culturally entrenched belief that certain types of professionals have a *duty* to donate their time and effort to those less evolved.

If you see a man choking in a restaurant and yelp for a doctor, the nearest medical professional will surely rush to the man's help. Afterwards, it would be unthinkably crass for the doctor to present you with a bill for services *you* ordered. Seemingly unthinkable. (Not to say that in the real world it does not occasionally happen.) But why is there an expectation of a freebie? If, instead of choking for air, this same stranger desperately needed a Vodka Martini, and you'd yell for the bartender's help, there surely would be a bill to pay.

The public has an entrenched notion that many types of professionals—men and women who gave up a big chunk of their youth in order to pursue a craft—have an obligation to serve the public. So long as the cause is deserving and the client cannot pay, the closest professional should drop everything and donate whatever time and effort is required, at any personal cost, even of putting personal safety or economic survival at peril.

Boston Legal, in many respects a brilliantly realistic legal show, opens with two exceptionally talented lawyers working to help a black kid who was denied the part of *Annie* in the eponymous Broadway musical. The child's mother is not exactly a client of their firm, the famously successful Crane Poole & Schmidt. The mother is a walk-in, or rather, a storm-in. She appears in the posh lobby, demanding that the law firm sue the musical's producers who—she asserts— had wronged her and her daughter. The point that she has no money to cover the fees never enters her diatribe. Of course, not only do some of the lawyers offer the free legal help she had requested, but these high-priced lawyers must compensate their own law firm, Crane Poole & Schmidt, for the loss in fees. It is a pay-to-work situation for these normally highly compensated lawyers.

But that's not what's interesting here. What's really fascinating is that the premise of high-priced lawyers, admittedly cynics, tripping all over each other to deliver free services to a woman they just met *feels* perfectly normal. We hardly pay this twist any mind at all. The requisite suspension of disbelief is virtually automagical.

Instead, imagine that the same woman would present her woes on a TV show called "Boston Roofers." See her storming into a roofing company, wailing about a leaking roof, demanding free help. Suppose also that the next scene on the show portrays two strapping roofers rushing off to help, competing with each all the way to see which one can fix the roof quicker and better. That sort of twist in the script would have gotten laughed off the networks, don't you think? At minimum, such roofers would be seen as an example of almost surreal angelic warmth and altruism. They would be immediately branded as the "over the chart good guys." On the other hand, Boston Legal's attorney Alan Shore—the lawyer who eagerly took free representation of the young star and her very pushy mother—hardly gets any special recognition at all for this large chunk of free work. He is *expected* to offer free services because he is a rich lawyer and that is his duty.

Art defines life and, of course, every divorce client—at least on some level—is persuaded that free legal services can be had, *if only the lawyer is persuaded that the client's case equals fighting for Truth and Justice.*

Which brings us back to Bella, the young damsel who stiffed me for three years' worth of work. As I said before, she was not entirely at fault for refusing to pay in the end. After all, Bella was a *woman with a just cause.* In her own mind, the just cause deserved free legal labor, and I just happened to be standing around with a law degree, ready to be drafted into the role of selfless Wonder Woman.

The reason I drag up this anecdote is because it seems to be a basic impulse for a woman bereft of her husband's support to barge into a private law office, grab the first lawyer by the lapel and strive to open the lawyer's eyes to the *injustice* of it all, until the lawyer sees that there's no choice but to donate six solid months of free labor to cure said injustice.

To be sure, I understand the client's impulse, I am not a monster, even if sad experience had taught me to take a jaundiced view of certain human proclivities. But here's the thing: I said at the start that the trick to successfully stiffing lawyers is to try and see the world from the lawyers' point of view, if only for a minute. And here's the lawyers' point of view:

Law practice is a business.

No matter how important your case seems to you, for a lawyer it is just business. As soon as the lawyer stops seeing it that way, he'll go out of business. The Shangri-La of free divorce lawyers fighting for the good spouse against the bad spouse is just that—a fairytale land of fiction.

Am I telling you that justice cannot be snatched without paying hard cash for it? Of course not. This whole book is about how clients can, and actually do, snatch oodles of free legal work. What I am warning you is that getting unpaid legal services is a subtle process, and going into a lawyer's office to *demand* free work is a very bad idea indeed. That kind of behavior is a doomed strategy based upon a counterfactual cultural mythology of entitlement.

Your first step is to simply refrain from fessing up that you are, in reality, a dangerous risk of non-payment.

It's that easy.

WHAT YOUR BODY LANGUAGE RE-VEALS

DO NOT BE UPSET if the previous chapter opened your eyes to the fact that what you had previously considered a cleverly crafted pity-pitch is, in actuality, a total bust. Do not despair even if this book made you realize that you may have already screwed the pooch by unwittingly admitting to your lawyer that you are out to con him.

Do not fret about your previous naiveté. Quite the opposite, you should celebrate the fact that you now are able to see the matters clearly.

First, that means you are paying attention. Your world is in right focus. You finally see things from a perspective other than just your own. If you can broaden your view of divorce to include your lawyer's angle, you can beat your lawyer at this game. So celebrate your progress! Stay optimistic!

Besides, there are worse ways of spoiling your client-lawyer relationship than telling your lawyer about your plan to never pay.

What could possibly be worse?!

There are a good many things. As the famous saying puts it, "Let me count the ways"!

Play-acting your plan to chisel your future lawyer, for instance, is infinitely worse than just *talking* about such a plan. What do I mean by that?

It usually happens at the very first, "get to know each other" meeting. There is usually a several hundred-dollar price tag attached to those meetings. And there also probably a couple hundred different ways in which clients unwittingly revealingly play-act their true deadbeat nature.

Imagine this scene:

Ana is shopping for a good divorce lawyer. A pleasant first meeting is rolling to its end and the time to pay the lawyer's consultation fee has arrived.

A following exchange ensues.

Ana: (passionately) I am so glad I came to see you—everything is so clear now that you explained, and you *are* the lawyer for me.

Lawyer: (untouched by the laudatory tirade, but eagerly anticipating a new client) It's all in a day's work, Ana. My consultation fee is $300, as discussed. Do you have a check for me? Or would you rather put it on the card?

And this is when Ana says that she has no money with her. She just this minute realized it. She can run out to the bank, Ana says. She banks with the Bank of Ozz, the closest branch of which is on the South Side, now in the direction with the rush hour crush of traffic.

Of course, Ana had booked the latest appointment in the day, and it is 4:40 P.M. when she discovers the unexpected: she did not bring any money to the meeting. Without a helicopter or an ambulance, her bank is unreachable before close. And, of course, she doesn't have an available ATM card.

Can she just bring the money tomorrow? Ana suggests.

The lawyer (no longer really sure he wants to be retained) says "Absolutely," in a tone capable of stopping dead the progress of global warming everywhere. Ana's file now has the Lawyer's mental note: stalled first PAYMENT.

What just happened? Ana just lost all of her creditworthiness. She might still be accepted as a client, but this law office will now monitor the accruing receivables with the cold-eyed watchfulness of a circling hawk. The lawyer now *sees* Ana in his mind's eye as a would-be cheater, visualizes Ana fumbling though her purse, checking her phone for time (funny, she remembered to bring her phone) and even leaning to check under her chair as though her checkbook might have jumped out and hidden itself there. That acting-out image will stay with the Lawyer for an uncomfortably long time, breeding visceral distrust every time Ana's payment is a little late. Ana did so much worse than just *telling*. She *play-acted* with an amateurish performance that would have gotten an atrocious review if dared by a middle-school drama club. A picture being more vivid than mere words, this Lawyer now *sees* a cheater every time he catches sight of Ana.

BEFORE we move on, let me answer the logical question you may be asking at this point:

"But what if that one consultation is really all I need? Shouldn't I try to get out of paying the 300 dollars, or the five hundred dollars, or whatever the fee happens to be?"

The answer, of course, is the obvious one: just don't pay.

If all you needed was one hour, and you got that one hour for free, you win. Declare victory and go home. No need to part with your hard-earned money to make a good impression on the lawyer whom you never plan on needing again. And there certainly are occasions when you only need to see a lawyer once: a quick situation assessment when you are only toying with the notion of divorce, a second-opinion consult when you are only double-checking your primary lawyer's opinion.

But this comes with a caveat: there are also plenty of occasions when what had initially seemed like a one-time thing develops into a bigger problem, and you all of a sudden discover yourself in need of a lawyer again. If that's the predicament, skipping on that first hour will work to your disadvantage. The lawyer will have only lost the one hour of pay, but won the long game. That lawyer now knows that you are a cheat and will avoid you like a plague. You, on the other hand, will be stuck with the chore of looking for a new lawyer to fill the void. Good luck.

ONCE you established that you need the lawyer beyond the first meeting, make sure you do not *play-act* your plan to chisel him later, sometime after the lawyer has done a lot of work on the case. Pay close attention to that first time when the lawyer *watches* you parting with your money. Compared to the cost of the case, the consultation fee is trivial, but *how you pay* it is critical.

Ana who had "forgotten" her initial payment may have actually made an honest mistake, but she now *looks* untrustworthy because she tapped into the shopworn "banks closed already" routine so familiar to lawyers as a means to cheat.

There are—oh so many—routines that immediately peg you as a bad credit risk. Are you in danger of unwittingly performing one of these routines? Read on.

Betsy asks if she can charge one hundred dollars on her card, and pay the rest in cash. The Lawyer says "yes" and runs her card for the hundred. The card works fine. Betsy looks for the rest of her fee. She ostentatiously empties her wallet, all three compartments. The keys, receipts, goldfish cracker crumbs and one half-rotten banana spill out onto the conference table. Betsy counts and counts and counts and . .

162

. comes up woefully short. She remembers the key compartment of the purse, and pulls out two one-dollar bills. Still short, but she has some cash in her car, she says. The trip to the car takes a little while. She returns looking frazzled and carrying a handful of wet ten dollar bills. Coffee spilled, she explains. She counts again, and is now she is only $50 short. The Easter egg hunt for the fee took half an hour. The Lawyer is OK with $50 short, if she *just leaves*.

Clara declares she will pay all cash. She has it prepared, she says, exactly the amount. She reaches into her purse and pulls out a stack of bills in five- and one-dollar denominations. Clara insists that she must re-count. She does, and comes up five dollars over. The Lawyer says: "that's Ok, just deduct the five dollars," but Clara wants to be precise and "fair to us both." She counts again. This time, it is three dollars short. Lawyer says that's OK, too. She would not let up, and counts again. It is now off by ten. Twenty minutes later, she is still counting . . . . "Maybe I should just bring a check the next time I come?" she suggests, and the Lawyer is happy to just get her out, and get on with the day.

Deborah happily offers a debit card. The card is in the name of Mark Smith (not her husband). Deborah explains that Mark is a "good friend." Lawyer wants details. "We met in rehab, I am handling his expenses until he comes out. He will not mind," explains Deborah. The Lawyer minds, though. Lawyers cannot just run an absentee person's card and hope for the best. Deborah has no other means of paying. The Lawyer tells her to send the check later and is grateful to never hear from her again.

Eva, mercifully, offers a credit card in her own name. However, apparently as a big surprise, the card gets declined. She insists it must be a mistake. Lawyer runs the card three times before Eva finally remembers that she "maybe" maxed it out the day before. She is so sorry and will mail the check. And she does, eventually. Was the poor thing just sloppy, or did she set the stage to stiff the lawyer only to realize that it's not the optimal time yet? Either way, her file gets a red flag.

Frank (my personal favorite) accompanies his sixty-year old mother for moral and financial support. When it is time to pay, he reaches out across the conference table to hand the check to the Lawyer. Instead of placing the check on the table, he halts his hand mid-air, waiting for the Lawyer to reach out and accept the payment. But as the Lawyer touches the check, Frank jerks back as though suddenly hit by a painful muscle spasm, then shakes his wrist, waving the check around like a child playing "catch" with a cat. The Lawyer freezes, hand still reached out in the air. Frank's mother stifles a proud smile and drawls "Kiddo, stop playing and give the Lawyer the money." The forty-year old "kiddo" reaches out as if to hand the check. As the Lawyer tries to accept, Frank jerks it away again, this time rolling into uncontrollable laughter: he made a lawyer beg and dance for the money today! Funny joke, you obnoxious jerk.

Gina blushes when asked if she brought the payment, and hands over a small blue linen envelope with her initials in raised gold. She is visibly embarrassed by the vulgarity of handling the money. The corner of a check is coyly peeping out of the envelope. The next day, the Lawyer tries to deposit the check and discovers that it was never signed.

The variations go all the way to **Yana**, but you get the point.

These hopeful clients—who capably and jovially pay at the malls, hotels, spas, yoga retreats, garden clubs and body studios—all find paying a lawyer a debilitating, challenging struggle. They simply cannot go through with it. It is so painful that any observer with a measure of empathy gets uncomfortable watching them try.

When I was a young divorce lawyer, the one part of my first consultation hour I used to dread the most was collecting the payment. I am not an exception. Just about every lawyer regards asking for his fee with dread and fear. Here's what I learned over the years and what every experienced lawyer knows to be true: clients who pay promptly the first time will continue paying promptly. Clients who stall, will continue stalling, sometimes stalling all the way to a complete stop. I never learned how to deal comfortably with clients who find paying painful, so I learned to just avoid them.

Clients like Ana, Betsy, Deborah, Clara, Eva and Frank make lawyers feel physically and mentally uncomfortable.

Despite some of my cynical tough-talk verbiage above, I am in reality only too often taken for a sucker. Asking "Do you have a check for me" often feels to me like I just asked the poor client to physically cut out the proverbial pound of flesh. So many clients make it *painful* to watch them pay. Their faces turn pale and tight-jawed, their eyes glisten, their breath grows shallow and raspy. I feel responsible for their physical discomfort. It is a horrible feeling. I never want to witness a client putting on display like that.

"Do you have a check for me?" I ask, and she looks up, eyes welling up. The lips start trembling:

"Do I get a discount?" she finally manages.

I just hate watching physical pain, so I say: "Make it a hundred dollars less."

Her lips tremble more, then she says: "But do I still have to pay *today*?"

I do not say anything, and her hand goes into the purse. Did I not rationally know that it's impossible, I'd be pretty sure that her checkbook is heated to scorching temperature and sears her fingers when she touches it. In pain, she looks up again, hoping I will stop the torture.

"*Today?*" she repeats with piteous dread.

I could counter that she had her consultation *today*. All three hours of it. And that I am charging for just one hour. Which is an absolute bargain. But I'm such a milquetoast about the agony of arguing and bargaining. So, instead, I just nod "yes," in a half-hearted attempt at firmness. The checkbook comes out, and she starts writing, every letter causing her to squirm, like it is etched in pinpricks on her body instead of the paper of the check. She writes in the dollar amount, lifts her fingers off the pen and swallows hard, visibly suppressing a sob. Then she looks up again, exhausted from the pain, ever hopeful that I will give a signal and relent—so she can stop the self-mutilating effort of writing the check.

All I have to say is "It's OK. It's free today," and the look of agony will be wiped of her face. It is so easy for me to be a wimp and surrender.

I admit, when I was younger, I've succumbed on many, many, many occasions. I cannot stand being in the same room with pain. If I could, I'd probably be a doctor. I've said "Do not worry about it today. You can pay when you have the money." Radiant smile. Sigh of relief. Big, big sigh and smile. It is a sensation of both relief and satisfaction as if I had just miraculously cured end-stage cancer.

There is no rational reason for my consultation fee to cause such acutely visible physical pain: my clients are typically a long, long way from being poor. They do not worry about putting porridge on the table for their children or keeping the proverbial wolf away from the walnut wood door. My clients worry about their facelifts, and fillers, and trust interest, and garden sculptures, and trips to exotic places.

Perhaps the pain is psychological: writing a check to a lawyer is the symbolic end of the marriage. Or, as I cynically suspect, the display of pain is a training session for the lawyer's benefit, designed to train the lawyer to charge less going forward. I do not know for certain.

I want people to be happy they came to see me, not in pain. So does every other lawyer. So guess what: you should act happy and I will like you more!

Your first payment comes when the lawyer sees you for the first time and makes the very first impression of your integrity, financial ability, your sense of responsibility, and—perhaps most importantly—your ability to value legal services. Fiddling with the money and frowning that you have to pay not only tells the lawyer to red flag your file, but also creates a *visual memory* that you will never be able to erase completely. Whether or not you are planning to stiff the lawyer eventually, you should never start out by raising red flags that may have a lasting negative effect on the relationship that follows.

There is only one proper way to handle the first consultation fee: pay it cheerfully, promptly and in full. Smile as you write a check. Chuckle as you rapidly count the hundred dollar bills. Beam as your card is swiped. Be grateful. Thank your lawyer for his excellent advice, as the money exchanges hands. Exude the impression that, in the wisdom-for-money exchange, you got the better end of the bargain. Then your file will be in the "happy people" file—and you get to start running up a tab that you may never plan to pay in full.

Every lawyer remembers how the client handled these first few hundred dollars. Pay easily, and you will save yourself thousands of dollars in future fees.

WHAT CHARMS LAWYERS (HINT: IT IS NOT WHAT YOU THINK!)

IT HAD BEEN A DELICIOUSLY PLEASANT Friday afternoon until the mailman delivered a package from a lawyer who claims to work for your soon-to-be ex. It's not so pleasant news: you are subpoenaed for a deposition.

After quickly googling the words "subpoena" and "deposition," you surmise the meaning of this unpleasant surprise: the shyster whom your not-soon-enough-to-become-ex had hired to make your life miserable wishes to grill you under oath, asking about unspecified but doubtlessly unpleasant subjects. This egregiously inconvenient waste of time will commence in exactly one week, Friday next, and, according to the papers, will be going on "day to day, until it is over." The madness is expected to stretch out "at least three days." There will be a court reporter to take down every word you say, every possible embarrassment and slip of the tongue.

Up until this unfortunate afternoon, you and your spouse were successfully negotiating your divorce without lawyers, or at least that's what you were led to believe. You had suggested to the other half that there was no need to make it ugly, and the response was "Of course, dear." The two of you could just as easily do it yourselves—divide your few possessions, sell the house, and schedule the kids' visits. You thought the negotiations were going well. But, obviously, you'd been duped. The notion of a peaceful and harmonious finale was not getting the expected traction with your worse half.

After a brief contemplation, you see that the natural gentleness and benevolence of your character is being mistaken (again!) for weakness. You resolve, therefore, to fight back with all the vile force available to you in our very complex and capricious justice system.

And so, gritting your teeth, you spring into action with steely resolve.

In response to your spouse's tool of a lawyer, you will hire a mercenary of your own, and you will make sure to find the meanest, the nastiest, the trickiest pettifogger in the whole State of South Duck. You'll even import one from New York, if necessary!

You are decided! If it's to be guerrilla warfare, so be it!

There is only one itsy-bitsy little problem: the budget. Your discretionary-fund resources are right now at a relatively low ebb, maybe a few hundred dollars, a thousand at the most. And you reckon the going rate for confronting what's lying in wait for you next Friday is at least a few thousand.

So there you have it: one week to troll for, hook, and serve up the meanest, nastiest, trickiest possible lawyer—and yet, succeed in stiffing your attorney for those fees that you can't and won't pay. Your mission is to save on the legal fees, *but not scrimp in the least on the legal services*, a.k.a., to "dine well, dash fast." Let's go!

Preparation

Here's what you need to know in order to prepare for your meeting with a lawyer. There are four elements to the perfect meeting with a lawyer, and all four must be considered before you even appear at the lawyer's office. The elements, in order of importance are:

Schedule the meeting for late afternoon;

Demonstrate that you are creditworthy,

well-organized and

able to stick to the facts.

Schedule for the Afternoon.

Scheduling is crucial.

For the reasons that will soon become clear, you must schedule for late afternoon, the later the better. Nothing earlier than 3:30 PM, anyway.

Be creditworthy

In order to persuade a lawyer to work on credit, you must prove you are creditworthy. That seems like such a basic concept, yet so many clients start out with blurting out: "I don't have any money!" But you've read this book, and you will not blurt. The way you deliver the first few hundred dollars can make a difference between being pegged as "crook to be watched" or elevated to "VIP, creditworthy."

Which one do you want to be? I thought so!

Everything about your first meeting, including the payment for that first consultation must be as smooth as the bottom of a six-week-old spaniel puppy. It's all in the presentation.

If the lawyer takes personal checks (most do), carefully prepare the check in the precise amount, the amount ascertained ahead of the meeting from the attorney's appointment secretary. Prepare the check before your departure from home, but take the checkbook along with you as well. Make sure that every line of the check is in order: the signature, the date, the numeric entry in the box and the matching printed amount on the second line. You want to present the image of a resolute, conscientiously prepared client.

172

If the lawyer's office does not like personal checks, or if you do not want the trace of payment to a lawyer to appear on your accounts, procure the exact amount of the consultation fee in the largest bills possible. Pop by your bank. Ask the banker to put the exact amount for the first consultation in one of those nifty little envelopes that banks so eagerly give out. Ask the teller for the newest, crispiest bills available. Use hundreds and fifties. Do not stoop to offering up mere tens, fives or dollar bills. Got it? Be smooth. Look creditworthy. Act efficient, eager, and generous.

Be organized.

Skip this step and go directly to Step 4 if nothing has been filed in the courts yet, and if you have no prenuptial, postnuptial, separation or any other agreements with the spouse. (On the other hand, you may find this section enlightening if your situation is moving in the direction of court. Hey, it wouldn't hurt to learn something, right?)

Good organization is important. If there is a prenup, postnup, or separation agreement, for cryin' out loud, make copies of these crucial documents and bring them with you. Otherwise, your lawyer will hardly be able to understand the true state of your situation. It matters little what you "thought" those agreements said; the written words are the best, and often the only, reliable accounts of what's really going on.

If there is a court fight in the works already, bring a copy of your court file that relates what happened so far. (Refer to the *For the Geeks* write-up at the end of this Chapter for additional instructions on how to prepare a court-file copy.)

Stick to the Facts

At the first meeting with your future lawyer, you will be asked to summarize the story of your marriage. After the summary is completed, the lawyer will ask about your goals: what are you looking for at the end of this divorce? What would make you happy? Of course, the lawyer should be understood to be asking only about goals and results that are susceptible to being achieved via the legal system. For instance, having your ex consigned to the most excruciating pit of Hell is not one of those. Seriously, give some thought to asking for things within the realm of the possible and don't waste your time (and, worse yet, the lawyer's expensive time) on unrealistic fantasies.

If you were looking to pay the maximum price for the lawyer, that would be a simple task: you'd just say the first thing that comes to mind and fumble inarticulately and meanderingly through your goals.

But if you are not looking to pay full price, telling your story becomes a more delicate task. Obviously, your story now is your elevator pitch, your chance to charm, to present yourself as The Best Client Ever.

Do you know what charms divorce lawyers? Most people get it all wrong.

Novice clients think that a way to a lawyer's heart lies through proof of virtue. Clients spend a lot of time and energy working to present themselves as virtue incarnate, unjustly trampled upon by a villain. This approach is wrong, wrong, wrong.

Maybe that would be a good way to win the heart of a civil rights lawyer—being virtuous. I don't know. Civil rights folks are financed by various interest groups and an important source of their sustenance *is* the limelight and fanfare and the satisfaction of soldiering on in support of all that is right and just. So perhaps the moral character matters there. But I can tell you for a fact that expounding on your virtue is decidedly not the way to the heart of a typical divorce lawyer. Yet, countless clients in my practice have used their first hour to sermonize, portraying a verbal hodgepodge roadmap of their marital discord, bursting with incandescent images of their spouse's depravity and their own resulting sufferings. Apparently, these clients imagined that, if they provided me with an irrefutable proof of their spouse's many unprovoked and singularly heartless villainies, this proof would inspire me to take more interest in their case and represent them with more zeal and a lower bill. That expectation is absolutely incorrect.

Indeed, you should not want a lawyer who will only be your friend so long as you are apparently the virtuous party in the marriage. A lawyer who seeks out only clients "in the right" suffers from a God complex, which is a trait unacceptable in the service industry. Your lawyer is not supposed to pass judgment on your virtue. Your lawyer must be duty-bound and devoted to working for you just because you are the client, not because you are on the ever-so-debatable side of the angels. Who is right and who is wrong is not the lawyer's place to judge. If clients were to view the actual legal merits of most divorce case with clear-eyed objectivity, they might be very glad that a competent lawyer's efforts are not calibrated by the degree of personal empathy with the client.

To be sure, if you absolutely must launch a tirade to prove your innocence and marital martyrdom to your divorce lawyer, the lawyer will find it totally understandable and even expected. Most divorce lawyers are professionally attentive listeners adept at asking open-ended questions and nodding sympathetically and compassionately: "Oh, my!" "Oh dear!" "Your husband seems like a horribly cruel man!" or "How did you suffer your wife for so long?!"

Nevertheless, conversations like this do not improve your appeal as the Dream Client.

Another thing you might keep in mind is psychological: once you get started talking about your divorce, it is hard stop. It is even harder to resist diving into a shrill, compulsive never-ending spiel.

Divorce *is* distressing. One *does* need moral support. Divorce lawyers *are* professionally adept at persuasively taking your side. A good divorce lawyer will have no trouble agreeing that an errant husband's adultery killed the marriage and that he is, consequently, tyrannical for holding against his wife her own tiny indiscretion, which was a mere meaningless one-time fling with a friend. Divorce lawyers are *the* professional adepts at proxying for the kind of emotional support often given by best friends. Attorneys are ready and able to provide you with emotional alliance. But let me ask you: are you ready to pay a divorce lawyer's hourly rate for emotional support? Why not use lawyers for legal work and reach for emotional support elsewhere? Many people are much better suited to comfort you. Most of them work cheaper or even free: therapists, clergy, primary care physicians. Your mother is often a good choice, and always free. Your best friend may be a good choice—unless your spouse is sleeping with your best friend. Facebook is full of "supporting each other in divorce" groups. Talk to your mother. Talk to your friends. Talk to the fellow-sufferers on Facebook (but do be careful not to give out too many personal details). These resources might not heal all of your emotional scars, but unlike your divorce lawyers, they are cheap or even free. They will cost less even if you become quite a successful practitioner in the art of stiffing an attorney for his fees.

Well, then what is the best way to charm a divorce lawyer? It is simple: create the appearance of becoming the lawyer's calm and coherent partner in the upcoming battle. Become a client who is eager to help their own lawyer, rather than a client who is a perpetually hysterical victim, a needy, petulant deadweight who does nothing constructive to advance the ball. That's what makes the difference to a divorce lawyer. As your first meeting is progressing, the lawyer might wonder:

Will you actively help the lawyer work for you?

Will you follow your lawyer's instructions?

Or will you throw a fit, refuse to cooperate, and make the lawyers job three hundred percent harder?

Will you tell the lawyer exactly what you want to achieve in the divorce?

Will you demand that the lawyer does something illegal or impossible, thus signaling a future rocky road of client complaints and dissatisfaction?

Will you break down and feel sorry for yourself in the middle of the courtroom hearing and start screaming at the judge, the opposing lawyer, or even your own attorney?

When the lawyer asks you to round up your bank statements, get a letter from your employer, or organize twelve months' worth of utility bills, can you be counted upon to comply quickly, competently, and without griping?

When you are asked to compile a list of marital assets, including such things as jewelry, collectibles, and financial assets, will you do that promptly, accurately, and without bursting into tears at the heartless imposition?

A client who predictably will make the lawyer's job easier is a desirable client, whether or not this person was a model spouse. On the other hand, even the most sympathetic spouse is decidedly not a desirable client if they do not cooperate with their lawyer, concentrating all the energy on playing the victim instead.

MIA was a poster child for *not being* her lawyer's perfect partner. In fact, she was twice fired by her own lawyers. The stated reason was her repeated "refusal to cooperate," a particular demerit that pushed her into the category of a get-all-money-upfront customer.

Mia's story was not an original one. Her husband, a brazen cheat, got caught red-handed. As Mia had discovered on home security cameras, her insensitive husband entertained his many mistresses (Mia used stronger synonyms for "mistress") all over the marital home—including Mia's own lavender scented bed and her favorite jetted bathtub.

"In my tub, with my bubble bath," Mia decried her humiliating fate. "She used my bubble bath, all my bubble . . .. All!"

I did feel sorry about how Mia got her first inkling of her betrayal. It is hard enough to accept the news that your husband is cheating on you even when you are all dressed up and looking your best. But Mia's discovery came while naked and alone and preparing expectantly for a luxuriant soak. The bad news burst upon her when she reached out for the bubbles dispenser and came up with an empty. It was like the fairytale Baby Bear's moment of realization that Goldilocks had been there. And, as it became clear, there had indeed been a goldilocks blond in Mia's tub, and she was bare, and so was Mia's errant husband . . ..

For lack of some bubbles, Mia's bubble of marital tranquility had been rudely burst. Moreover, that demoralizing moment of realization took on an over-the-top, near-hysterical degree of importance in Mia's mind.

Every time we spoke, Mia reminded: "Have you done anything yet about the bubble bath? He stole all my bubble bath, for his filthy whore of a mistress!"

"Make him pay and see to it that the blond bitch regrets every bubble," she demanded.

Mia obsessively dragged her bubble bath plaint into every conversation we had.

Still, I did not pick up on the fact that something was demanded *of me*, not until the bubble disaster festered and burst into a real problem.

"You are doing nothing to make him pay," Mia announced.

"What sort of payment are we looking for here?" I wondered suspiciously.

The affair itself and its offensive circumstances had served to spice up Mia's rather substantial alimony claim, but that goose had long since been cooked, served and eaten. I thought that we had already won, but Mia clearly wanted more, something beyond the monthly check large enough to buy a veritable sea of bubbles.

I started to worry. Was I missing something about the value of the bubble bath?

"Mia," I said, wondering if I had somehow grossly undervalued the asset, "what sort of a bubble bath *was* it?"

I had initially assumed an average bottle filled with a concoction of salts, oil and soap. But was I wrong? Was it specially flown from Paris? Was the bottle made of Swarovski crystal? Did it break? Was there gold dust mixed in the bubbles? Mia's estate was of a sort that made all these enhancements a possibility.

"Mia," I said firmly intent on digging down to the truth: "What did you pay for the bubbles?"

"That's not the point," returned Mia sulkily.

"How much?" I pressed in my blunt way.

"I do not remember."

"Will you recognize the make?" I took out a list and stumbled over exotic names:

"Ahava Deadsea for $22?

Catseye London for $25?

Molton Brown for $30?

Diptyque for $78?

Honest Co Bubble Bath, Tangerine Dream for $11.95?"

"I dunno," sulked Mia, "You are not on my side on this. I should have fired you. You don't understand me."

"How much for the bubbles?" I demanded again.

It took an hour, but I beat it out of her. Her particular bottle of bubbles hailed from the local drug store where her maid had picked it up for twelve dollars new. It was only half-full when the mistress got her hands on it. You could not get six dollars for the potion on e-bay.

"I do not want six dollars for my bubble bath, I want

justice," Mia eventually revealed her goals.

"In what shape?" I inquired businesslike. Delivery of justice was my direct job description, and I would not falter in my duty.

"I want the judge to tell *him*," Mia never had the strength to say her husband's name, "I want the judge to tell *him* that he was wrong to waste my bubble bath. She had no right to use my bubble bath! Not for that slut!"

"You want the judge to scold your husband in public? For misappropriating a half bottle of ordinary bubble bath?"

"That's the only way he'll ever understand."

That framing of my commission flummoxed me. It is not that the judges never scold the litigants. (They do.) It is not even whether the judges *should* be in the business of scolding the litigants. (In my point of view, scolding is not the judges' job, but nobody had asked for my view, nor would they have paid any attention to it.)

In Mia's overblown view, my fatal failing was that I'd never prepared a *motion for scolding*.

How would I even name such a request to the court?

"Wife's Motion to have Husband Scolded"?

Or "Wife's Respectful Request for Reproach"?

Or "Wife's Brief in Support of Upbraid of the Bubble Thief"?

Or just "In re Bubble Bath"?

What would be the "relief sought from the Court"? Mia did not want any money. She did not want her husband to do anything, nor to refrain from doing anything. Neither damages, nor injunction, nor even attorney's fees. All she wanted was a public humiliation of her Ex. I was not aware of a statute creating a remedy for "humiliation" and I was fairly sure that the general powers of the divorce courts did not reach that far. The statutes authorizing public pillorying of offenders had, after all, long since been relegated to dusty history books rather than law books.

A motion for scolding could get us both sanctioned, punished by the court for wasting its time with a petition that had no adequate basis in law.

"Mia," I said pleadingly, "do you just want to make your husband suffer? We could do it the old-fashioned way—bury him under discovery requests."

Requests for Admissions could do the trick. Answering them would not only cost him legal fees but also produce considerable personal anxiety and waste of time.

"Mia, I can send him fifty questions and force his lawyer to work for days on end responding "yes" or "no" to crafty questions that do not have an easy "yes or no" answer. Will that make you feel better?"

"Your questions will be about the bubble bath?" came the predictable response.

But there was nothing left to litigate about the bubble bath.

Mia did not want the money, she wanted her bubbles back or, worse yet, the dignity that the bubbles had irrevocably burst. Not another bottle, not even a better bottle, not even an identical bottle. She wanted what was *hers*. Her bubble bath. Her life. Her husband. She wanted the whole world to hear that her husband—that monster—bathed another woman in her bubble bath... both of them naked... in her bath... with her bubbles . . ..

Mia's demands were understandable, but there was nothing more the law could do for her and, consequently, nothing I could do to deliver more justice.

Although definitely the innocent party in her marriage, Mia was far from The Best Client Ever. Ironically, The Best Client Ever was the very villain of the bubble story, Mia's husband. From what I glimpsed in the pleadings, he spent very little time at his lawyer's office, was always upbeat, knew exactly what he wanted in this divorce, and did not ask the lawyer to fight about much of anything.

To be sure, I liked Mia very much. I tried my darndest for her. She got an excellent alimony deal and 65% of all marital assets, which was a solid bargain given that she did not work a day in her life (nor would she ever have to). But every conversation I had with Mia was more exhausting than an hour of on a treadmill set at high speed and steep incline. She got my best efforts, but she was not getting any discount on my fees. Far from it.

―――――――

IF your goal is to distinguish yourself as The Dream Client, you should aim to be the antithesis of Mia. Ask your lawyer to solve your legal problems, not the problems of your heart for which the laws of your State unfortunately provide no recourse. Aim towards imperturbability and efficiency.

Here are a few Dos and Don'ts:

Do Talk Business

Talk about the issues (some of which only you may be able to identify).

Are you prepared to tell the lawyer what you want to achieve in your divorce? Keep the house? Prefer the cash instead? What about the sea-side condo? Would you like your ex-husband to take the kids off your hands for the Summer? Would you like to make your spouse suffer at any cost to you?

Say what you really want, right away, even if you think it makes you look like a bad spouse, bad person or a bad parent. Be straightforward. If you have no idea what you want, say that too. Talk about the marital money. Who makes how much, who minds the family business, what's in your 401Ks, whose parents are paying for what.

Don't Talk Feelings

Don't talk excessively about your spouse's character flaws. The fact that you are divorcing sufficiently shows that there were Big Problems. Bad spousal behavior is much less legally relevant than most clients think, so listen carefully for signals from your lawyer as to which conduct issues might actually make a difference and which don't.

Don't Sugarcoat

Say what you want out of this divorce. Is getting full custody of the kids not what you have in mind? Just say so. If the goal is to have your weekends free from the kids, nobody is judging. Say it..

Don't pretend generosity. "I don't care about the money" directs your lawyer to perform an entirely different set of tasks than "I want to get every single penny I'm entitled to." The lawyer is fine with either direction, really. So long as it's your sincere direction.

Do Say What You Mean.

This is not the time for political correctness, beating around the bush, and relying on your lawyer's ability to interpret the subtlest of your hints.

Please do not hint.

Tell your lawyer exactly what you mean. Otherwise, you might get a result you did not order.

186

Don't dramatize

Of course, if you *are* upset, shaken, foggy or drugged out on Xanax, your lawyer needs to know. But if you are feeling reasonably steady, do not work yourself up into a frenzy for the lawyer's benefit.

Whatever you do or don't do, eschew the belief that lawyers seek out clients with a dramatic flair, would-be impassioned stars in the witness chair of a crowded courtroom listening in rapture. Every divorce lawyer's life is brim-full of melodrama already. The clients sigh, wail, snivel, swear, and decry their rotten fortunes. The opposing lawyers scream, swear, wring their hands, and yell indecipherable obscenities. Judges roll their eyes, swivel the chairs in disgust, run out of the courtroom, threaten and scream "contempt," "jail," "involuntary dismissal." It's a never-ending circus. With loud roles played by opposing lawyers and even judges, the life of an average divorce lawyer is already exhausting. Don't pile on.

A divorce lawyer's consultation day is sold by quarter-hourly increments of dealing with the rotten romantic misfortunes of angels unjustly soiled by their unfortunate associations with diabolical spouses. An additional dose of drama from the client is not exactly a consummation devoutly to be wished.

I am not saying lawyers are in any position to complain. The meter is running during the client's performance, just as it would in a taxicab. The "cabbie" gets paid even when the customer cries bitter tears and directs the driver on useless detours that only run up the bill. Enduring the clients' dramatics is part of the compensated job, but it does not mean that it is the sort of job a lawyer would seek out, given a choice.

I am only saying: divorce lawyers do not *go looking* for drama. They are already well-supplied. Drama finds divorce lawyers every day.

If your goal is to charm the attorney and to distinguish yourself, try a presentation that is organized, objective, efficient and honest. You will be far along to earning the coveted classification as Dream Client.

With these general principles introduced, we return to the exercise in beginning of this chapter: find and stiff a divorce lawyer in one week. Step by step, starting on Friday.

Friday

Friday afternoon is when you realized that your spouse had hired a lawyer and is looking to depose you in one week. Take these steps: panic briefly, locate a good lawyer in town, schedule yourself with the lawyer for Monday, 4:15 p.m.

You are done. Commence your habitual Friday evening routine.

The Weekend

Relax, re-charge, re-read Chapter 2 of this book, get zen,

as close to a mental state of tranquility and peace as you can manage.

Monday 3 p.m.

Slowly and deliberately come out of your relaxation phase. While still clinging to the zen mindset of mental tranquility, dress for comfort.

Monday 3:15 p.m.

Depart without haste. Stay zen.

Monday 4:00 P.M.

Arrive at the lawyer's office on time. Decline the soft drink, and swiftly commence the Dream Client routine. Like a trained karate master, you will deliver your precisely calculated moves —PUNCH! KICK! JAB!

In one smooth gesture, quickly and cheerfully hand over the consultation fee in impressive fashion, following my directions in an earlier section to provide the fee either in crisp large bills neatly stacked in the bank's envelope or via a neatly written check. Lead with the money, then turn on the charm. Smile. Say you are so grateful, you are relieved, and you feel better just being at the Lawyer's office. PUNCH!

Now go on and begin to explain your case to the Lawyer. We talked about preparing your file, providing the relevant materials. Hopefully, you will be able to hand over the well-organized stack of court filings. If that process was, for whatever reason, too much effort for you, then you will just have to take a little more care in explaining the case. KICK!

And finally . . . relate the rest of your situation precisely and dispassionately.

Concentrate on what happened in court, skipping melodramatic but legally irrelevant details of what happened between you and your spouse.

Gloss over juicy irrelevances such as the role of erectile dysfunction in discovering your husband's affair by your shrewd counting of the number of blue pills remaining on the bed stand.

Smooth over the steamy particulars of adultery and dalliances with co-workers or traitorous mutual friends. If there were five incidents of cheating, just say so, firmly and precisely. There's no need to spice things up with graphic descriptions, dragging out a saga resembling the ten seasons of JR's adulteries on the TV show Dallas. You would not say: "I want you to see the text where, on our wedding anniversary yet, I get denounced as a worthless shitfaced slut." Then you would not waste the next ten minutes searching for the aforesaid text on your phone, while the lawyer waits with eyes rolling. Instead, you would relate the same content in thirty seconds by saying only: "My spouse cheated on me, and called me abusive names, and I have records that prove it."

In the middle of the meeting, you will not take the call from your errant spouse, engage in a two-party screaming session, then re-tell your lawyer all the offensive expletives just communicated over the phone. (The re-telling is, in any event, superfluous because the telephone conversation was almost loud enough to make it audible to passersby in the street outside!)

In short, you would act like it is a business meeting. Because that's what it is, business.   That's it. JAB! With any luck, you now made yourself into a Dream Client.

You took my advice and dressed comfortably. You did not come jingling like a Christmas tree, you did not leak mascara and foundation on the office furniture, you came across as low maintenance and relatable.

You took my advice and paid the consultation fee cheerfully, and so you came across as responsible and appreciative.

You took my advice to be cooperative with information sharing and, generally, were a pleasure to be around.

By considering the situation from the point of your potential mark (the Lawyer) you achieved the very station so many men and women seek in vain—your Lawyer likes you and can relate. You are all around lovable as a client. Yes, the lawyer did not need to hear about your many marital sufferings in order to like you. Indeed, it was just the opposite. The case, as you presented it, offers the lawyer a carefully crafted, alluring impression of sanity—even if that seductive first impression may turn out to be a mirage—as, if you turn into a successful grifter, a mirage it will turn out to be.

Congratulations, you made the Perfect First Impression, and it is roughly 4:55 in the evening on a Monday.

Look at the time! In under one hour, you nearly disarmed all of the Lawyer's defenses with your masterful technique of appearing to be a Dream Client.
Consultation fee delivered happily—PUNCH
Well-organizes stack of court filings—KICK!
Your story related precisely and dispassionately—JAB!

Monday, 4:55 P.M.

And now it's time for the knockout: commit the lawyer to your case today, right away. That is important. You may be thinking: what's so hard about signing up a lawyer? Doesn't the lawyer want new business? Isn't getting new business the whole point?

Signing up a good lawyer (you do want a good one, right?) is slightly more delicate than, renting a bike in a seashore spot where you push the dollar in a slot and ride off into the sunrise. Most good lawyers resist being hired on the spot because they are keenly aware of the serious obligations that the resulting contract imposes on any licensed attorney. In prudence, lawyers need a little time to check out the client. Is there a history of arson, hardcore drugs or mental problems? Did the prospective client have a prior lawyer? If so, it does not hurt to discreetly investigate how that liaison ended. And, most important of all, is the litigation schedule.

192

When I take on a new client, the first thing I do is call the courthouse scheduling clerk. I never take the client's word that "there's nothing scheduled in court." I had to learn that lesson the hard way, getting burnt too many times. No lawyer wants to sign on a client and discover—surprise! —that some judge has scheduled a crucial event—a hearing, a deposition, a discovery response, or even the trial itself—only a few precious days ahead.

In short, a prudent lawyer needs time to check out the client before committing to the representation. A client wanting to chisel a lawyer, on the other hand, needs to cinch the contract immediately, because as soon as the lawyer signs, he is on the hook to do all urgent work, even if the payment is still "in the mail" and the lawyer is confronted by an unexpected (for the lawyer) mess.

Getting back to 4:55 on a Monday when you, the Dream Client, eagerly explain that you would like to get your contract with the Lawyer signed immediately. Predictably, the Lawyer shields your last punch with a prepared defense: "Happy to be your lawyer, but take my contract home, read it over, come back in a couple days with the retainer."

That's of course, not what you want. But do not despair: you had softened up the Lawyer, and his defenses are now weakened. Any law firm would be happy to have you—a cooperative, sane, respectful, ready-to-pay Dream Client. By now, the lawyer dearly *wants* to take your case. You just need to contrive a plausible reason for making an exception and signing you on today.

It is time to be insistent and persistent.

Can You Stiff You Divorce Lawyer?

Say that you will not sleep a wink tonight unless you know you have this impressive Lawyer on your side. Insist that you looked high and low, and your mind is made up that this law firm is the onliest for you. Say, maintaining a straight face, that there is a karmic connection. You just need to give the Lawyer an excuse to do what the Lawyer already wants to do—take your case. Just a little well delivered push. Then, Lawyer agrees to make an exception and the clock on the office wall says 5:05.

KNOCKOUT? Not quite yet.

Monday, 5:05 P.M

With the Lawyer committed to representing you, now is the time for that knock-out.

You persuaded the Lawyer that today is the day and now is the hour to sign the contract. The contract comes out, and with the contract, comes up the matter of some serious money, the "retainer" fee.

The consultation fee, which you had paid with notable cheerfulness and alacrity is a mere pittance compared to the retainer. Retainers for a lawyer are like the first month's rent and security deposit when you lease a condo—payment in advance in case you skip. Divorce lawyers' retainers vary widely. It could be $2,000 or $50,000, or anywhere in between. One thing that does not usually vary is that retainers are paid the day the contract is signed.

194

Finagling the signing of the binding attorney-client contract but not paying the retainer is what we are after. Then, the hook will be firmly set.

So, now comes the part for which you so studiously prepared.

The lawyer asks for a $10,000 upfront retainer. The Lawyer's goal now is to collect the retainer in case you do not pay the future bills. Your goal is, quite the opposite, to put your Lawyer in that exact position of being stuck working for you with as little pay as possible. Remember, once the Lawyer formally contracts to take your case, it will take a while for him to get out, and lawyer's professional obligations demand that the lawyer continue doing his job during that time.

You say: "Ten thousand, not a problem. Tomorrow morning . . . First thing."

The Lawyer's prudence will now battle the Lawyer's own optimism and greed. (You presented yourself as a client to covet, after all). Now your job is to help the optimism along.

You might say that your wealthy Aunt (and doting Godmother) has graciously offered to finance your legal severance from your "mistake" of a marriage to a person "clearly beneath you." Auntie had never approved of this marriage. Money in hand, Auntie will drive from her house out in the County, but she is old and fussy and *needs to see the contract first*.

Or, you say that the tax refund just came, and it is processing through your bank.

Or, you say that a Certificate of Deposit matures tomorrow.

Or that you had already put through for a loan with your 401K (show papers).

Or that your doting Dad is in the process of selling off a subsidiary.

Truthfully, it does not matter what you say, so long as you say it with sufficient persuasiveness. Divorce lawyers are a surprisingly gullible lot. Your story will sail through, especially if you have some supporting papers to show. Present a Certificate of Deposit, your application for a loan against your 401K, your aunt's itinerary, or an appraisal of the diamond that you are planning to pawn.

And now you are grateful for your foresight in arranging things so that it is already ten minutes after five o'clock and you cannot get $10,000 after the bank closes, but you can still say convincingly that "the cash will be there the next business day. First thing."

Now sit back and watch quietly as the Lawyer's prudence battles his greed.

Since you had paid your consultation fee in full and without a complaint, you have the benefit of a doubt.

You might hear the suggestion that "the money and the contract all will be done tomorrow."

Easy enough to push back: "Auntie is bringing me the money. She'll need me to show her the contract in completed form."

Or: "I cannot sleep tonight unless I know that 'the best lawyer in town' is signed up on my side."

Go ahead and say it: "the best lawyer in town." You may come across just a touch odd, but it is flattering to be dubbed "the best lawyer."

"Where's the harm in signing the contract just a few hours before the money arrives," the Lawyer will think, "especially if I get such a grateful, eager, sane client. A client so good that, heaven forefend, why risk a change of mind before coming back tomorrow. Better close the deal now!"

Lawyers are trusting. Most likely, you will be rewarded by a shrug, a grin, and an "Oh, fine." And at last you will have delivered the KNOCKOUT!

Raise your arms and spread them high: you have a licensed attorney professional obligated to take care of your problems until some judge says otherwise.

Congratulations! You are now on the right side of the door. All you need to do from now on is just keep your place. Turn to the next chapter for that.

(Unless you are the sort who enjoys obsession over technical detail, like me. In that case, sub-section below is for you.)

For the Geeks:

Make a list of what you want accomplished in your divorce. This will be a private list, for your eyes only. *Nobody else* will see this list: not even your best friend or your mother, nor even the lawyer for that matter. Your goal here is to get honest with yourself. Do not hold back. What do you really want: spend more time with your kids? Or time for yourself so you could finally go to graduate school, finish your novel, finance your patented invention? Or do you just want to drag out the process so your ex-spouse receives a good dose of richly deserved misery? Or would you rather end your divorce quickly and move on to the next chapter of your life? Do not lie to yourself, not even a white lie. And do not write down "I just want what's fair to both of us." Because, as a practical matter, there is not really any such thing as "fair to both."

From the list you just made, pick out the three things you most want your divorce lawyer to accomplish.

If your case has already begun to be litigated, organize and maintain your own copy of the court file. This will not only help you stay connected, but also will give you your best shot at getting an objective look at how the judge sees your case. Remember, if something is not part of your court file, the judge does not know about it.

As your case progresses, update your copy of the court file.

Make copies of all the *court filings*. You will recognize a court filing by its first page with the characteristic rectangular box for the names of parties (i.e. <u>Mr. Husband v. Mrs. Wife</u> or <u>Kramer v. Kramer</u>), the name of the court (i.e. Ducklingburg County Court) and the docket number (i.e. 15-CVD-12345)

Got all the court filings? Great! Now organize them. Place all the documents in reverse chronological order, most recent on top. You can use a three hole-puncher and a binder if you are a tactile, hard-copy person. If you are forward-looking, scanned PDF files work just as well.

There are usually two dates on each court document—the date it was signed by the judge or a lawyer (look to the last couple of pages) and the date it was stamped by the clerk (look for the stamp on the very first page). Most of the times, these two dates are the same. However, when these dates do differ, go by the latest, which will be the date of the stamp on the first page. That's the date when the document hit the official court file and began its official existence. Note that you do not need the original signature and stamp—any legible copy will do. But if there is no stamp at all, you are likely not looking at a document that is part of the official file—perhaps a draft that never got filed, or a draft which got filed in a different version. Start a separate pile for those strays.

Make a list of the court documents. List them by name of the document (usually appears on the right top side or middle, immediately after the box on top) and the date of the file stamp. Your list will look something like this:

1/1/15 Complaint

1/9/15 Motion for Extension of Time

2/9/15 Answer

8/4/15 Motion to Compel Production

9/5/15 Order

An additional advantage to being well-organized is that, should the other side try to pull a fast one, you will have, at your fingertips, all the necessary proof to fight back. Study your court documents. Know what they say. Should the opposing lawyer stand up and lie that "my client never said

ABC," a well-timed comment will save the day: "Judge, there's a motion filed on March 12, that proves otherwise on page 5, line 2." This is *your* case. Lawyers may understand the law better than you do, but there is no reason *you* should not be an expert about the facts of your case, about what's going on in it.

THE POWER OF DELAY

ONCE YOU SQUEEZED BETWEEN the Scylla and Charybdis of attaching a lawyer to a case without a retainer in exchange, you deserve to relax, enjoy and reap the benefits of a game well played. For a while at least, you are sailing on silky-smooth seas.

The first two steps—the task of attaching a lawyer to your case without sacrificing all of your Christmas bonus money—were not easy. They required a panoply of skills—from Emmy-winning acting to a sense of timing worthy of a professional bomb defuser. As my kindergarten teacher liked to proclaim, "What's well begun is half done."

Now, though, just keep that velvet-gloved iron fist of

yours firmly clasped on your lawyer's throat, lest there's talk about halting the work until you pay. Fortunately for you, that's not how the law and the Bar's canons of ethics operate, and your lawyer knows it. In a pinch, let the lawyer know that *you know your rights*. The magic words to use are "the canons of ethics" and "code of conduct."

The task before you can be described quite simply: squeeze as much work as you can before the lawyer dumps you. (And dump you he will, he just needs a judge's permission if the case is in court.)

You have a window of time, maybe longer than you think.

Let's get back to our hypothetical Friday deposition. You signed on your new lawyer on Monday, four days before launch. Here's how you will spend the rest of the work week:

Tuesday,
3 days to launch

You had promised to bring the retainer "first thing in the morning." It is due today.

Of course, you are not going to deliver the money. (You had to ask?)

Instead, sleep in late, have a quiet breakfast, sip your coffee, watch some TV, listen to some music. Enjoy yourself. Later that morning, you might relax yourself by putting your ex's best cherished garments through a commercial-grade shredder. Have some refreshments. In short, do whatever brings you the most inner peace. Leave all the worries to your newly hooked lawyer, because right now it's the lawyer's job and obligation to worry about you.

Call the lawyer's office.

Leave a message with the lawyer's receptionist: "I have the payment in hand, but will not be able to deliver until late afternoon." Discussing money is probably above the receptionist's pay-grade, and she probably does not even care (her own paycheck does not depend on whether you pay or not). No matter. Tell her that you had planned to deliver the pay by early this morning, but an unfortunate emergency has intervened.

What sort of an emergency? Blame your car that would not start, a sudden illness of your children, your boss, your pet, your childhood friend, or even just a forgotten dental appointment. Any supposedly unforeseen event that passes the straight-face test will do.

Politely ask if it is convenient for everybody if, instead, you bring the money at 4:30, in the late afternoon. Thank the receptionist profusely, apologize for the inconvenience, inform her that you feel horrible, and compliment her on her speaking voice.

Or her efficiency.

Receptionists love compliments, and they are unfairly

starved for a kind word. Nobody notices the receptionist until she misses the mark and something goes wrong. People never ever think of writing a card to the office receptionist to thank her for showing up before sun-up, for never dropping one call in the queue, for always taking all messages accurately, for not complaining when the regular secretary gets tied up and dumps a load of double-sided copies to be made in a jiffy. Did you ever think to thank the receptionist? Didn't think so. But this changes today! Write down the full name and use it, together with her title, at every contact.

The receptionist is your buddy now. Her full name is Mrs. June Flowers. You will not forget.

Tuesday, 4:30 p.m.
3 days to launch

Call in to your lawyer's office again. Hopefully, your friend Mrs. Flowers, the receptionist, picks up the phone. Leave a message for the lawyer, again.

This time, say:

"I really planned to drive by as I told you when we talked earlier, but it seems that the gods frowned on that plan. I have a terrible headache (toothache, the runs, heart palpitations, ingrown nail pain, flatulence, cramps)."

"If it's really, really necessary, I might be able to brave it and bring the money, but I really would rather not drive because this condition caused me to black out in the past."

Without a doubt, your lawyer's receptionist will tell you

to stay put, and...

... and you are done for Tuesday!

In fact, the condition that causes black-outs buys you at least until Wednesday afternoon.

> NOTE: Both times you call (after you'd dis-
> cussed the delivery of the money) spend a few
> minutes to leave a message regarding your
> case. The lawyer needs to know that you're
> checking on the job.

A new detail, a question about a legal point, or just plain reiteration of your concern about the Friday deposition—anything goes. Ask Mrs. Flowers, the receptionist, to write it all down and "just pass it on when my nice lawyer isn't busy with anything else." This will keep your lawyer from forgetting the most important point: the lawyer must work equally hard, whether or not the client is holding up on the obligation to pay. The lawyers' license is on the line every time.

Wednesday, around 3:30 p.m.
2 days to launch

The Misdirection

Today, you need to distract your lawyer's thoughts away from that overdue payment.

To this end, you might:

Call your lawyer's office, and, in a tremulous Very

Weak Voice ask to speak to your lawyer directly.

If the lawyer does pick up the phone, make sure you speak first, and open with discussion of the work that needs done. The deadline is breathing down the lawyer's neck, which means that a smallest inadequacy in preparation should and will destroy the lawyer's emotional balance. And that's just what you need to do. *Destroy the balance* by throwing in the unexpected.

Ask that, in preparation for the deposition, the Lawyer interviews a new witness. Insist that there is a whole line of defense that rests on the information available from this witness. If the lawyer resists, insist: "she is a critical witness, and my case will crumble without her. I am devastated that you had not realized the need for this person's involvement."

You will hold the lawyer personally responsible if your case is lost because of this oversight, you might say. In fact, warn the lawyer that you feel so strongly about this that you're going to put your request in writing, via an email, "just so that we have a record" of your suggestion. Even if the lawyer knows your request holds absolutely no water, the little paranoid voice that always hums in the lawyer's head will start screaming "What if?" And that's all you need: *the misdirection.*

There are lots of misdirection possibilities. Conjure up an important bank account, a police report, a tax return, a transcript of an obscure deposition in a Federal Court where your feuding spouse's second cousin was once involved as an eyewitness. Insist that the lawyer is amiss if this "critical evidence" is not at his fingertips and, thus, is available to refute the inevitable lies and trick questions perpetrated by the opposing lawyer.

You should not have to answer why exactly this irrelevant junk is important, but if you find yourself in need of an answer, then simply say: "that will totally show the judge what sort of a person my spouse is!"

Whatever person, event or document you dredge up, the important thing is to mention it with passion and to repeat at least thrice that this is a *sine qua non* for the Friday event.

All the better if your explanation of the importance of this out-of-the-woodwork element is somewhat garbled and unintelligible. The less you can be understood, the more meaning the lawyer's paranoid mind will conjure, all by itself. So, go ahead and be as clear as a fortune cookie.

This conversation will challenge your lawyer's confidence sufficiently that any worry about the money issues will be pushed aside.

Now that you are ahead, go ahead: talk money.

Do not let the lawyer take the lead here, either. Make sure you are the one to initiate the money discussion, and to frame it as an indubitable assertion that: "the check is in the mail." You are so sorry that the unexpected disaster in your life (as reported in the message left with the receptionist) has made it impossible for you to deliver it personally as you had planned.

In sum, you can embroider the delivery, but the core of your conversation should always be this three-punch move:

COMMENCE with the inadequacy of your lawyer's preparation *and* your recently occurred life-threatening condition. Perhaps these two points could even be suggestively intertwined, gently hinting at possible causation.

> *Example: "I fear you are going to lose this case for me, but my doctor forbade me from worrying until I get proper medical attention. We can discuss this more when my doctor releases me."*

VEHEMENTLY assure that the check's in the mail—before your lawyer even mentions money. The dramatic effect may be enhanced if this line is delivered in a single breathless run-on sentence.

> *Example: "Honey, I must hang up now, my whole left side is feeling numb and my face is burning... I must see the doctor, but do not worry, I mailed you your money, you should get it tomorrow."*

FINISH by terminating the phone call with an enigmatic sound that makes it impossible to discern if you are still functional or if the burdens of life might finally have smashed you down into quivering helplessness.

> *Example: "Oh my gah..." hang up a receiver as the sound of suffering still rings in the lawyer's ears.*

After the conversation is completed with the requisite

artfulness, I recommend a field trip. If you have a friendly primary care provider, visit the Doctor and vent about your *acute stress*. Never feel bad about mentioning your acute stress. You are getting a divorce. If you are not suffering from the acute stress, you are not paying attention. You had told your lawyer that you needed medical attention, and it is best not to lie to your lawyer. And it does not hurt to get checked out either: divorces are hard on anybody's health. Let the doctor take your pulse, study your tongue, and recommend that you do more yoga.

Meanwhile, the old "check in the mail" routine buys you another day, until Thursday.

Thursday, around 3:30
1 day to launch

Since the check is supposedly in the mail, there is nothing you *must* do. But a proactive approach works best.

Call your lawyer and, in a weak, tremulous voice, firmly demand to know where the work stands. Express a keen interest in knowing what's going on. Ask when you can see all the drafts, charts, research, lists of witnesses, or whatever is relevant.

Praise something.

Criticize something.

Suggest something.

While you have the lawyer on the phone, interrupt yourself mid-sentence and ask the lawyer to hold—you have an incoming Call Waiting message and the Caller ID is your doctor; it may be a matter of impending healthcare crisis, even of life and death.

Since the full payment is purportedly on its way, you are entitled to be a little *demanding*, but remember that there are two schools of thought on whether you should be *critical* of your lawyer.

The "spare the stick and hurt the child" school teaches that the more you complain, the harder your lawyer works.

The "catch more flies with honey" school teaches that lawyers work better for clients who are sympathetic, the clients who do not complain about imaginary faults, or even real ones.

Take whatever approach suits your temperament and mood, and leave the contradictory theories to the unhelpful theoreticians.

Criticize, threaten, complain and nag, if you feel like it.

Praise, suck up, promise lavish gifts, if you feel like it.

It's your lawyer and your choice. You can threaten a Bar grievance or bring home-made cookies.

I had experience with clients who sometimes took both approaches alternately or even simultaneously.

It's your performance, and you should choose the path that makes you the most comfortable and, based on your own observations, seems best suited to "training" your lawyer.

Friday, sun-up

Rise and smile.

At last, today's the deadline for your work, and the lawyer is ready. You did hire the best lawyer you could find, yes? The best lawyer will be ready whether paid or not—the lawyer has a sterling professional reputation to protect.

Lawyers, like doctors, air traffic controllers, ambulance drivers, bridge engineers, rocket scientists, must do good work once the job is accepted. A surgeon will not do a half-hearted appendectomy, excusing lack of effort by lack of payment: the surgeon's license is on the line, if things go south. Likewise, a lawyer cannot come to court and tell the judge: "Judge, this client only half paid me, so I am only half prepared,"—or the lawyer will be only half-keeping his license and might get half-sued for malpractice.

Professional attorneys have an ethical obligation to do their very best at all times, no matter if they are paid or not. If you do not pay an attorney that lawyer may try to leave you ASAP or try to collect, but just cutting back to doing a slacker's job is not a viable option. There's the license on the line. For most professionals, the license is not only the source of making a living, but is intimately tied up with their whole identity, their sense of self.

In sum, so long as you had managed to hook a lawyer without pre-paying the entire fee, the unpaid work you get as a result will at least be good enough to satisfy all the ethical and legal requirements of the profession and, in most instances, as good as the work you'd get if you paid every cent. And now you are getting all that just for the piddling price of one consultation fee. Not bad, eh?

Friday, 8:30
launch day

Early in the morning, as soon as the lawyer's office opens, you call to check in. It is Friday, the D-day for your deposition, and the lawyer is still your lawyer. Ergo, your goal is accomplished—you got the free work! Today is your day. Enjoy your victory. But stay prepared in case your lawyer makes a play for the money.

Your lawyer might ask if you were happy with the services. Most of the time, this is not to trick you. Lawyers simply have slightly artistic temperaments and adore being praised. It is tempting to at least pay your lawyer partially in praise, since praise is certainly cheaper than paying in money. However, acknowledging that the job was expertly done might embolden the lawyer to make a request for the fees by then incurred. On the other hand, you do not want to appear an unpleasant ingrate—that's the sort of client who gets canned fast. A tricky balance here!

A client of mine once offered a brilliantly elegant solution to this quandary. Clara's alimony trial was one of those rare occasions when everything went our way, like a train on the express track rails. I was blessed with an audience, too:

212

Clara's whole family had been in full attendance to watch the court performances and hear the judge pronounce an alimony award large and long beyond our wildest dreams. Clara's clan thereupon spirited her away for a warm family-only celebratory lunch. She was gone before I could say the words "congratulations!" and "overdue invoices."

It was evening by the time my phone call caught up with Clara, and judging by the sound of her "hello," she had been mellowed by a few celebratory drinkie-winkies and was already in her jammies, out of make-up war paint, and relatively defenseless against my insidious lawyering skills.

"Great day in court, wasn't it," I started, fishing for a compliment and also aiming for a smooth segue into recovering that obscenely large unpaid amount she owed for my fees. As my grandmother (married to a lawyer) used to urge, "Strike while the iron is hot."

"Uh," agreed Clara listlessly, but did not add anything more to the conversation.

"Were your parents pleased," I pressed. "Did you have a good celebration over lunch?"

"Oh, no, no," sobbed Clara, and then delivered a response of pure genius: "My mother is very upset. Our neighbor's cat died suddenly. We loved it . . . that was *all* we talked about at lunch. I cannot think about my divorce, it seems like such a trifle compared to the creature we loved . . . not now!"

Not many people have a heart sufficiently frigid to respond to such a tearful and desperate plea by dredging up a crass reminder of overdue invoices. To be sure, I do have such a frigid heart, and I did ask for money. But in vain.

Clara just kept whimpering that she was too disturbed by Death to talk. It was a checkmate, a knockout punch. I admitted defeat and folded.

Saturday
day after launch

But enough of digression and back to your depositions which are now completed.

What next? If nothing more needs to be done for your case, delete your lawyer's name from your contacts list and just move on with your life. On the other hand, if a lawyer's services are needed further, you must contrive a way.

At this juncture even the most gullible of lawyers will not buy the "check in the mail" routine. You will have to spring for a little more bait, a carrot to put in the hamster wheel. Make a measured partial payment to prove your creditworthiness. Just a small part of what you owe.

People are funny that way: once your lawyer sees *a little* money, the hapless creature is easily deluded into believing that there is more where that payment came from. That's just how we are all wired: it is easy to believe in something if we just want it badly enough.

And then there is one more thing that powerfully works to your advantage: By this time, your lawyer has too much invested in you and too much money owed to just walk away.

As a practical matter, for your lawyer, firing you as a client and walking away means for sure forfeiting all the money already owed. Clearly, you'll never pay a dime more if your lawyer fires you. On the other hand, staying the course may feel like a ticket to get paid a growing stream of revenue from billed hours and reimbursable costs. Potential piles of money. Tempting.

Economists have discovered that most people find it irrationally difficult to walk away from investments in cost that are already in the rearview mirror, what the economists call sunk costs. "I've got too much invested in this to quit now."

Instead of doing the smart thing and cutting their losses, people often tend to compound the loss of effort and money by spending more energy and money in vain attempts to recover advantages deemed to have been already "earned." You do not actually need a degree in economics to notice that it is common to "throw good money after the bad."

It happens every day. People sit through horrible theater performances because they "paid for the tickets already," or keep gym subscriptions because they "can't get back the initiation fee." Some even go through with a wedding because the "the hall and the caterer are already paid."

Now that your mind is sharpened to this human infirmity, do take advantage. Bait your lawyer. It will be easier than you think to persuade the lawyer that now you will pay because that wishful thinking is what your lawyer desperately wants to happen.

So, send in a payment. Do not worry, I am not suggesting you give up and pay all you owe. That would defeat the purpose of the game. Pay a fraction of what is owed. Say, 20% to 30%.

If you owe $10,000, maybe deliver $3,000. If you owe $50,000, then $15,000 or even $10,000 might do the trick. Mail the check in and grease the way for your lawyer to embark, reluctantly but ever-hopefully, upon his next task.

> NOTE: *There is a risk to this strategy. The lawyer might pocket your partial pay, cut the losses and give you the boot. Heavy promises of large forthcoming payments may serve to minimize this risk.*

WEEK two, Tuesday, 11:30 A.M.

Your partial payment has arrived, and so has the need to explain its paucity. It's always a good idea to sugar-coat a bitter pill.

Get ready. Start by setting the mood. You must contrive to befuddle your lawyer so that your unpaid balance shrinks in proportion to other things that cry out for attention. If your initial approach had been to display a touch of unhappiness with your lawyer's work, capitalize on that. Turn up the complaining, just a teeny-tiny, eeny-weeny notch. Mention that the other attorney dominated the room, or that the judge did not seem to show your attorney so much respect, or that your attorney failed to mention a critical issue, or to object where you thought an objection was necessary. Say, with just the slightest touch of whininess: "I did not feel as protected as I would have liked."

Be saddened by the lawyer's shortcomings but graciously forgiving. It is important not to go overboard with the criticism. Lawyers hate being criticized much more than they hate being ripped off. You aim at planting a healthy seed of self-doubt, not at awakening the self-preservation beast who just might decide that the best way out of a mess is to just fire your complaining ass ASAP.

Likewise, if your original strategy was leaning towards praise, capitalize on that. Turn up the praise. Explain that the lawyer is your true savior. You can even bring a prop—I've received, for example, a basket of cheeses, a home-made pie.

Either way, the lawyer's impulse is to prove his colors. Most people do not realize this, but it is true: good lawyers are bitterly self-critical and perpetually insecure. Litigators especially are on a never-ending quest to prove themselves, to demonstrate that they are worthy of the title "Esquire," to make their mothers proud. I do not have the statistics to back it up, but I am confident that there is a reverse correlation between the quality of the lawyer and the lawyer's confidence. Plenty of piss-poor lawyers are uncannily pleased with themselves, but better lawyers are constantly dissatisfied. Maybe that's why they are better lawyers. Einstein had made an observation: "The more I learn, the more I realize how much I don't know." And Einstein was a guy who knew plenty much!

A few years ago, I was sitting at morning lecture in a ten-day intensive seminar program of the National Family

Lawyer Trial Institute, a program which attracts the most committed of the divorce litigators, those hoping to improve themselves. Institute participation requires its attendees to leave their busy practices, fly in from across the country, and pay roughly $4,000 for the privilege. Most lawyers in my class were divorce law veterans. Each had represented endless multitudes of clients, taken and defended oodles of depositions, argued file cabinets full of motions, and some even won in viciously litigated jury trials.

The lecturer took the podium and opened with a telling observation. Seizing each face in the amphitheater with the soul-penetrating look of his coal-pitch-black eyes, he blurted out:

"You all feel like a fraud, every one of you. That's why you are all here, in this windowless room on a Sunday morning."

The audience of distinguished legal minds gasped as one and issued an empathetic sigh of relief. We all doubted ourselves, we just did not realize that our neighbor was just as terrified. The truth is, every professional has a little voice inside his brain that nags on the hour: "I wonder how I screwed up today... ." That's what fuels the never-ending quest to get better.

Now that you know about this chink in your lawyer's armor, you are prepared to *capitalize*.

Imply that your payment is lacking because the results were lacking, that you paid what you thought was fair. And what with you being near your deathbed with a mystical (and

218

mythical) migraine on Wednesday and the lawyer's job being unsatisfactory to you on Deposition Friday, the lawyer
will not be able to stop wondering whether a better future
performance would not both validate his past performance
and also open your purse to full payment of the already incurred bills. This possibility will cause the lawyer to want to
"prove" to you that you were undervaluing the performance.

There are two things you'd do well to firmly keep in
mind when dealing with lawyers. First is what we just talked
about: good lawyers, like all good professional, constantly
doubt themselves—no matter what bold front they try and
turn to the world. Second is that lawyers make shoddy busi-
nessmen. They suck at asking for money. When lawyers
gather at their inner circle parties and lawyers-only confer-
ences, that's all they talk about. How they could not collect,
and whether there's a better way to "talk money" with clients
who are delinquent on their bills. The biggest problem with
collections is that the process makes lawyers feel awfully
awkward.

Enlightened and emboldened by these revelations, you
can now approach the *talk* more confidently.

And before you do, there is one more preparatory step
you could take. Some of my clients have found it helpful to,
instead of writing the deficient check themselves, have an
older member of the family write that partial check. This
way, when you are ultimately nailed by the question: "Your
payment was short?" and your original expression of disbelief and earnest shocked surprise is not fooling the irate lawyer, you can easily phase into the blame-shifting stage: "Oh

no! Grandma wrote the check. The poor sweet thing can be so forgetful at times."

"Grandma made a mistake," you would say. "but do not worry, Grandma will correct it. Please, please do not tell her that her little slip caused me trouble!"

Who could be upset with an old, forgetful, well-meaning lady? Who could break the sweet old lady's heart with guilt by suggesting that her forgetfulness might have left her dear granddaughter lawyerless?!

Then throw in a preventative strike.

"How much do you absolutely need right now, dear?" you might murmur wearily and resignedly in a manner properly suited to a person surrendering to the utterly unbearable minutia of life.

That routine almost always produces a pause, then some hiccups, and finally a number.

"Of course, dear," you will respond magnanimously.

> NOTE: *Be prepared that the number your lawyer throws back at you might go up, now that you have—let's face it—bad credit history with the lawyer.*

Whatever the number, do not argue or ask for discounts. Deep down, what do you care? This number is nothing but the lawyer's pipe dream. You will never actually pay that much.

You will, however, promise to pay, and with that the subject of the fee will be closed for now, and the subject of work will re-open.

With a new deadline looming (you always do have a new deadline, don't you?) the lawyer will roll up his sleeves and get back to work. It will be another few days or so until your lawyer comes to realize that there is no check in the mailbox for what now is close to two weeks of work. By then, you will have weaseled out several weeks of legal work for a mere fraction of the cost. For more work, simply repeat the same steps in a different tempo and tune.

Of course, relying on exactly the same gimmicks would be inexcusably amateurish, and disrespectful to your lawyer's intelligence as well as your own resourcefulness. Inspired by my educational tales, a smart person like you will, no doubt, invent your very own tricks, appropriate for the personalities and circumstances. A few thought-provoking hacks are listed below to start your creative juices flowing. They fit the classic urban dictionary definition of a "hack" as a "clever solution to a tricky problem."

The "Credit Card Authorization" Hack

This is something to have up your sleeve for those critical situations when you are losing your lawyer's trust. Suggest that you will empower the lawyer to simply bill your credit card any time he likes. You will leave on file with the lawyer your credit card number and all the secret security digits on the back and in the corner, and sign this release:

I authorize the law firm of Gull & Able PLLC to charge my credit card with all the charges for fees and expenses incurred in connection with my representation within 24 hours after I am presented with and approve the invoice, unless I conclude, after review, that I disagree with the invoice amount.

Make sure that you add this critically important sentence:

My separate approval will be required for each new charge.

Having a credit card authorization on file should mollify all but the most suspicious lawyers, at least enough to carry on working a little longer.

Of course, now that you have a hack to mollify the lawyer's fears, you are in need of the corresponding hack to prevent the law firm of Gull & Able PLLC from actually collecting on the bill. Consider some of the delaying hacks described below.

The "Let's Wait For A Better Stopping Point" Hack

When the dreaded invoice first arrives, and the lawyer asks for your OK to charge the card, you might say:

"Could we wait and invoice me after the [deposition is finished, motion is filed, letter is written]? I want to pay for all of it at once when I have a better sense of how the case is going?"

This approach often works because it appeals to the lawyer's need to prove the quality of work done.

Caveat: do not overreach by choosing a stopping point that will not occur until next month. Choose a stopping point that is only a paltry few days out. This way, the lawyer will be more inclined to feel that there is no harm waiting a little, to accommodate your natural request to evaluate a more finished product before you pay.

The "Card Switch" Hack

If a charge on the card appears imminent, stop it by this message:

I retract authorization for my card ending -1234, effective immediately. Do not charge anything!

In post scriptum, explain in plain English: "So sorry, but the card you were about to charge has just been reported lost (stolen, over-drafted, closed, unexpectedly suspended by the issuing bank's security check regarding suspected unauthorized use, etc.) Do not worry, I will get you the new card number just as soon as it is issued."

The "Card in the Mail" Hack

Yes, the *credit card* in the mail, you read this right. The brilliance of this move is precisely its absurdity. Lawyers these days are fighting back against your "check in the mail" routine with requesting a credit card to keep on file.

You had promised the lawyer that your card can be charged, but now the lawyer is asking for the card number. So, it is time for you to engage in a hysterical fit of paranoia about the transmission of your credit card information.

Because of the identity theft, you fretfully say, you do not want to trust your credit card number to the email or the telephone. To protect yourself, you will be *sending* your credit card number by snail mail. (Alternatively, you will stop by to personally provide it.) And, by the way, before any of this happens at all, you'd like some written assurance about what security measures the firm has in place to safeguard the handling of this precious information once it is actually received.

No self-respecting lawyer will press you to expose yourself to worries about identity theft, however unlikely the risk might truly seem. If the lawyer counters that the firm has a "safe portal," all you have to do is insist that you do not trust the internet, even when it's supposedly safe. There have certainly been enough hacks into "safe" internet places to validate your paranoia.

There is a more generally useful trick that is applicable here. When you put a worry or objection to something in a writing, even via email, lawyers tend to fret about how that might be construed as having put them "on notice" about a risk for whose consequences they might, if lightning indeed strikes, someday be held responsible. Lawyers are worry-warts and, when there is an easy way to avoid a risk, will usually jump at the bait. So, create a risk and be sure to do it in writing.

It is not hard to see how a hack like this can give you an extra day or five. This move can be used in conjunction with the "Card Switch" or as a free-standing hack. Use your imagination!

These are just a few examples of hacks that work to delay making payments while your lawyer soldiers on, working hard on behalf of your cause. With patience and perseverance, you will discover your own style and your own hacks.

WHY TRICKS AND HACKS WORK

WHY DO TRICKS and hacks work? Why would your lawyer fall for the old routines like the "check in the mail," the "401K loan is processing" or "Auntie is coming with funds for the payment"? Why would a basket of cheeses melt a lawyer's heart? Why would lawyers believe such tall tales? Are divorce lawyers stupid? Sounds silly at first, but there is a perfectly reasonable explanation: the tales mimic precisely the jam and pickles that befall the well-meaning, God-fearing clients who harbor no intention whatsoever of skipping on their bills. I have been describing a would-be grifter in order to get your attention, but the behavior of more honest clients is remarkably similar. It is harder than you might think to tell the cheaters from honest clients who are bedeviled by real problems and concerns.

A new client came to see me once. We spent a productive hour. At the end of the hour, she got up and looked in her purse, and went a little pale: she forgot to bring her wallet. Three days later, I received a letter with the check from her. She never meant to stiff me—she just was (understandably) nervous getting up to see a lawyer. In the next few months it took to sort out her affairs, her payments were always prompt.

Another client told me that he put in for a loan against his 401K to hire me, but it did not come through yet. He really needed somebody in court with him the very next day: his wife had brought a domestic violence complaint, and losing it would be devastating for him. I took the risk of non-payment rather than letting him handle this serious matter without a lawyer (a course that is almost always a losing proposition in domestic violence defense hearings where the lawyerless party is figuratively bringing only a knife to a gunfight). His 401K loan came through a week later, and he ended up a devoted client. He never intended to stiff me.

The trick "credit card in the mail" comes from a client of mine who never intended to stiff me either: she mailed her credit card numbers by snail mail because she really did have an over-the-top, paranoid distrust of the internet and the telephone. (Whether she also wore a precautionary tinfoil hat at home, I cannot say.) The important thing is that she paid her bill in full, as had always been her honest intent.

An Armenian immigrant whose income was too small

to pay my fees supplemented her "pay-what-you-can" financial effort with a basket of home-made bread—the best bread I ever tasted. It was a sincere and kind gesture, which in my eyes, mostly made up for the dollar deficiency. Maybe not totally, but it was enough to keep me on her legal team.

Life is notoriously harder to believe than any fiction. Perfectly well-meaning clients frequently end up in situations that are impossible to distinguish from a con. Which is why whatever con, trick or hack you implement, it may have happened in real life, to clients who meant to and did pay. One just never can tell. That was the good news for a would-be successful rip-off artist.

And now for the bad news . . ..

If you do not pay your lawyer, he will eventually Houdini out of your case. Because of the lawyer's entanglement with Bar and court requirements, this day may come later rather than sooner, but the day *will* come. What do you do when this day comes? With the wolves of litigation at the door, most people hire the next lawyer. Simple enough. So what's the problem? The problem is in the transfer. As my grandma use to say: "three times move, one time burn," which took me years to parse as "stuff get damaged in the move." Just as in moving from one house to another, your damage when moving from one lawyer to another is multi-faceted and hard to predict. Agreements which your first lawyer had made with the opposing lawyer all of a sudden get disavowed and undone, promises get forgotten, documents lost. Even the judges change their minds and what seemed a sure win suddenly becomes . . . complicated. The day you transition to your next lawyer, you best have your every possible loose end double-tied with a sailor's knot.

In the next chapter, we talk about some unintended consequences of transitioning to a new lawyer.

Part Two

Donny Comes Undone

BEFORE I MET LYNDA, there was Donny.

Most of what I know about stiffing lawyers I learned from Donny Beaver, although, to be fair, there were nuances Donny did not anticipate either. At times, we learned together.

When Donny and I met, we were not on even grounds.

He was much older and richer, but it was more than just our thirty-two-year difference in age and thirteen-million-dollar difference in bank accounts. It was the difference in life trajectories. I was surely going up because one cannot fall below the nadir. Danny was . . . so far up there, I could not really tell which way he was heading. Coasting, I think.

Donny had reached the apogee of his career a long time

before we met, perhaps around the time I was playing in kindergarten. He had made his first two million dollars before I made it to college, and lost all of his ambitions for business (but not his interest in money) before I entered law school.

While I was clawing my way through learning the law, Donny was floating through his golden years, complacently rich and tastefully bored. Then a romantic catastrophe jettisoned him out of a bland marriage and plopped him into a poorly air-conditioned condo on the second floor of the two-floor, fifty-year-old walk-up badly in need of a new roof. That condo was also double-tasking as the home of my one-week-old law firm.

In the week since I had opened my doors, Donny was the most promising prospect.

Donny's call was only the third incoming call which I had handled that week (it puzzles me why any new lawyer would bother to hire a receptionist, but some do).

The two previous calls were both from women, each of whom led with a vociferous declaration about wanting a "woman lawyer," a desire which I could presumably satisfy with indisputable biological qualifications.

The first woman called on behalf of her drunkard son, who was in custody for repeated DWIs. The incarcerated son (the woman-caller said) could pay *if* I bailed him out. She herself regrettably had no money for the bail—or anything else. "Woman to woman, he is my son," she begged, "you understand?!"

I understood, but elected to wait for the next caller.

The second caller's desire was to sue her husband's

lover for alienation of affections. There was a million dollar award in her case, she was sure. Also, she could pay as soon as her tax refund came in at some hazy future time. Upon learning that my initial consultation fee alone was $250, this second prospect, the Woman Scorned, mumbled bad words about sleazy, greedy lawyers and hung up.

This prelude set the stage auspiciously for Donny, my third and (obviously!) most promising prospect. On the phone, he did not appear fazed with the $250 consultation cost, asking only if I was available on Friday afternoon, so, he said, he'd be able to come after work.

Of course I was available then! It was the Memorial day weekend, and I was in luck because the early heat of Duck-lingburg Spring drove most of my divorce law competitors to the beach. At the end of my block, where the zoning abruptly switched from multimillion single to posh restaurant and retail, the outside seatings of the popular joint called *Pick-Up&Tequila* were gaining decibels.

Every other business was shuttered for the holiday. I, however, was ready and able pretty much any time of day or night. Donny and I agreed on half past three.

DONNY HIRES A LAWYER

DONNY ARRIVED at 4:45, over an hour later than scheduled and ten minutes after I gave up on him and changed out of my "dress for success" office clothes.

We liked each other right away.

Donny was smooth, worldly, and confident. I was enchanted with him.

I was young, energetic and passionate about the law. And gullible. He was pleased. By everything.

Donny's shoes cost more than I hoped to make that month. My own office shoes (now resting in the kitchen) were bought in my days as a corporate lawyer, before my Alice-in-Wonderland-like fall into the rabbit hole of family law. They were reasonably expensive in their own right, but known ceremoniously as "the shoes." I also owned "the suit" and "shirts number 1 and 2," but lamentably no "shirt 3." A three-day court appearance could have become an embarrassing sartorial dilemma—assuming an observant judge. But dress-to-impress problems were the least of my problems in those days. First priority was latching onto someone to impress.

Donny carried up three boxes of documents, darting up the two flights of stairs at an impressively good clip. He did not even show the slightest sign of getting winded. He unloaded the boxes in an uneven line in the middle of the living room. Then he resolutely docked his linen-clad bottom on my ivory leather couch (happily, I had spent a good forty minutes the previous night washing and polishing the leather in careful preparation for his arrival).

Donny immediately dominated the flow of conversation.

After informing me that the weather was hot and promised to get even hotter, he loosened the top buttons on his fashionably wrinkled linen collar. He did not wear a tie, and I do not think he was actually coming from work. Then he started to expound on his quest.

My mission, he declared without inquiry into whether I'd accept it, was to help him shake off his *very troubled* wife so he could quietly unite with a more attractive woman. Donny was not a starry-eyed novice in the world of romance and deceit and he was adequately prepared to withstand the blows of the heavy hand of the law. In a way, Donny's family had been planning for this moment since his birth: it was family money that fueled Donny's business.

The current Mrs. Beaver had arrived in the marriage with no assets except for the ones on her chest, and those, upon inspection, turned out to be two parts marshmallow foam and three parts shimmer bronzer. Donny's love was rather disillusioned by the woman's attempt to marry into real money in exchange for fake boobage; and not just fake— painted on! Thus, he did not even feel bad watching his fiancée cry genuine tears while signing away her future alimony rights in response to his ultimatum presented on the morning of their wedding day. She signed the legal papers while the guests were already waiting in church, and slept with her back turned to Donny during the entire honeymoon.

"That prenup fixed the alimony problem," Donny said pensively. "Now I just need you to fix the property division."

"You didn't 'fix' the property division in the prenup?" I asked, mirroring his lingo.

"Sure we did," snapped Donny, "but the thing is, there were a few snags."

"Snags?" I caught myself repeating everything he said. Somehow, I had to snap out of it.

"A few details, so to speak. You'll just have to work out the glitches for me, study a few details."

As we spent a while studying the *details*, I developed "the headlines" grasp of the problem: Donny was caught in a predicament best described as a straw-man scheme gone rogue. Straw-woman, in his case.

At times during the marriage, Donny had to move some property around, and sometimes it ended up titled into Mrs.

Donny's name. There were good pressing reasons for that—tax reasons, a brief SEC investigation-related scare, a short spell when Donny fell so blindly in love with his wife that he wanted to share his fortunes. According to Donny, just about all of those transfers were "undone," "no more," and "reverted back" to Donny. "You'd need to understand the details," he said. "Some might be faultily titled," he admitted. "But it's clerical. You'll see that all the business property should be mine after all. Mine alone."

It was in the details, indeed.

And he was going to trust me with every detail of his business, he said. "Every detail that *matters*, anyway," Donny's smile had just the slightest hint of condescension.

———

OF COURSE, there wasn't time on that remarkably hot and long afternoon to study *every* minuscule detail of Donny's exceptionally full life. Some minor details got prioritized out, including the one bit that was proximately responsible for bringing Donny to see me. Donny had not told me that day, but it eventually came out: he'd fallen victim to a Mistress Ultimatum.

After three years of waiting patiently in the wings, Donny's Mistress had approached him with this vapid fiat:

"No more sharing with that stuck-up B—" the mistress announced, staring in the air above Donny, and gesticulating wildly, "I get the whole of you, or you never get to see—," she proclaimed with her arms frozen dramatically at shoulder height, both index fingers pointed to the lower part of her Rubenesque belly.

Donny was already all too familiar with this particular form of diatribe. As a matter of fact, he had heard this very ultimatum uttered with an increasing frequency in the past few months, so often that he even could not resist lip-syncing along. The incantation exerted the power which familiar refrains have to seduce their listeners into joining the chorus. It was like an annoying commercial which has everyone cringing but singing along anyway, even if only in the recesses of the brain. Brainwash. Magic. Donny was singing along: "You never get to see this *again*," Danny's brain could not help re-echoing over and over the Mistress's tune.

But this time, something about her *lyrics* had sounded different, as was also the accompanying gesture.

When Donny got to the word ". . . again . . ." his voice trailed uncomfortably alone. She had a different refrain today!

"*Never*, not once!" she smirked smugly and rotated her wrists slightly up her belly, fingers still pointed inward stiffly. The gesture was subtly new, with an alarmingly different point of focus, one slightly above the area that heretofore had been the asset being bargained over. Donny knew in his gut, even before his brain had time to process: this was not her habitually empty threat.

After years of trying every angle, Donny's Mistress got hold of an entirely new and far better pressure point in her quest for her woman's happiness: now there was a bun in the oven. She was forty-six, and it did not seem possible, but it happened, the miracle of miracles! She suddenly had *leverage*!

Donny Junior was on the way, and that changed everything. Any remaining shred of Donny Senior's devotion to his childless marriage was gone like a bad dream. As a result, Donny launched himself on a quest for a competent lawyer who'd be amenable to handling his intricate divorce situation for what Donny thought was a *reasonable* fee. (Donny's idea of a reasonable rate was roughly ten times under the going market rate for a divorce of comparable complexity.) A miracle of impending birth set underway a chain of events which, in what seemed another miracle, brought Donny to my doorstep. It figured. He was here, a multi-millionaire client wanting to hire *me*, days after I opened my one-woman practice. Donny's case was the break which, for most new lawyers, does not come for years.

Donny's voice took over my small living room which served as "conference room number 1." He spoke with the well-modulated certainty of a radio shrink, accustomed to talking into the rapt attention of the whole syndicated area audience. Donny's voice was one of his true talents. His voice made one buy every word he was selling. It was a voice that could be so warm that one felt all worries gone and troubles disappear; or so stern that one felt the sadness and injustice of the whole world, and knew instantly that all those horrible things were singularly one's own fault.

We discussed Donny's business.

He had alluded vaguely to the mistress, but not to the

upcoming baby nor to the ultimatum. The matter of the baby did not come up at our first meeting, nor in any of our later conversations, for that matter. In fact, the baby did not come up at all until Mrs. Donny Beaver testified at trial, catching me off guard and shifting the judge's attitude from gratuitously unfriendly to moralizingly hostile. But I digress. As I said, that first day we met, Donny and I just discussed details of his business.

Donny's business was on the decline, or so he told me.

Back then, I did not yet fully appreciate that there was *always* a direct correlation between the decline of a husband's business and the proximity of the separation date. But no matter. Donny's investments (except for a few million dollars here and there that were squirreled away in stocks and in gold) were in real estate—mostly commercial buildings which he leased out to commercial clients. I remembered Pepsi was one of Donny's tenants, leasing a small warehouse; all of the other tenants had unfamiliar names. Donny painted a grim picture of his financial status in the stumbling market: tenants skipping payments, insurance carriers increasing premiums, City of Ducklingburg suffocating him and his tenants with fines, taxes and zoning challenges.

It all seemed glamorous, even his problems. Donny used words like "triple net lease" and "capital gains" and "1031 tax shelter." Faltering business or not, he was a client who really did *have* real money. The times may have been hairy and liquid funds tough, but he was surely good for his legal bills. I thought.

Donny's immediate problem, he explained to me in his authoritatively deep, faith-inspiring voice, was his wife's *incredible stupidity*.

Donny's wife, the Spiteful Witch, with no business sense but plenty of initiative, was about to bring down the family business into ruin.

"The Spiteful Witch went off the deep end," he said.

Among other things, The Witch was on the verge of fire-selling a warehouse, the Beavers' crown asset. (I could not tell you now why the warehouse was important exactly, but in Donny's mind, it clearly had the symbolic significance of a king in a chess game.) For tax purposes which Donny had since grown to deeply regret, title to the warehouse in question was recorded in the name of Mrs. Donny solely, a fact which arguably empowered her to put the warehouse up for sale—a "totally stupid" step she had already taken. The crown jewel of the Beavers' little empire was on the block. What's worse, there was an eager buyer, who would not take Donny's hints to walk away and leave it be. And what was decidedly horrible was that the buyer was Donny's vicious competitor, hiding behind a facade of agents and layers upon layers of nearly indecipherable corporate Matryoshka doll structures. If completed, this sale could quickly cripple Donny's business, and lead to financial ruin and personal disgrace, Donny confided with sadness. The sale might even cost Donny his hard-earned retirement nest egg. *The sale had to be stopped.*

"Can you stop the sale, can you do it?" beseeched Donny eyeing, with theatrically exaggerated suspicion the shelf that supported my law school diploma (very good quality, but much too fresh). "Can you put a stop to this disaster?"

"Well, that depends," I said. I am of the school to never promise.

When you are a lawyer, prudence dictates to answer absolutely every question with "Well, now, of course this depends... ."

But in my heart, I knew that I could do it—and I intended to prove that I could do it to myself, to Donny, and to everybody else who cared to watch in awe of my awesome lawyering.

I was hooked: Donny played his first card masterfully. Lawyers—litigators especially—are a compulsively competitive lot, constantly needing to prove their worth to themselves and anybody who will listen or watch. It is an obsession with any litigator to prove that he is better than the guy down the road, just as quick-draw gunfighters are reputed to have done in the Old West. Those who make it to the top of the competition do not stop until an untimely heart attack puts them down during an opening statement in a courtroom full of aghast spectators. Those who do not make it to the top often find solace in a bottle of booze. Litigators can be pushed to their limit if you promise them an equivalent of a gold medal, maybe just a paper certificate with a silly title like "Outstanding Lawyer of the Year." (Just check out their office walls and shelves for tangible relics of their success in the hunt.) Lawyers are a lot like professional athletes that way, with a competitive wiring that overshadows even the pursuit of mere money. That is their strength and—as is always the case—their weakness, their Achilles Heel to be exploited. In my case, Donny discovered his mark's weakness almost immediately, and manipulated the situation in the space of a few minutes.

"Will you take my case," challenged Donny, "or is it *too complicated* for you?"

He looked around my make-shift office again, and seeing it through his eyes made me regret the decision to open a law practice in my walk-up condo.

The four-unit condo building in question was a decrepit wart on the polished forehead of a swanky multi-million-dollar development. It was also by far the cheapest buy in the surrounding three square miles. I liked the price and did not mind the imperfections. Indeed, the bohemian ways of my fellow condo-owners were comforting: we did not much care to keep up with the emerald green grass yards and the well-fed brand-name rose-bushes that adorned all the *other* houses, as far as the eye could see. While our neighborhood sprinkled, aerated, fertilized, de-thatched and blew their dead leaves off their lawns, our condo board steadfastly preserved the "natural" look of the condo's front-yard grass and stood firm in our irrational belief that the three leggy azaleas in the front could rely on nature alone for their sustenance and their flowering inspiration. Our window frames showed character, even if the fascia along the front was badly in need of repair.

Up until that moment, I saw my haphazardly maintained "office building" as independently whimsical. The front of the building had the distressed look of impoverished nobility, relaying to my clients the message that I do not charge them extra for the snazzy overhead. Or so I told myself.

The back of the building was the real problem, though, and I knew it.

Right now, the first floor neighbor on the right was chilling in a pair of flip-flops and not much else, chowing down on her holiday beer and pizza. With the first floor neighbor on the left line-drying her underpants on three teetering racks stacked across her patio, the back entrance provided a crowded view that, while arguably "interesting," did not convey the ambience of a high-class, sophisticated law practice.

I had determined that the clients of my law firm would come and go through the *front* entrance—the inside stairs abandoned by the condo residents in favor of the easy access from the back. The ploy had worked, but now I wondered what I'd do if Donny (whose entrance I had carefully corralled through the front) were ever to push his way through the back stairs where the first floor neighbors' unkempt patios yawned embarrassingly open for the clients' inspection. He would thus see my law practice for what it really was—a Potemkin village. I shuddered and switched back to listening to Donny.

THE TRUE MEANING OF "COMPLI-CATED"

ACCORDING to Donny, he'd talked to three lawyers before me and each of these lawyers could not take his case for the same reason. "'Too complicated,' they said." Too much to deal with, even for the Big Wig who kept the office on the corner of Swan and Lake, charged $600 an hour, and was the object of envy and hatred of the rest of the local jackal pack. Even for the Big Wig, Donny's case was "too complicated." At that moment, I saw my niche and mentally measured my wall for the "Outstanding Lawyer of the Year" certificate.

What I did not know in the first days of my Duckling-burg divorce practice was that "too complicated" was not so much an honest assessment of a case, but the industry code for clients with high expectations and shallow pockets, those likely to pay badly and never be happy.

That was not the meaning of the term I expected. For corporate lawyers, which was what my law school specialized in preparing its graduates, "too complicated" meant just that: "too complicated for some lawyers, probably for the lawyers of a lower caliber than those with our prestigious law degree, but certainly not too complicated for *us*." If, that is, we deign to accept you as a client.

As it turned out, for divorce lawyers, "too complicated" has an entirely different meaning. It is code. "Too complicated" is the term for clients who will squeeze the life out of a lawyer, demanding work day and night, but will not pay. It is a polite way of turning freeloaders out of the door, the dating world version of the rejection code "it's not you, it's me."

We did not cover that meaning of "complicated" in my elite law school and my brief but even more elite corporate law training. What we did cover, instead, were the stories of complex business restructuring which saved important corporate clients, and with them, the economy of the entire country. We studied the legends of corporate takeovers and resistance. We took away the notion that the way to riches and glory in the legal profession *is* to deal in matters too complicated for ordinary, humdrum lawyers. The legendary attorneys who invented the *poison pill*—the tiny provision in corporate charters that changed everything in the merger and acquisition terrain—those epic pioneers, did not shrink from "complicated." Quite the opposite: complicated was

245

the reason that respected corporate lawyers were hired and that the Wall Street Journal called for an interview with the elite legal counsel involved. "Complicated" was a *good* thing in the world from which I had just taken a tumble. I should have noticed that my world was different now, but I did not yet have the sense to let go.

"Lawyers who say a case is 'too complicated,' are just lazy losers," I thought to myself. "If filing an injunction to stop a wasteful sale of a marital asset is too complex for this local bunch, I can be a star in this town."

I told Donny nothing was too complicated for my little firm, and, by jolly, I'd take his case right away. I was going to win big and prove myself! I was going to be famous! The Best! The go-to gal for the complicated cases in this little town. I already planned a new line on my website: "*No Case Too Complicated!*" I was going to have a niche. Donny's case would launch my career. The guy with the office on the corner of Swan and Lake—the one supposedly "best and notorious" in this divorce lawyers' community—would be ashamed to show his face in the courthouse after I win the case that was "too complicated" for him. In that hour, it did not even much matter what (or if) Danny offered to pay, because his case was going to put me on the map. It was the Launchpad to the reincarnation of my stellar legal career that we were talking about here.

But Donny did not disappoint with the first consultation's $250 payment either. Without the least nudging from me, he stopped mid-sentence, smiled magnanimously and said: "I nearly forgot—what an embarrassment." He then produced an oversized checkbook. "Let me pay you," he declared, tearing off and handing, with a grand sweeping gesture, a check already filled out in his firm, clear hand. If he were offering me the million-dollar payment that goes with the Nobel prize accolade, he could not have been more grandiose. Plus, he brought up the matter of additional future payments immediately. "I know you will need to be paid in advance going forward," he said, "I know lawyers." In his days of business dealings, he'd dealt with more lawyers than you can shake a stick at, "and I will make sure you are paid a generous retainer," he announced. Because of the marital "complications" in his business affairs and the state of the real estate market, he unfortunately did not have much *liquidity* just then, he explained. Right after the holiday weekend, he'd take care of his cash-flow problem promptly because he knew how important prompt payment was to lawyers.

"I will pull sufficient funding for your work out of my 401K," he disclosed to me, like it was a dirty secret.

As (almost) his lawyer, I could not ignore the tax consequences:

"You may be taxed on the 401K withdrawal," I reminded. "And there may be a fine for early withdrawal. You best check with your accountant first."

"I'll take a hit," he sighed stoically. "Do not worry, I'll put in the papers and cash it out as soon as the bank opens and I can get the paperwork rolling. How much do you need?" I ball-parked getting an injunction against his wife at a week's worth of work straight, and said ten thousand. Not a problem, not a problem at all, he amiably agreed. Then, in response to nothing I did, he leaned in so close that there was almost no space left between us and, looking me intensely in the eye, pleaded in a deep, low voice, almost stage whisper: "Trust me. I will pay every penny for your work. But this real estate sale is an emergency. You can start working this weekend already, right?"

Every lawyer knows that it is stupid to accept responsibility for a litigated case before the payment cleared. That's elementary. Once a lawyer gets into a case, it is almost impossible to get out without a judge's blessing, which means that it is impossible to get out for weeks or months, depending on the glacial pace of the local court. That's weeks or months of forced labor, whether the lawyer is paid or not.

But from time to time every lawyer does it, anyway. Leap and the saving net will appear, right? Makes one feel alive. Sometimes one has to take a chance, and nothing kills a once-in-a-lifetime chance as surely as prudence and good planning. It's the classic war of the conflicting proverbs: "Fools rush in where angels fear to tread" versus "Opportunity knocks but once"!

One must try and do the prudent thing, of course, there is no denying that. It is prudent to wait for the retainer to clear before signing on the client; prudent to wait and *not* start a law firm before saving six months' worth of living expenses and getting approved for the six figure-sized business loan; prudent to never talk to strangers; and, for that matter, not to run a law firm out of your home.

Doing the prudent thing is great, but let's face it: nobody has achieved greatness by sticking obsessively to what's prudent. Besides, I had already opened my practice with no money in the bank, let alone six months' worth. Prudent was not going to happen, so I might at least be consistent.

DONNY was in a jam—the fire sale of his largest asset was scheduled for the following Wednesday.

I could wait for his 401K funds, or I could get prepared for court, but there was no time for both. The thought that Donny would bring the payment the day of court, and I'd come to court unprepared shot cold panic through my already dizzy head. That was far more terrifying than not getting paid.

Yes, signing a client without payment was not the recommended plan, but let's face it: recommended plans are for mediocrities. Did any of the visionary computer billionaires follow a conventional "recommended plan"?

Besides, if everything had gone according to the usual plan, Donny would probably be standing on the twenty sixth floor of the Lark Tower, talking to one of Pincher Pincher & Pong PLLC's three hundred lawyers. Instead, in a rare stroke of luck, he brought his multi-million dollar legal troubles into my walk-up condo.

It was a career-changing chance, and I took it eagerly. You'd do it too in my place.

Can You Stiff You Divorce Lawyer?

Or, maybe you'd be a better crystal ball gazer?

DONNY and I shook hands and signed the contract for representation. I was firmly embroiled as his lawyer now. The clock had progressed to a quarter past six, the time of day when the heat of the South Duck Spring afternoon was imperceptibly tuning down. The air temperature on my walk up patio lessened from scorching-maddening to pleasantly lethargic. But I was not tired in the least, I felt needed and energized. Bring it on!

I did not say it out-loud, because it was not a prudent thing to say, but in my mind, I knew I'd move mountains for this man who had just put his trust in me. He was risking millions of dollars. I was touched by his confidence and vowed to protect his best interests with every iota of ability I've got. Donny, on his part, did speak his mind and assured me once again that he'd indubitably pay "every penny."

Then, he confidentially explained the dangers of the sale that had to be stopped. It seemed every transaction in Donny's business depended on that crown jewel warehouse property. It was irreplaceable. Without the warehouse, all other business parts would turn useless, like unattached appendages. He claimed that the collapse of his business interests would be like falling dominoes.

"She sells this, and the rest of my business will be about as useful as lids when you break their jars," said Donny. "Let me explain how this works."

As he talked, he pulled out short piles of paper from the boxes he had carried up with him, ten pages or so at a time, and stacked them around the floor of my living room, all designed to underscore that the numbers supported his story. I had no time to look at the numbers, but it was comforting to see them spread out like that—I was figuring that I'd reverse-engineer his chaotic filing system after he left. The boxes of records were mostly bank statements, which did not help much, but there were some disjointed pages of articles of incorporation, from what looked like at least three different companies. And, judging by the way Donny enthusiastically displayed these piles of papers, they must surely be stuff that was helpful, right?

By the time we finished, almost every square foot of the floor was covered with short paper towers.

The paper barricaded the front door, spilled over the living room doorsill into the den that separated the living room from the kitchen, oozed further and took over my kitchen, leaping onto the wooden kitchen isle, then the glass of the smooth top range.

We followed the stacks into the kitchen, talking like he had been my client and ward for years.

"The judge will see the truth?" he asked me hopefully.

"If I can help it," I responded lawyerly.

I was sure of the win, but it would be in bad shape to boast.

HE left through the back door in the kitchen, the entrance dubbed "private" because it opened to a bedraggled porch with a swing and rickety pinewood stairs very much showing exposure to the elements. Donny navigated the precarious stairway descent gingerly but quickly. At the bottom of the staircase, where the two steps were rotten, he skipped over both steps in one energetic leap, like he was jumping for joy. Donny's gait was notably straighter and his step even lighter than when he had first walked in. As I watched him leave, all his sorrows behind him, I felt downright proud. As if on cue, the sprinklers in the rich neighbors' yards came to life all at once; the air felt fresh; the shade of the penthouse next door circled around and chased away the wilting heat from my porch swing. The multi-colored climbing roses in my pots breathed a sigh of relief—the poor things came with the label of "sun-loving," and were melting off their petals on my torrid porch. Perhaps the sunlight consuming those roses was an omen about the proverbial "too much of a good thing."

It was a Friday evening, and the start of a long, happy, hot weekend.

Alone, I dug into Donny's file, which in the absence of the magic of his commentary, turned out to be an almost incomprehensible mess of disorganized papers. The stacks on the floor were mostly random pages and numbers, not really supportive at all of the story Donny was telling with such authoritative passion.

But I was determined to find the support which, so I thought, must be there somewhere, just awaiting my grasp.

MY BOYS FRIDAY

By midnight on Friday, two things became clear: Donny's financial affairs were very tangled, and there was not enough time for me, working alone, to untangle them before the Wednesday sale of assets deadline. I needed help. Urgently, and (since Donny had not yet paid much) cheaply.

The time period in question was before the proliferation of outsourcing, but there was already Craigslist as a "ready reserve" resource. I had to resolutely disregard interesting-but-unhelpful search terms with advertising of local people looking for "casual encounters" and "rants and raves."

In the possibly more helpful Craigslist category enigmatically titled "Gigs," I typed in:

Can You Stiff You Divorce Lawyer?

Lawyer seeks help.
College drop-out preferred. Long hours, pres-
sure-cooker environment, unyielding sched-
ule. Pays all the Ramen noodles you can eat.
Great opportunity to broaden your horizons
and enhance your resume!

It was a truthful description of the job, and conse-quently, I did not expect many takers.

THERE were twenty-five e-mails in my box by four A.M. when I emerged from un-refreshing, fretful nap. I picked two kids with the best pedigrees. Now we would be a law firm of three, three lost souls excited about our newfound distinc-tion as protectors of Donny's fortunes—and by the prospect of mucho Ramen noodles. You do not have to believe me, but it is true: in the city of Ducklingburg, South Duck, there were two college dropouts even more street-stupid than me—and I found them.

THE ensuing frenzied holiday weekend passed like we were on an episode of Trump's "You're Fired." My window-less den converted perfectly into our war room. My pair of Boys Friday painted all four walls with dry-erase paint, and

254

filled the walls with diagrammed schemes of corporate ownership, sufficient to prove the true identity of the evil-minded buyer. (The Secretary of States' websites divulge quite a lot, if one only knows how to look.) Acquired on a quick foray to Best Buy, three plucky home-use-sized laser printers were spitting out hot fumes along with prototypes of charts and graphs for the future courtroom exhibits. My basic Westlaw on-line legal search account was getting a vigorous workout. Nova litigation support services—the only profit-minding grown-up-thinking players—were methodically grinding out color copies of our charts and exhibits.

The warehouse sale dreamt up by Donny's wife was indeed a horrible idea, and we were determined to demonstrate just how wrong-headed the sale was, demonstrate it in every medium available to humankind and in all the colors of the rainbow.

In South Duck divorce courts, where email service is not allowed even today and nothing can be e-filed, lawyers end up spending untold time and effort making paper copies. Most other parts of the South Duck courthouse system have already moved on to this century: motions can be uploaded to the courthouse website and emailed to the other side; the exhibits can be scanned and pulled up on personal monitors for the judge and the witnesses in court; the documents are shared on flash drives and other electronic media. But not in divorce court. Everything presented in divorce court must exist in paper, in a profusion of copies. We needed one copy for the judge, one for the court file, one for the Wife's lawyers, one for the Wife's witnesses, one for us to keep. That's five. And always the sixth copy *just in case.* You always want to have things *just in case* when you are in court.

"In case of what, exactly?" asked one of the Boy Fridays, wonderingly.

Boy Friday #1 was operating a Canon ImageClass MF4770n, a flimsy machine not intended for the volume of business that we were foisting on its lightweight frame. I could see why the kid wanted to know, because we were torturing both ourselves and our equipment in order to produce copies. The aforesaid Canon copying machine presently sat in a small cloud of hot fumes that reeked suspiciously of burning electrical innards and scorching paper. The copier had puffed out the first complaining cloud at the three hundred fifty seventh page, and now was puffing with increasing frequency, by all appearances in an attempt to convert our workplace into a sauna.

"Things happen, Boy Friday #1," I explained more authoritatively that my actual experience would justify. "You need to be in court to understand."

In fact, never having been to Ducklingburg divorce court before, I had not a clue what nameless worries we were guarding against. Unexpectedly, Boy Friday #2 came to my assistance with a colorful example: "Suppose the Honorable Judge takes a copy to the bathroom over the break and accidentally Honorable-pees all over it."

"I'll make *two* extra copies," reacted the cautious Boy Friday #1.

The copying machine made a rasping noise like a ghost of litigation rustling rusty chains, but nobody paid any heed to its complaints anymore.

We were ready five minutes before midnight on Monday, a whole eight hours before the courthouse even opened for business and we could set out in search of a judge to hear us out.

––––––––

A motion for injunctive relief is deemed a legal emergency. The judge-on-call must hear it right away. The urgency is the law and, more importantly, the local court rule too. However, there is no law or rule that requires the judge to regard the emergency's rude intrusion upon the already hectic progression of the court's tightly packed judicial day with kindness or even with good grace.

It is a rare judge who'd exclaim: "Whoopdee, what a great morning, an injunction motion! Welcome to my courtroom!"

The Honorable Jane U. Nettle was most certainly not about to express this jolly sentiment. My motion in the morning was about as welcome as a flat tire on the way to work. But although I could not boast a warm welcoming, I was not turned away either—and that was warmth enough for Donny and me.

In response to my lengthy request for a hearing that had hit the judicial e-mail box just before the open of court on Monday, the Honorable Jane U. Nettle directed her secretary Tonya to provide a succinct reply. Tonya-the-secretary's email eventually reached us in the late afternoon, just after I had lost all hope.

Tonya-the-secretary wrote, in the subject line, "Injunction, Beaver."

The text of the email was shorter still: "8:55."

One of Boys Friday cracked the code as setting the hour that we were summoned to present ourselves before the judge. That made sense to me: five minutes before the start of Nettle's regular court schedule.

———————

AT 8:15 a.m. the next day, I was already waiting outside the locked door of Judge Nettle's courtroom, striving to spy inside through the tiny square glass window. There was movement: the judge's sheriff dawdled down the aisle, wielding a contraption appearing to be a mirror welded onto the working end of a golf club. He shoved the mirror haphazardly under a few of the empty benches, apparently with a view to check for explosives. I thought it was a sure bet that he had no plan for what to do if he'd actually find what he was looking for.

Except for the one-man bomb squad, the room looked empty. My shy tap on the glass elicited his ready invitation to come right in. He unlocked the door and ushered me to the front of the coliseum, where the low railing corralled two empty desks for the fighting gladiators, the opposing lawyers. There was no trace of anybody from the team of

Donny's Wife.

"Which side you want me?" I ventured.

Everything about the courtrooms is regulated, including where one must sit.

By custom, the table closest to the jury is reserved for the plaintiff; the table furthest from the jury—for the defendant. But there is no jury in Ducklingburg divorce court. I think there is no real jury for divorces in any of American States except for Texas. In a so-called "bench trial," the judge decides everything from the bench. The jury box would stay empty all day except for a stray lawyer who'd wander in and settle on the cushioned seat, waiting to get the judge's attention for a scheduling request or a signature on a settlement.

"Sit here," pointed the judge's sheriff to the side already checked for bombs. I figured that his choice was not so much out of concern for my safety as to keep me out of his field of work, like the cleaning lady would direct the traffic out of the way of her broom and water puddles.

I settled at the desk closest to the jury box and started to prepare the field of combat. I set out three stacks, a foot high each. A copy of my Motion to Stop the Sale on top, fortified with charts and graphs of ownership. Then the draft Order that I hoped Honorable Nettle would sign—one page and punchy. The filings rested on the foundation of a dozen of cases and statutes which probably nobody would read, but which were nevertheless considered indispensable and were, therefore, faithfully reproduced in full and highlighted in their important parts.

Each of the stacks was marked according to its ultimate

destination. The one to my right sported a yellow sticky "for the JUDGE," the stack to my left was "WIFE'S LAWYER." The stacks were identical except for one minor detail: the charts and graphs in the Judge's stack were performed by the wizards of Nova litigation support in professional techni-color and made to impress. But at $1.99 a page, we had skimped on the Lawyers' copies. Those were in black and white, amateurishly colored over with Sharpie highlighters of the appropriate hues.

The third stack was mine, and not nearly as neat, bris-tling with tiny stickies filled with reminders. That stack also refused to behave itself, to keep straight, on account of col-orful magic markers which impaled it in four places. The color sequence had a meaning. The margins of everything were crawling with all the critical points and the right turns of the phrase, starting with the one on top: "MAY IT PLEASE THE COURT."

Lawyers on TV—at least the ones who play the good sort—never have the smallest problems with their memory and organization. All the exhibits are always at their finger-tips, they never forget a date, they have the statutory Codes memorized cold, even when they must quote what is a five sub-paragraph deep citation. The task of keeping a thousand points together never has them one bit concerned. Not me. To this day, every time I enter a courtroom, I feel like I was supposed to study harder for an oral exam, and that my shortcomings will be exposed and, thus, doom me to shame-ful failure.

Re-reading my own notes for the fiftieth time, I wondered: *How do they keep all that stuff memorized?*

At 8:51, the sheriff unlocked the door again to let in a human spring—she coiled, jumped in, recoiled, bounced over her rolling case and jumped into the chair at the opposite desk. The Wife's lawyer, I gathered.

"Welcome, Attorney Boom," grinned the judge's sheriff abandoning our risk-the-life-together-searching-for-explosives friendship at once. My loyalty was forgotten, displaced by the enemy's tight clothes.

Her clothes were tight like the Pope is a Catholic! As Boom was unloading her rolling case, the bow of her violet-colored top stood starched at attention over an ample bosom. Below, she was resplendent in skin-tight purple slacks, her bottom punctuated by the visible outline of thongs encasing two oversized buttocks. The wiles of Boom's feminine buttocks were boosted by at least five degrees of hip rotation accomplished by a pair of seven-inch spiked heels in flashy metallic gold, decorated by two purple flowers that were a precise color match to the form-fitting slacks. The top of her suit was buttoned snugly shut and holding on for dear life over size D breasts that were no doubt fortified by the latest in miracle-wear uplift engineering. Mrs. Beaver's lawyer showed no skin at all, but left none of her Rubenesque form to the imagination. I forced myself not to stare.

What little experience I had with the courtrooms and lawyering had narrowly limited my own choice of wear to expensive, monochrome, somber-colored fabrics. This display of burlesque femininity was an entirely new concept.

Maybe Boom was at a party last night and had no time to change?

I briefly wondered how it would sit with the judge. And whether I was at an advantage.

There is a protocol for greeting the opposition before court: one crosses the invisible line between the counsel tables, says one's own name loudly and shakes hands. Or hands each other the exhibits. Either way, the idea is to project goodwill, and the spirit of civility. Well, at least that's what they teach in Moot Court, the pretend litigation class in law school. My own courtroom experience was limited to watching senior lawyers go at it in New York. Pearl Street did not much differ from my Law School Moot Court. But here it did not apply.

"I'm Portia Porter, you must be Mrs. Boom," I was doing my very best to keep my eyes off her ready-to-burst battle-uniform. "We made you an extra copy of the motion, if you'd like."

Strictly speaking, one of my Boy Fridays had delivered the exact same stack of documents to her office earlier in the morning (or late at night, depending on your view) but I was not taking any chance with the service.

"Did you have a chance to look at the proposed Order," I offered the papers.

"More and more bullshit," snorted Mrs. Boom and coiled back to her seat, ignoring the stack on my stretched out arms. That was completely off script. I guessed that Moot Court was taught differently at Ducklingburg Law, edged my stack onto the corner of her desk and retreated, aiming to stay in her blind spot.

Without un-tightening her coils, my counterpart rolled her eyes, shook her head, and let out a low-pitched laugh, then gave a sideways look to the judge's sheriff—our only audience for the moment. The sheriff hurriedly took his eyes off her awe-inspiring form and slapped on an oily smile.

I straightened my back, tightened my jaw, and sat down to wait for the impending fight.

ONE always looks smarter when one writes something, like there is a great legal thinking in the process..

On my blank yellow-pad, I duly wrote: "Beaver, injunction," and put today's date.

There was nothing else to write, so I added the hour. Eight fifty-five.

8:55 A.M. Judge's bench still empty. It's just me, Ms. "Human Coil" Boom and the sheriff.

9:10 A.M. No change.

9:20 A.M. No change.

9:25 A.M. Starting to lose hope. The judge forgot about us probably.

10:10 A.M. The back door opens . . . false alarm! It's the Judge's Secretary Tonya, the author of the cryptic email.

Tonya's eyes met with Human Coil Boom, she pantomimed "ain't got the slightest idea," and sashayed to the low desk abutting the judge's bench. She never took the slightest notice that I was in the room.

One's brain begins to conjure up crazy thoughts. Maybe there is not even a judge available. What if I am in the wrong courtroom?

10:31 A.M. Started composing an explanation for the client. "I thought that the judge meant today, but she did not mean today. Apparently. I do not know what she meant. (Wow, that sounded completely incompetent.) But, after all, Ms. Boom is here too.

10:32 A.M. But what if Boom is here for something else? She must have other clients!

10:33 A.M. It *has* to be the right courthouse. Could be the wrong day?

10:34 A.M. A breakthrough! I have a solution. I'll just wait indefinitely, however long it takes. Never leave the courthouse. Eventually, the judge has to pass by her courtroom.

10:40 A.M. All hope is lost. There will never be a hearing, never.

10:55 A.M. I have no feeling in my left toe.

11:15 A.M. Took off the left shoe. Feeling continues to be absent.

11:30 A.M. The sheriff just took off. Lunch?

11:45 A.M. A cleaning lady stared at me. I nodded in perfunctory acknowledgment. End of the day?

11:45 A.M. Sheriff screamed "Stand for the Judge."

Wait—where? Darn! Stand for the what . . . That so was *not* a cleaning lady!

JUDGE Nettle turned out to be a short, stout, solidly built woman with a face that put one in mind of Cubism. Without a robe or even a jacket to conceal her unsightly street clothes, the judge blended into the courthouse background. Indeed, she could have blended anywhere, her hands shoved up to her wrists into cavernous pockets of black polyester pants—the sort of a pant that would not turn heads at the gym or on a fellow in Walmart shopper. The counsel tables are arranged so that the attorneys face the bench and the door to the chambers, ready to greet the judge. But today she sneaked in from behind, walking through the commoners' entrance.

"Stand for the Judge!" the bomb-sniffing sheriff, still holding the doors for the Judge's arrival, almost saved me. I sprang up, trying to catch Judge Nettle's hostile gaze, but got disoriented by two rows of eyes—no, wait—those were just sunglasses *above* her eyes.

The sunglasses were in her hair—cheap plastic frames, the kind one buys off a help-yourself rotating stand at the mall, for $17.99 including tax. The plastic rims held the graying strands of hair out of her eyes, but not out of the air where her rapid stride made stray tresses bob asymmetrically, like a street woman's do. So I greeted our judge with a nod and a stare. Not good.

But at least we do have a judge. Phew.

———————

"**BEAVER** VERSUS BEAVER, let's go! Why'm I here?" called out Judge Nettle, bee lining for her bench.

The secretary Tonya was not quick enough to clear the passage for the Honorable's frame, and as Judge Nettle ramped up to squeeze behind Tonya's chair, the grocery cart brimming with today's files jerked and bumped into the Honorable ribs. This caused the judge to gasp, and I saw an opening.

"May it please the Court . . ." I started, but before I could speed into the speech I'd been silently playing on repeat in my head for the last three hours, Ms. Boom uncoiled and sprang into action like a blacksnake hunting a frog.

"In all my fifteen years of experience, Your Honor, I've never seen anybody so unethical as Ms. Porter," Ms. Boom declared in a sonorous voice that drowned me out as easily as a trained Church singer dominates a background rustle.

That was not an auspicious beginning. In divorce courts, the judges rarely have the time to read anything, and lawyers rarely bother to submit much in writing (even though I did). Time is short in divorce courts, passions are intense, and a verbal brawl between two lawyers is often the only basis of the judge's ruling. My voice was no match for Ms. Boom, and I was staring at a certain defeat. But there truly is such thing as the beginner's luck—and it came to my rescue.

The judge's eye stumbled into the cart of today's cases

and spotted Donny's file on top, spilling out its technicolor charts. Her Honor's open palm jumped up in the universal "stop and wait" signal. I croaked helplessly, Ms. Boom wheezed, and thick silence descended on the room.

The Judge was reading my motion!

Under the table, I performed a quiet jig with my right foot (the left one still was not responding properly to the signals of my dazed brain) and sat back for the Judge's decision like a kid waiting for Christmas.

If she would just read my argument to the end, she'd see it my way!

Huddled over my motion, the jurist appeared to take it all in. I was winning! I had to be! Her Honor's gaze crept through my motion and finally arrived at the last period of the first page. Nobody moved. I held my breath, waiting for the Judge to turn the page. No go. Presently, the Judge raised up out of her chair. Her palms were flat at shoulders' width, firmly planted on the top plane of her bench, straddling Donny's motion, floating above the surface in what resembled a freeze-frame of the static top of a person doing a pushup exercise.

Twenty seconds passed.

Forty.

A minute.

Unless the Judge could see through the pages, she seemed to be repetitively re-reading my introductory paragraph. Over and over and over. And over.

Was there something wrong with my first paragraph?

In total silence, we waited.

What was she seeing in that first paragraph?

Mostly to assure myself that the Judge had not been paralyzed by some abrupt coronary attack or other seizure, I broke the silence and started anew:

"May it pl . . ." I hiccuped, and stopped because the Judge had pushed herself erect, her stare ablaze with strong emotion. *Her Honor is still alive*, I astutely diagnosed.

"Chambers!" Her Honor's finger stabbed, indicating the door adjacent to her bench.

Judge Jane U. Nettle was a woman of few words. Today, the Judge's ratio of sounds to pantomime majorly favored the pantomime. The audio transcript of the hearing would prove gravely deficient as a means of figuring out what happened.

My opponent Ms. Boom, apparently experienced in Judge Nettle's ways of doing things, was already standing at the feet of the bench where the small back door, equipped with an imposingly mega-sized push-button lock, was guarding the way to Judges Nettle's chambers.

How did Boom make that leap so quickly?

All *I* had time to do was to follow the Judge's finger with my eyes. And there was Ms. Boom already perched at the door! A yank at the heavy handle, and Boom was holding the door graciously open for the Judge. Superpowers! I thought I saw a halo behind the silhouettes of two women and the door sprang shut behind them with a loud clunk.

"You should go too," reminded the sheriff, propelling me out of my seat where I was frozen in horror.

Crap! Can they decide it all without me?!

Whether from the draft of the shutting door or from my jerking up to my feet, the carefully equilibrated stack of papers stickied "for the JUDGE" careened crazily and slid off balance. It slowly oozed over the distance between my desk and Ms. Boom's, spreading like a multi-colored flower opening its petals in slow motion on the Nature Channel. I made a dive for it, my still-benumbed left foot gave in and landed me on the carpet from whence I assessed the gravity of the disaster.

First, the sheriff was the only one watching. That was good.

Besides that, my predicament had nothing to recommend it. The stack of documents for the Judge was utterly ruined—there was no chance of assembling it back while on the wrong side of the door from my legal argument in chambers. If the Judge was making a fateful decision that very moment, it would be hard to explain my absence to the client. The client! The thought of Donny and all his millions which he entrusted to my incompetent care was horrifying. How does one explain to a client losing the case because I ended up on the wrong side of the door? Some lawyer! The charts were MIA and so was my left shoe. Covered under the papers somewhere?

And then I came to grips with myself.

It is not the wardrobe and props that make performance. I gave a parting glance to the courtroom, and with neither speed nor grace, traversed the ten paces to the door, and yanked the handle.

———————

NOTHING happened. The door to the enchanted garden did not yield.

I yanked again. Nothing.

"You gotta slide your lawyer card," noted the sheriff helpfully. "You not got it?"

I did not even know that there *were* lawyer cards for divorce court.

"How do I get in there without?" I gave the door a desperate push.

"Take double doors out of the courtroom, left, left, elevator to the tenth floor, get out, take one flight up, small door into the corridor and then the inside stairs back down."

I saw quite clearly: this was the end of my brief Ducklingburg career as a divorce litigator. I'd never make it to the other side of the door, Judge Nettle will have the whole thing thrown out, and when it comes down to the inevitable malpractice suit, the sheriff will rat out that I did not have the accursed lawyer card. Never mind explaining all that to the client. How do you explain it to the State Bar when it levies a charge of incompetence?

"Or I can just open it for you," the helpful sheriff finished his thought. "You going in or what?"

After the helpful ministration of the sheriff, the door popped open. I limped warily into the blinding sunlight that lay beyond.

The architect of the cake-shaped courthouse ran a glass

loggia behind the windowless semi-circle of the interior courtrooms. The loggia was narrow, with floor-to-ceiling glass. Courtrooms were rooms without windows, circled by the corridor of windows without a room. A security feature against a sniper intent to attack a judge on the bench? I wondered if the floor to ceiling glass was bulletproof. It most definitely provided no defense from the heat.

JUDGE Nettle was mid-sentence: "What do I need to sign . . . where is the Order?"

A hand stretched out towards me through the light made me wonder the obvious, but after a few blinks the view cleared up. I was part of a circle (an oval, really). Wife's lawyer Ms. Boom, Judge Nettle and Tonya, the Judge's secretary. Tonya, the Helpful Hannah who had set us up with the 8:55 notice for the 11:45 hearing.

The Judge was still talking: ". . . sign?"

Apparently, Judge Nettle had already cut to the grand finale of the hearing, and was ready to see the Order, but I was not tracking. Indulgently, the Judge nodded, acknowledging my tardy arrival, and started from what she thought was the beginning.

"You opposed the sale," started Judge Nettle, looking at the plain wall in front of her and addressing neither of us in particular. She had the air one assumes when talking to an acquaintance whose name and connection lamentably escaped one's mind. We've all done that: it is rude to ask "who are you," but it is hard to go on. It occurred to me the Judge had no idea which one of the Beavers wanted the sale and which was opposed. Or maybe which lawyer represented whom.

"May it please . . ." I started out again.

"I'll grant it. You want the sale stopped?" the Judge turned towards Ms. Boom.

"If I'm honest, it's fine with me. My woman does not want to sell it either. Anymore." Boom shrugged her shoulders in ennui. The Judge gave an energetic nod, and again reached her hand in my direction without looking—a movement reminiscent of a surgeon reaching out to her PA for the carefully placed tool: "Pen!"

"Use mine," Boom produced a ballpoint pen, a promotional plastic with her name emblazoned in shiny letters, and placed it in the Judge's palm with solicitous familiarity.

"The Order?" commanded the Judge without a nod to the pen.

That means I won, I suddenly realized. Judge Nettle was asking for my draft of the Order so she could sign it and stop the sale!

"In the courtroom," I panicked, and made for the door like we really were in surgery and my speed meant life or death. The egress back to the courtroom was locked with the same slide-your-card technology, apparently to discourage terrorism. I banged on the door like an escaping hostage.

WHEN I finally made it back, clutching three copies of the Order, the circle around Judge Nettle had gotten wider, attracting lawyers passing by the chambers' corridors. The Judge's taciturn mood was gone. She was finishing an anecdote from her earlier years. It was about a lawyer everybody in the crowd knew, which apparently made the story funnier. "I granted his request," went on Judge Nettle, "it was one of those cases where I could see it going either way. Wouldn't get appealed either way. But I ruled *his* way."

The audience drew the air in anticipation of a twist in the story: the lawyer must not have been well-liked.

The Judge delivered: "He hands up the Order. I ask for a pen, but his pen won't write. He is patting his pockets for another ... no pen. Rushes out of the courtroom. We wait, me and Tonya. Finally, he gets back with another pen ten minutes later, I'm in the middle of my lunch. Can't tell ya where he got that crummy pen, but it leaks indelible blue on my fingers . . ." roared Judge Nettle, and the chorus of anticipatory laughter ricocheted off the walls.

". . . this pen leaks on my fingers, on my robe, and on the *Order* he wants me to sign . . . and so I put a cross on the Order and write:

Denied for want of a pen."

The laughter got louder, then stopped abruptly like somebody snapped its neck. In their imagination, the lawyers were trying it on for size on their own necks.

"He never came to me without a pen again, that's for sure," finished Judge Nettle triumphantly.

A pensive older lawyer muttered "Explain *that* to your client," and the mood palpably plummeted.

In haste, I surrendered three copies of the Order into the Judge's expectant palm, and stopped breathing. One cannot help but feel the touch of destiny at the moment any Judge holds a pen over any Order. Or maybe it's just me.

She did not sign right away.

Nettle scrutinized the first paragraph for twenty seconds, but it apparently did not yield up any failings. Then she lifted the Order by the first page and flipped to the last page, giving every intervening page a brief look of disdain. She lifted the second, identical copy of the Order, and flipped to the last page again, as though trying to catch the second copy with some dirty secret that its sister copy refused to betray. The second copy of the Order stood steadfast.

We watched in a trance.

"Where's the property y'all fighting over?" Nettle finally said under her breath addressing neither of us in particular, and while I recited the address, she flipped to the last page of the third copy and placed a wavy line of her signature on the last page: approved!

The Order was signed.

The sale was stopped.

I won.

Somehow, it did not feel in the least like a win.

"My clerk will stamp," declared Her Honor, handing the signed and instantly valuable paper to Tonya, the same wizard who'd missed the time of court by almost three hours. I had my doubts about Tonya, and was determined to see her do the right thing with that stamp. On the way down the corridor, I snuggled behind her so closely that she pushed back.

"Step away from me," snarled Tonya, and just like that, I made an enemy for life.

AFTER all the of anticipation, preparation, wait and strife, the whole affair with Judge Nettle took exactly six minutes and twenty-three seconds, and would have taken only half the time except for my own clumsiness and inexperience.

It was an undignified episode. But no matter. I won: the Witch's stupid sale was blocked, Donny was victorious.

Following the Moot Court script, I sought out Boom and leaned in to shake hands with her.

"Thanks for use of the pen," I said politely, "seems, I could have lost for lack of a pen."

"Say what?" Boom did not deign to notice my extended hand much less my feeble attempt at a little humor.

"I am glad we could agree," I retrieved my hand.

"You obviously don't know what you are doing, running the clock on your client. Working the case: I should turn you in to the Bar," Boom did not reciprocate my spirit of cordiality.

She might not have been wrong about the first bit: none

of what just happened made sense to me, so maybe I did not know what I was doing. But the rest of her tirade was puzzling.

I muttered: "What changed your mind about the sale, if you don't mind my asking?"

"I mind! You abused the process, you'll be hearing from me!" And with that she was gone, the sheriff's gaze wistfully glued to the undulating wonders of her retreating shape.

Like the slow kid on the playground, I was alone again, with all my toys still strewn on the floor. The Judge and Tonya disappeared while I tried to mend fences with the opposition. Never again, I decided.

Tonya's low sitting desk was littered with planners and papers, but my precious Order was nowhere to be seen. At least not in plain view. Maybe if I climbed up to take a look at the Judge's bench . . ..

"Excuse me ma'am, I got to lock up," the sheriff was now all business.

"No more court today?"

"Looks like you'all booked for the full day."

"Have you seen the Order?" I asked. "Tonya said she'd stamp it. Have you seen it?"

With an end of a pen, the sheriff carefully lifted a bright piece of clothing off Tonya's desk and gave it a perfunctory look.

"No Ma'am. You can ask Attorney Boom."

That might've been meant as a sneer, but I could not prove it. The sheriff continued confidently: "But don't worry, you'll be fine."

"Why?" I could not resist.

"Judge Nettle would never let the sale. She never does. You'll be fine."

"She never?"

"No. Don't worry. Everybody knows."

So my legal triumph was not really mine?

And everybody knew that?

"You saved my life, officer," I said sincerely.

There was nothing left to do but be grateful and celebrate. As my mother is fond of saying, the child may have been born covered in icky slime, but who'll know after the first bath?

On the way from the courthouse, I called Donny with the joyous news: We won! There would be no sale of his precious crown asset!

THREE hours after I appraised Donny of the news of his legal triumph, my bank called me with the news of its own, not as joyous: Donny's oversized, well-calligraphed, beautifully executed two hundred and fifty dollar check had bounced: insufficient funds. The call from the bank went into my voicemail because my team of two juveniles and I were too busy celebrating our dubious victory and the imminent rewards.

The days of fame and riches were a sure thing, we decided.

Still, the current accounting was troublesome.

So far, Donny's representation produced no income. It was not, however, without its monetary costs.

$350 NOVA litigation support copying service

$109 Groceries for crew (Ramen noodles quickly lost their appeal)

$38 Hammermill copying paper (1 box)

$47. Russo Tacos, celebration (felt rich; ordered 2nd round of tacos)

$299.99 x 3 Printer Canon ImageClass MF4470n (refurbished, bought on credit)

TOTAL: $1,443.97 all told

Plus, there was the matter of Boy Fridays' salaries. I'd have to pay my poverty-stricken assistants something at some point, or risk seeing them disappear. After the weekend of round-the-clock work, I was further in the hole. And, frankly, I felt even more a fraud. You know that stupid feeling when you realize your garden sprinklers are competing with a thunderous hail storm?

Nevertheless, I figured it was not what business was about and texted Donny:

"Hate to bother you but check bounced."

WHEN Donny learned of his *faux pas*, he did not dilly dally a bit in responding. In the first fifteen minutes, he texted, he emailed, he left a message on my landline, on my cellphone and on my fax machine. He tried connecting on Facebook and Twitter. I almost expected a carrier pigeon to land on my windowsill.

Every one of his lengthy messages started with the words:

"I am absolutely mortified! This has never happened to me before. I hope you do not draw the wrong conclusions."

We connected human-to-human the next day, albeit on the phone. He started by repeating the same apology verbatim, complete with being "mortified," then mobilized himself into a long-winded and flattering description of my legal abilities, concluding with an offer to be friends forever.

"You do Visa?" he urged, "I'll be right over!"

An hour later, he drove in to personally watch me phone in his Visa for $250, and his whole spiel started over. He was "mortified," "embarrassed," "incredulous," "in agony." "His check was his bond," and he would "sooner starve" than break his bond.

His agony over the bounced $250 was, to all appearances, so sincere that I did not bring myself to mention the bigger issue: a week after I plunged into his fast-paced litigation, we were still only talking about my mere first consultation fee. There still was no retainer! At our first meeting, Donny swore he'd look to his 401K for the ten thousand dollars I asked to start the case, but he has not mentioned it since. And when I emailed my first invoice after the "Stop-Sale" Order win, his only response was "thanks!" Presumably, Donny was tending to it. The paperwork was probably wending its way on its labyrinthine pathway through the bank's bureaucracy. I simply could not add to the upset of such a nice, already-devastated man with crass inquiries about a delay in plundering his retirement nest egg. Donny was an important client, and obviously pleased with my services. There was no need to offend with cranky, tactless expressions of unfounded suspicion.

————————

A skilled con artist is not the one who never missteps, but the one who, once a wrong step is taken, finds a way to turn this apparent failure into an advantage. (Is that what Churchill meant by success being going from one failure to the next?)

I doubt that Donny intended to bounce the $250 check. But having bounced it, he discovered a valuable piece of information. He learned what most lay people do not realize: lawyers—especially the young ones—hate bringing up money matters, especially if asking for the payment comes across as a sign of distrust and impliedly casts aspersions on the client's character or financial trustworthiness. Many lawyers avoid conversations about money altogether in hope that the sterling quality of their hard work will shine so brightly that the grateful clients pay spontaneously, without nudging.

Bouncing the consultation fee worked to Donny's advantage even more than his first tricky ploy, the "compli-cated case challenge." The matter of money was bound to come up at the end of the week, and it did, but now the framework was different: we still discussed only the initial $250, the payment that should have been long since made and forgotten. Neither his ten thousand retainer nor the bill for the work on the Stop-Sale Order made it onto the agenda. There's only so much bandwidth in one meeting, and, after all the histrionics of the bounced checks, and assuring Donny that his character remained clear of suspicion, I had neither time nor energy left in me.

I ran Donny's credit card for $250, learned from my merchant account rep that the funds should transfer into my bank in three business days, and, secure in the knowledge that Donny and I had talked money, went back to work. (In a "truth stranger than fiction" twist, three days later, Donny's super-secure card stopped payment to my unfamiliar ac-count to investigate a "suspicious transaction," not con-sistent with his shopping practices. Neither of us could have seen this one coming!) And I was too busy working to even look.

There was a lot of work yet to be done.

WITH the immediate disaster of the fire sale averted, Donny outlined the long term goals. The goals were ambi-tious, but the outline was simple:

"Nothing. The Witch gets nothing."

She came into the marriage with nothing, and would come out with nothing, Donny decreed. Our job was to leave the Witch with no alimony and no assets.

It was an ambitious plan, made even more difficult by the Witch's character. Bluntly, there was decidedly nothing wrong with the Witch's character: no self-destructive fits, no addictions, no craziness, no late night Facebook chats with former boyfriends or even colleagues. None of these things should have mattered from the point of the law, but judges are human. Our mission—to dismiss the wife of three decades without so much as a severance package—would be easier if we could present the Judge with some shameful character flaw. Unfortunately, with the exception of her recent bad business judgment that almost cost the Beavers a disastrous sale, the woman had no notable faults. Still, the law was mostly on our side: she signed the prenup, didn't she? All of the later transfers into her name were just minor details that could be explained away. We just had to prove that—and so we set out to work.

THERE was something else that chilled my billing enthusiasm: the "Stop-Sale" Order for which I invoiced Donny was technically nowhere to be found. Sure, Judge Nettle had put her wavy scrawl of a signature on it, but where did the signed Order go afterward? It was not in Donny's court file, not with Tonya, not even (apparently) in the unfriendly offices of Attorney Boom. The document just disappeared. We all saw it signed—me, Tonya, Boom. And that was the last I saw of it.

It may seem counter-intuitive, but the judge's *words* mean nothing until they are clothed in a proper *paper* of an Order. To be valid, an Order must be in writing, signed by the judge and file-stamped by the clerk. This written, signed and stamped order was nowhere to be seen. Where was it hiding?

I waited a week hoping the "Stop-Sale" Order would pop into my mailbox, then organized a search.

"Look for it where?" wondered the cautious Boy Friday #1.

"I'll get it, Boss," jumped in the boisterous, self-confident Boy Friday #2.

I tossed Boy Friday #2 my car keys and he zoomed out of the parking space, a care-free child-genius on a quest for the Holy Grail, the signed and stamped Order.

He was back in seventy-five minutes with sad stories of utter defeat.

His first stop was the last person who saw the "Stop-Sale" Order, secretary Tonya. According to my Boy Friday, he cornered Tonya in Nettle's regular courtroom, the same place where the late "Stop-Sale" Order was last seen. The ensuing episode went something like this:

TONYA: Help you?

BOY FRIDAY: Here to pick up the Stop-Sale Order in Beaver v. Beaver. It was signed in chambers on Monday.

TONYA: And you are?

BOY FRIDAY (extending hand for handshake and approaching Tonya's desk) My name is not really Raccoon, but they all call me Raccoon. You can call me Raccoon too, I don't mind.

TONYA: Sheriff!!!!

SHERIFF (snapping the handcuffs on Raccoon in a clumsy set of slow moves) Sorry, kid, you can't approach her like that.

The sheriff ushered the Raccoon out of the courtroom, but then released the handcuffs and offered a good lead about the whereabouts of the missing Order: "Try Family Court Administrator. They have a box for processed orders."

The Family Court Administrator has a tin box where judge's secretaries drop off the processed orders and lawyers can go to pick them up. Raccoon reported that the tin box housed at least three hundred signed Orders, dating all the way to the prior calendar year. Still, nothing there for *Beaver v. Beaver*. The helpful staff suggested "checking in with the Judge," which was, of course, useless. But they gave another excellent lead: the file room.

After the file room staff had a good hoot about Raccoon's nickname, Donny's file was found in no time.

But, alas, there was no Order in Donny's file.

They repeated the suggestion to "check with the Judge," but this time the advice was not all bad. Instead of going through Tonya, they advised: "try Judges' Chambers Central on the top floor."

Raccoon took the elevator to the top floor, and buzzed

the button for the Judges' Chambers. At that point in his story, he became incoherent, his eyes assumed the shapes of triangle warning traffic signs, and I could not get any more intelligence about what transpired. Whatever had happened, it must have been an ugly scene to have so upset the fearless Raccoon.

The bottom line was that the duly signed "Stop-Sale" Order was still MIA.

My own subsequent efforts yielded these curt and inadequate responses from Tonya and the Judge:

"Ms. Boom has it, ask her for a copy," emailed Tonya coldly on Monday.

"It's in the mail to you, wait till the end of the week," she promised on Tuesday.

On Friday, Tonya reproached: "I put a copy on your desk on Monday after the hearing, you must have left it there."

"It's in the Family Court basket," she advised Monday next.

"We mailed it two weeks ago," came straight from Judge Nettle.

"The Judge never signed any orders in Beaver v. Beaver," contradicted Tonya.

"What Order?" Tonya wrote coldly about three weeks into our correspondence.

And finally, I had to stop the inquiry after Tonya requested: "Please stop harassing me."

With each subsequent response getting colder and colder, I decided to let the sleeping dog sleep. *De facto*, the sale was stopped: surely, Mrs. Beaver would not venture to go against the Judge's wishes, even if I did not have in hand the proper documentary proof that there had been such an Order. Still, I couldn't seem to shake a queasy, uneasy feeling that I was somehow letting Donny down.

We'd compensate by working more and winning his case in the end, I decided. And so we went to work, building the best possible factual and legal case that "the Witch should get nothing" pursuant to Donny's directive.

FOR twelve weeks since I was hired, my little legal team barely slept. We drafted, we deposed, we subpoenaed, we filed, we researched and re-drafted. We attended mini-hearings where we fought with Boom and her minions over discovery and scheduling disputes,—the petty battles that holds no glory but in most cases determines the eventual outcome. I studied the law, and my Boys Friday mastered the art of communicating with the office of Attorney Boom, who made every step nasty and difficult.

In that entire time, I worked up the courage to discuss money only once.

Donny answered my call on the first ring, and told me he was on the way with additional money. He had it all ready and would bring the check at once. Two hours later, he called to apologize. He was calling from a dealer's shop. His car developed a brake problem. It was unsafe to drive—he barely brought it to a stop at the corner. He would stop by as soon as driving was safe.

"Don't you worry about the money," he said. "You just worry about doing the job. Money will not be an issue. Trust me."

MONEY became an issue that could no longer be ignored at the end of the third month. After I paid the Nova printers, and the office credit card bills, there was none of mine left. I could not afford what it was costing me to work for Donny anymore. None of us could. When I say it bluntly like that, it seems really stupid of me. At the time, I still devoutly wanted to believe that this was just a tiny, transitory accounting problem.

I called Donny again.

"You need to pay," I demanded.

"Certainly! On my way," came his eager response.

He was at my door in half an hour, holding up a small envelope. I felt bad about ever suspecting him.

"Cash," he announced proudly, and pressed the envelope into my hand.

I was not an expert on cash payments, but it seemed thin for ten thousand dollars. I tore the flap to look inside, while Donny waited patiently, watching me with the patient grace of a painfully honest man unjustly and viciously accused.

It felt horrible, but I still did it: I counted the cash.

There were a few one-dollar bills, one crisp fifty and eighteen well-worn ten-dollar bills.

"This is $246?" I wondered.

"Yes, the first meeting," explained Donny, probably thinking that the bounced check and his declined credit card incidents had both slipped my mind.

"You need to pay for the rest of the work," I insisted.

It felt rude to speak to him like that, but I stood firm.

Much to my chagrin, Donny stood even firmer.

"I cannot do that just now," he said coldly.

"Why on Earth can't you?" I was just as stunned as if he told me that the sun was not going to set that day. It was my first time getting stiffed, and everything seemed new and surprising.

"You see," explained Donny in his low, mellifluous, carefully enunciating voice, "I said I'd use the 401K, but the Judge has not yet decided that I can keep my whole 401K. What if it goes to my wife?" It was the first time he called Ms. Beaver something other than "The Witch."

I suggested that Donny tap one of his other accounts, like his Wachovia account. But Donny had the same concern: what if the Judge leaves the 401K to him, but gives the Wachovia to Mrs. Beaver. "What about the Bank of America account?" I asked.

"Can you guarantee that the Judge will not leave me the 401K and Wachovia, and give Bank of America account to my wife?" objected Donny.

The couple had roughly a million dollars in cash and

stock distributed between various banks, but whatever account I suggested, I got the same response:

"Can you *guarantee* that account will not go to my wife in the end?" He put very strong emphasis on the word "guarantee."

I was still not totally following the logic of his objections. Money was money. Cash from one bank was the same as cash from another bank.

"Donny," I proposed, "It is dollars. I am not asking for your wife's favorite Faberge egg. You can cut your wife a check from your account to cover the difference. What difference does it make to the final settlement if the money comes out of one source rather than another?"

Donny's voice became deliberate, slow, and patient, like he was talking to a very slow-learning child. "Ms. Porter, you are advising me to move marital money. That violates the laws. Can you *guarantee* the Judge will not be upset?"

It was impossible to tell if he was buying his own logic, but I tried the Kantian approach.

"Donny," I began, stringing my words together carefully. "If everybody thought that, people would never be able to use *any* of their money during the year it takes the judge to divide the marital assets. Heck, sometimes the process takes years. What then?" I looked up at him hoping my logic was registering, but Donny settled into the superman pose, standing firm and gazing over my head, at the crack in the ceiling.

"Look," I went on, "the divorce process lasts forever. Yet, everybody goes around still paying for necessary things.

Groceries. Gas. Electric. And paying their lawyers. Nobody gets a free extension until the money is divided."

My logic seemed solid to me, but I had a tough, immovable audience.

Donny stood straighter and lifted his chin.

"No matter," he did not yield, "if other people are not ethical. I am ethical, and I am honest, and I do not want to appear dishonest and upset the Judge. You are setting me up. Jeopardizing my case." He unglued his stare from the ceiling and moved towards me. "What happened to you," he inquired, grabbing my shoulders. "You used to care. Did the other lawyer get to you?"

"No, but," I started, but he was speaking over me.

"Spending this money will jeopardize my case," Donny was firm and angry. "You were bought off, I see it now. I will bring a Bar grievance, and I want you off my case. You are jeopardizing my case; you are pitting the Judge against me. You are a vindictive, untrustworthy woman."

Had he told me that he was not paying because he did not like my work, or that he was returning to his wife, or that he just did not like my hourly rate, I would have found something to say. But this idea that every penny he had was under a cloak of judicial preservation—that was an entirely unexpected notion. Most importantly, I could not decide: was he grifting me or genuinely confused? Was he a phony or did he truly believe in the nonsense that he was spouting?

"Donny," I started again, "you drove here, right? How did you pay for gas?"

"I borrowed some money," insisted Donny, adhering

290

unyieldingly to his story.

"Donny, I cannot work for free anymore. *We* cannot. I'll have to get out."

"Wait!" brightened Donny. His voice was warm: he found a solution. The end of his case, the final hearing was just two weeks away. The Judge would make the decision then, and he would pay the entire invoice—for every hour worked.

"Every penny," repeated Donny, "and do not worry about getting paid. I am an honest man, don't worry. Just worry about the work."

"Unless you think you cannot win this one," continued Donny. "If you think the Witch's lawyers are better than you are?"

It was well played.

"Of course I am better than those schmucks," I cried out.

And I was going to prove it! I was going to win this case for Donny, and Donny would write us the check when he felt it was safe. After all, law is the service business. It is about making the client comfortable, even when the client is a little bit cuckoo.

THE fateful day of the property division trial arrived at long last. All would be decided in Judge Nettle's courtroom.

My little legal team hauled in seventeen boxes of exhibits. For witnesses, we lined up three of Donny's bankers, each more eager than the other to speak authoritatively to the right shade of truth: Donny's vast premarital fortune never transmogrified into "marital property." Mrs. Donny must therefore keep her undeserving hands off the Beaver empire. We were prepared to the eyebrows with all the proof possible. I orchestrated a show of force. The cautious Boy Friday #1 secured the rear, typing verbatim transcript on a tiny Apple. At the forefront, the Raccoon sat ready at my desk, dexterously in charge of exhibits retrieval.

Judge Nettle (who caught this case despite her best efforts and ours) was finding our enthusiasm grating, but we were mostly right on the law.

The Judge was torn.

All trial judges are motivated by two fears—of criticism by the appellate court and of investigation by the judicial ethics committee. That year alone, the Honorable Jane U. Nettle had already been twice reversed by the Court of Appeals, and the year was not even over. Four reversals a year was a problem for any judge, according to an unsubstantiated courthouse rumor. I was most certainly capable of bringing an appeal.

"YOU want me to do what?!" Judge Nettle believably faked a semblance of an apoplectic fit.

"You want me to give *him* the buildings? Give *him* the money?" The Judge air-punched a stubby index finger towards me and Donny.

"HIM?!" (stab towards Donny) "And HIS illegitimate child?!" The Judge pronounced 'illegitimate' as though it was two words, *Il Legitimate*.

She went on: "And you intend to kick out this poor woman!" Hand sweeping gesture, palm to the sky, towards the other side of the courtroom. "The woman who gave her life to this duplicitous man, and what is his plan? You want me to kick her out?!"

I did. I wanted to kick out the poor woman. That was the result supported by the law, anyway.

"Your Honor," I said, "the State of South Duck does not discriminate against children born to unmarried parents. Mr. Beaver's child is not, in any proper legal sense, 'Il Legitimate.'"

That was a bad start.

Then I made it worse:

"Your Honor appears to have formed an opinion on the ultimate issue before the evidence is introduced," I began digging my own grave, "and this constitutes grounds for recusal and we therefore respectfully ask for a recusal," I asked the Judge to move off the bench.

"No," came an unexpectedly swift and peremptory ruling. It meant my motion was denied.

I had another suggestion: "May we have a hearing on bias before a different, a neutral judge? Not you?"

"No."

"We are entitled to a neutral judge, Your Honor!"

"No!"

"Respectfully ask for a finding of facts, pursuant to Rule 58... I mean 52," I was losing my cool.

"No."

"Respectfully notice appeal and move for a stay. May it please the . . ."

"Say what?"

The morning had barely started and I already managed to alienate the Judge.

How is Donny taking this?

Donny was seated to my far right, glued to The Raccoon's right arm, perfectly still, staring stolidly at the cracked plastic cover of the court-desk Bible, like there was some answer lurking there in the Good Book. Did Donny think I was botching his case? If I told him I was following the law, and that the *Judge* was not, would he believe *me*?

My attack on the Judge stirred up the opposition. Boom saw an opportunity:

"May I be heard on a housekeeping matter, Judge?"

In respectful homage to the Judge, Boom's not-so-subtle behind was lifting from her seat as she spoke. Her head had not yet caught up, still buried in the papers on her desk. She resembled a digging fox terrier whose tail wags violently at the master.

"Judge, first time I see these affidavits," complained Boom. One by one, Boom held up three affidavits of Donny's bankers and speedily lied: "I have not seen these before to-day!"

This particular trick was Boom's trademark: she never admitted to receiving anything we sent her. Boom just plain never got her mail—snail or fax.

As the litigation rolls, lawyers on opposite side must exchange dozens of papers. Motions, Affidavits, responses to discovery requests. Whenever and by whatever means the opposition sent to Boom, there'd always be an issue with delivery.

"Judge, we faxed those over on Tuesday," I rebutted, prepared for Boom's tricks, "we have the fax logs."

"I'd like to see those fake fax logs," refused to shy away Boom, "we should all look at them now. Judge, I ask to halt the hearing until she produces those logs."

True to form, prudent Raccoon was on it. Without taking eyes off the Judge, he twisted his left arm in the socket and was spot on, pulling from one of the giant boxes directly behind his chair proof that the Affidavits were indeed faxed."

But Judge Nettle was not interested in my fax logs. She'd seen that play before. "Hold your horses, you both," ordered the Judge, "we are not stopping this trial."

I sighed relief.

"And you right," the Judge was addressing Boom, "I ain't gonna look at their affidavits."

What???

". . . because she submitted them late, after the dead-line," the judge stabbed in my direction so there would be no doubt whose affidavits were late.

Before I could protest, Boom was on her feet: "No testimony either, Judge?"

"N-no," said the Judge, with visible hesitation. "They were late. I need not hear from *him* either. (Nod in Donny's direction). That means I'll just hear from Mrs. Beaver, and then I'll be ready to rule."

Preparing for court, I thought of dozens of setbacks and challenges I might see in this trial, but this one was utterly unexpected. Late affidavits?? But we filed everything on time!

"May it please," I started meekly, not sure what followed.

The Judge turned her torso towards me: "That should teach you. To do your work. On time!"

"Thank you, Judge," hissed Boom like a triumphant tea-kettle.

It was the ultimate trial lawyer's nightmare. The trial under a gag order, watching the other side spin their story, but unable to respond. I was pretty sure that my budding career as a divorce lawyer was over. There was no way to go but up, so I protested.

"May I be heard on the timeliness of the affidavits," I rose urgently.

The Judge shushed at me, and gave her sheriff the "get ready" look. I persevered, talking twice faster.

"We submitted all the affidavits three days before the

deadline. I am not sure where the misunderstanding lies," I pushed on as quickly as I could.

Before the Judge could react, Boom was up.

"This is nonsense, Your Honor, please make her shut up now! Three days? You can see she's making it up, making up stories as she goes along," Boom screeched. "The deadline was on Monday, and she did not bother to obey the orders, now she is misleading the court, but I have her affidavit here, and it was filed on Tuesday. Here's the stamp, Your Honor!"

She jumped around her desk, to my side of the courtroom. One of the affidavits in question, firmly in her two hands, one hand clasping the top, one bottom, arms outstretched. When I reached for the paper, she jerked it away, and, swiveling on the rubber heel of her shiny shoe, held up the paper for the Judge to see the filing stamp.

"Is it true, counsel?!" the Judge was looking at me. "You filed on Tuesday?"

"Yes," I said, "but the deadline—"

"Don't ever interrupt me again!"

I thought of saying that I was not interrupting, but thought better of it.

"You misled the court," concluded the Judge, "telling me that you did not file after the deadline, and you filed after the deadline, and here is the proof. Tuesday! We can all see the stamp. On Tuesday!"

"The deadline was on Friday; we were three days early." I finished, without much persuasion.

"No, I can't believe it!" The Judge's tone graduated from self-righteous to furious. "I already found you misled the

Court once, and now you are misleading the Court yet again?! We all know when I set the deadline. She knows!" The Judge nodded approvingly towards Boom who sat firmly in her chair with a look of a cat who had located a bathtub filled with tuna salad.

Just a few minutes ago, I thought that nothing was worse than missing a deadline, but, as optimists like to say, I was wrong: it could get so much worse. Here it was, something so much worse: being accused of lying to a Judge. I briefly wondered if one could get disbarred for that.

I was interrupted by a sharp pain in my right side. That gave me hope: if I was having a heart attack that would cause me to be rescued from this courtroom by a team of EMTs. Hopefully, I'd die, putting an end to all problems. But that was not to be my fate. The pain was only mechanical: an elbow lodged in my side by my ever-vigilant assistant. The Raccoon was seeking attention to his pencil note. In huge block letters filling out the entirety of the 9 1/2 by 11 page:

Deadline was Friday.

We filed Tuesday.

Three days ahead the deadline.

"*Three days ahead*" was underlined four times, resulting in a tiny tear in the paper.

Underneath, he added in longhand, in case I still was not totally clear:

Deadline Friday, <u>not</u> Monday!!!!!!!

I groaned under my breath: "I know," but the elbow persisted.

"What?!" I grunted hatefully.

The Wife's affidavit was pushed in front of me, and the Raccoon was circling in green marker the filing stamp in its upper right corner: Donny's Wife filed on Friday, later than we filed Donny's. Wife's lawyers filed their damn affidavit *on the date of the deadline*, and three days after ours. That was a game changer. That could sufficiently prove my innocence of all charges . . . If only I could catch the Judge's attention.

But pushing a word in edgewise was problematic: the Judge was not pausing even for a breath of air. Her diatribe moved off the self-righteous, sped through the mildly furious, and now she was working herself up into a proper rage:

". . . Misleading the Court! Stand up!" she crescendoed, even though I was still standing.

"Contempt! I am considering holding you in contempt of court! Sheriff . . . I am considering holding in contempt . . . and fining you . . . you could go to jail for that, misleading the Court! I found you had already misled the court! You could go to jail for that until I . . . .."

The sheriff reacted to the Judge's chant and was parked behind my chair, but I did not care.

"Friday!" I yelped, speaking *over* the Judge and slowly picking up and fluttering the Wife's affidavit like a white flag over the rebels' barricades. The Judge halted, just long enough for me to point at the filing day stamp:

"FRIDAY! *They* filed Friday, *on* the deadline! *We* filed Tuesday! *Before* Friday . . . deadline . . . .."

The Judge had abandoned the effort of talking over my Tarzan speak. I almost added: "Me Portia. Me Early. Boom On Time." That seemed like a good follow-up reiteration of what had happened with the ill-fated affidavits.

The Honorable's brain was now working through the days of the week: Tuesday before Friday. It could not both be true that I was late *and* that Boom—who filed later—was on time.

"May it please the Court," I started up again, in a lame attempt to balance my boldness, but the Judge regained her speech before I damaged my plight any more:

"Recess!" Judge Nettle alighted from her bench, lifted her robe above her shins, and, clutching its hems in both hands, jogged out of the courtroom, as if responding to an unexpected and urgent call of nature.

"*Now* you blew it," snarled Boom.

BOOM was not wrong. Interrupting the Judge was a suicidal move in itself. But that was the least of my sins. In one quarter hour, Nettle framed me for missing a deadline, lying to the court, *and* disrespecting a judge. Missing a deadline alone is known in the industry as *the* leading cause for getting sued by clients for malpractice. Donny's multi-million-dollar business was so much beyond my policy limits that I might as well have no policy at all. But that problem paled in comparison with the next one: lying to the Court could easily leave a lawyer without any means to pay off anything, if the Bar's ethics committee were to side with the Judge on this.

Maybe I should appeal?

"Stay seated," announced the sheriff.

The Judge returned. I stopped breathing. Nettle did not wait until making it to the top of her bench to start talking:

"The Court finds that both lawyers missed the deadline for affidavits."

"Say what?" I thought, but kept my mouth firmly clamped shut. That was an entirely unexpected turn. I had to give Nettle a kind of grudging credit for having found a logically consistent, even if contrary to fact, way to avoid admitting that she must have been wrong about the filing deadline.

"I could ban you both," went on Nettle. "I could just dismiss the case today and go home."

"Go home to two appeals instead of one," I thought, but kept my lips sealed still.

"But, tell you what . . ." The Judge was pointing at Boom, "Attorney Boom, you were absolutely honest and forthcoming that you missed the deadline."

Boom developed a blank expression of stilted unconcern. Of course, Boom was *not* "forthcoming" about missing the deadline, because *she did not miss it.* Suddenly, *Boom* had a situation of her own that would be hard to explain to her client.

Boom hiccupped, and reached out for the plastic water carafe, which she lifted with too much force and splashed all over her desk.

"Honesty," carried on the Judge, "Honesty must be . . . in my courtroom . . ." she stopped and inspected both of us.

"You were both late, both of you. But only Attorney Boom was honest about it," continued Nettle's terrifying

301

proclamation.

"Here's what I'll do," the Judge declared, "I will let all of y'all give all the testimony you want. I will not close your client's testimony today," Judge Nettle nodded in my direction, "just consider this a warning."

Outstanding, I am free from a suit by a client! Life's looking up.

". . . I'll decide on your punishment later, I'll hold it open," the Judge waved the sheriff away from my side of the courtroom.

Just peachy. No jail time for contempt of court today.

All the threatening and screaming was heavy work, and the Judge felt exhausted. "Y'all fightin' and arguin' and actin' as children, that took up all the time we got. Y'all outta time. Tonya'll give you the time to start tomorrow. I'm meeting with lawyers in a big case in the morning, so it gotta be after eleven. Thank y'all. Next case!"

We stood up, dismissed for the day. Judge Nettle was already talking over our heads to a new batch of lawyers, who were pushing their way into our warm seats like we stopped being visible. I swooped up my files and papers to get out of the way and nearly dropped them on the floor: my side again was being impaled with a blunt dagger.

"The recording! I got it!" Raccoon excitedly babbled into my ear while exhaling a puff of Ice chewing gum smell.

He was clutching the audio recording of the scheduling hearing—the deadlines for all the Affidavits narrated in Judge Nettle's own voice. Apparently, The Raccoon had slipped out undetected and managed to charm a young secretary next door into making him a copy.

The recording would clear my name!

"Your Honor," I mounted a new charge, now interrupting somebody else's hearing, "we recovered the recording of the scheduling conference. When you gave the deadlines. This will prove that the deadline for affidavits was Friday, as I had truthfully reported to the Court."

The new batch of lawyers paused, and I finished triumphantly, gasping with joy:

"May we play the recording?"

'Nah," came a prompt ruling.

"Your Honor, this is my livelihood and reputation. Your Honor is contemplating undeserved punishment, but I have proof here that I spoke truthfully about the Friday deadline. May I submit the proof to clear my name?"

"You know what," murmured Judge Nettle magnanimously, I am not punishing you this time. But I'll remember your duplicity the next time. Thank y'all. Next case!"

Publicly called a liar by the Judge, but not punished. In a divorce court, do we call this a loss or a victory? It felt a lot like I had been trapped in the world of Alice in Wonderland.

IT was over for the day.

The ever-busy Raccoon was packing up our papers, easels, boards, files and folders, three and two-hole punched and tying all those treasures to our wheels, all in preparation for starting our exodus.

Nettle had been clever. Now there was nothing to appeal because there would be no punishment.

Gingerly, I lifted from my seat, slid past the sheriff, and filed out of the courtroom before the Judge changed her mind on the jailing. I did not feel quite safe until the double doors of the courtroom closed behind me.

Donny was trailing behind.

We circled the court hallway and settled ourselves on the marble benches, out of direct sight of the courtroom doors. A stupid precaution: the Judge would not come into the hallway. Judges used the back door which leads to the private elevators. My pulse calmed down for a second, but then I looked at Donny. On second thought, a quiet time with the court sheriffs might have been more welcome that the explanations I owed Donny. The words of an older lawyer came to mind: "some things are just very hard to explain to a client."

"I understand." Donny obviously was reading my mind. "Do not worry, I understand."

"You sure?"

"It's elementary. We filed Tuesday, they filed Friday. For Friday deadline. She knows that. Everybody knows."

"She does?" I wondered.

"Yep." Donny was never in doubt.

He went on without bitterness: "That Judge doesn't like me very much, does she? She'd give my business lock stock and barrel to the Wifey just to punish me, but she knows you'd appeal that. She tried pushing you. Now she's trying to make me doubt you. A fool could see through that."

"How'd you know?" I was impressed.

"*Divide & conquer* is not a new angle. Old tricks, used them myself in business. If you and I started fighting, that'd leave me vulnerable. Judge was bluffing. She does not want an appeal, I can tell."

"How can you tell?"

"When appeal is mentioned, she wraps into her robe like it's gotten chilly in the room. And it'd never survive an appeal, her deadline trick," he smiled.

"So you and I stick together. Partner?" Donny's large, well-shaped hand with manicured nails stretched out to meet mine. We shook like buddies.

Donny did not need an explanation, and, what's more important, he was solidly on my team. The Judge's threats and bluff only worked to bring us closer. The threatened jailing, the contempt, the gag order—Donny did not buy any of it. Donny, the multimillionaire and a businessman trusted *me*, and I would do anything to win his case. Together, we were invincible.

———

By eleven o'clock the next day, Judge Nettle had calmed her nerves. She ordered us to reconvene and start the trial forthwith.

"How long y'all need to try this," she asked.

305

"Two days," I said.

"A week," said Boom on behalf of Donny's Wife. "We have extensive testimony about adulterous behavior, at least four days' worth. We intend to prove Mr. Beaver's unsavory character."

"It's a property division trial," I reminded, "by law, a party's character is not of any legal relevance, so long as the operation of his business is not affected."

Inspired by my own cleverness, I went on: "We move to exclude all testimony about adultery.

"It's irrelevant!

"It's prejudicial!

"It's inflammatory!

"And it unduly imposes a burden upon the Court's time, impeding the administration of justice!!"

It was a passionate objection, but whom was I kidding? Of course, Nettle wanted to hear the dirt.

"I'm allowing it," Nettle declared indulgently.

"Your Honor, this is a property division trial. Adultery has no relevance in property division," I protested again.

"I'm allowing," insisted Nettle, but popped out a disclaimer: "I'm not saying what *weight* I'll give it, but I'm allowing it...." and, likely recognizing that she was just about to set the stage for a week of irrelevant mud-slinging, Nettle gave a nod to my side too:

"But just three days. Give y'all three days. Ready? Set? Go!"

I was not sure if I was ready or set, but we went anyway.

Boom's witnesses got to go first, because Donny's Wife

306

was officially the Plaintiff. For two days, Boom put up irrelevant but entertaining stories of Donny's dalliances. Boom had hired a retired cop, now about three hundred pounds overweight and making a living as a private eye, to steal the garbage from the curb of Donny's mistress for three weeks straight. From the garbage, the Private Eye authoritatively concluded how many times Donny and the mistress had sex. "Unless, of course, there was oral sex," he added.

"Objection," I said.

"Denied," retorted the Judge.

"Move to strike the entire sex discussion," I said.

"Goes to weight," said the Judge.

"To weight of what?" I said, which was the wrong way to address a judge.

"Sit. Down," said the Judge, "before I hold you in contempt again."

I wanted to point out that she never actually held me in contempt before, but gave up and there was an hour more of colorful sex talk. The Judge cringed at some of the lurid details but took it in resolutely, like an alcoholic takes in his morning drink. She addressed a few questions to the PI herself, which went to the juicy details. There were photos of the garbage, and Nettle took an early lunch break to study them. I cannot speak for the Raccoon, but I skipped through the anger, embarrassment, outrage, and boredom, and by lunch just settled on numb. We shuffled through copies of the garbage photos over lunch, the garbage bags ripped open on a plastic table, the contents spread out. An unopened junk mail envelope addressed to "resident" at Donny's address was photographed front and center, proving the provenance of the garbage.

"What if Donny's being set up?" said Raccoon, his mouth full of courthouse cafeteria French fries.

"Doubtful . . . And for the umpteenth time, adultery does not matter in property trial. But tell you one thing, I am never taking *my* garbage to the curb, ever."

Anybody who leaves their rolling garbage containers curbside allows full access to inquisitive investigators, or neighbors or ex-lovers if the would-be sleuths are not squeamish. But roll the garbage bin back out of the public right-of-way and onto your private property—and it is off limits.

"We could burn the garbage every week, in violation of the City code," suggested Raccoon, adventurously.

"Let's do. Nobody will know," I said.

"Except for the smell."

"My garbage does not smell." I figured that was too much personal chit-chat, and returned to studying the photos.

Raccoon finished his fries, then my fries, then it was time to return to the courtroom for more dirt.

———————

BACK in the courtroom, an exotic dancer from the local "gentleman's bar" was Boom's next witness, testifying that Donny frequented the establishment. Without makeup, she looked rather like a he.

"Perhaps my client came for the buffet? You serve great lobster, really cheap," I proposed during my cross-examination of the he-dancer.

To my surprise, the answer came: "That's possible, many gentlemen do." Judge Nettle's face betrayed amusement. Was she a pervert, that Judge? Would there never be an end to the irrelevant trashing?

And then, after about ten hours of sundry sex-related testimony, it finally happened. The scandal became tiresome, the novelty wore out, the shocking images no longer shocked. Nobody, not even the sheriff, wanted to hear more about sex. Not this week. Not ever. Even Judge Nettle's heart was no longer into tarring and feathering my man Donny. The Judge's morals fought a good fight, but lost it to her healthy fear of the Appellate Court. The scandalous testimony went on, but everybody was probably thinking of the saying about "beating a dead horse."

At last, on the third day of trial, the Judge interrupted yet another of Wife's witnesses who was droning on and on about one more of Donny's scandalous erotic encounters: "I've heard enough, I am ready to rule."

"Due respect, we did not put up any testimony yet," I objected.

"Sit down," ruled the Judge.

Judge Nettle had already written out her ruling, and read it slowly, leaning into the microphone so it screeched at times. Boom was scribbling furiously and our team's appointed transcriber, Hoppy, was tapping his tiny Apple machine quicker than the girls of The Thoroughly Modern Millie.

Abruptly, the long-anticipated property trial was over. There was nothing for me to do but sit straight and control my face.

———————

NETTLE'S ruling commenced with an expression of her disapproval of Donny's way of living. Using language that suggested the horror and disgust of a fifty-year old nun forced into a sex-ed class, Judge Nettle dictated into the record a somewhat exaggerated summary of Donny's adulterous conquests.

The second part of Judge Nettle's order, the part called "Conclusions of Law," alluded briefly to the Honorable's disappointment with the South Duck State General Assembly. The good men and women of the lawmaking body did not afford the good judges of our State with a good statutory way to crucify those of Donny's ilk in cases of marital property division. That was disappointing to our Judge.

Left to her own devices, Nettle would not rule in Donny's favor even on a request for a potty break. Nevertheless, she was narrowly bound by the dictates of State law.

Jumping back to the findings of fact, Nettle spoke to Mrs. Donny. Filled with empathy with the wronged woman's long-suffering endurance, Her Honorable voice grew soft and tenderly embraced Donny's soon to be ex-wife. The Judge mused, getting deep into *obiter dicta*, how she wished she could do more. But in the end—Nettle's voice grew resolute with the sense of duty—in the end, the judge must follow the law.

Then came the third part of the Order, the "decretal portion," the really important part. Decretal portion is the very end of the Order, where a judge actually decides who gets what and when. Decretal potion is the bottom line.

Suddenly, Nettle's voice picked up speed and lost its crispness. She was reading off her yellow-pad so fast that Boom quit scribbling altogether and Raccoon broke the laptop space bar trying getting it all down.

The bottom line was unexpected.

THE IMPORTANCE OF A WRITTEN OR-DER

THE JUDGE KEPT READING, and Donny was sitting straighter and straighter as she read:

Donny could have the business. No sale. No asset sale. No shares to the Wifey.

We won.

It was a crushing defeat to the other side's dreams and hopes.

Donny, the revalidated owner of Beaver Global, stood up and hugged me. I think his eyes were misty.

We were jubilant.

Donny and I, we had stood tough together, resolute in the face of the Judge's ire.

(Actually, *I* stood tough. *Donny* spent most of his days in court sitting with his eyes downcast, the very picture of contriteness.)

We had trusted each other, and we were intrepid.

(Actually, *Donny* was intrepid. *I* was scared out of my mind.)

Our valor found its reward: Donny remained a multi-millionaire and his soon-to-be-born baby would enjoy a wealthy father. The Beaver empire would bloom and prosper and would live happily ever after. And I was the lawyer who made it all happen. I was sure that the local grapevine was already seething with the news of the spectacular newcomer, me. And then there was the handsome fee to be had. No more Ramen noodles!

———

LEAVING the Raccoon in the courtroom to pack up our papers for the last time, Donny and I returned to the marble benches on the opposite side of the corridor loop, the same place we had held our first conference.

What a difference three days made!

Donny was beaming and bubbling like a child who had just won a prize at the science fair. He was suddenly full of plans. Now that he was expecting a son (the kid would be a son, he was sure) Donny needed to grow. His business would blossom from "comfortable" into "globally awesome."

My own business was going to take off too. Donny's unpaid invoices added up to $80,000 and change, enough to propel my little practice to an entirely new level.

Reading my mind, Donny reported: "I am going straight to the bank, and see what's what to cut you a check. I might have to move some things around."

How did he know? I wondered if I had a tell somehow. Did my ears move when I was going to ask him for the money? Then again, maybe Donny was just a clairvoyant. Anything's possible.

"Do not worry," he said, "you will get paid, you were worth every penny and more."

He took my arm between his two hands, in a gesture that was something between a hug and a politician's two-handed handshake. His gaze was in the air, filled with visions of growth of his business empire.

"By the way," Donny descended to the terrestrial plane with astonishing speed, "I'll need some papers for the bankers today. Time to expand. Need to get my ducks in a row while prime's low. Can you write me a note that the business is mine now? Those tight-asses at the bank will not release a broken penny without some papers."

"I can't write you a note, Donny," I said still delirious.

"Don't worry, I'll pay you."

"It's not that."

"You trying to get something extra for it? I said I'll pay you," Donny was getting impatient.

"Not doubting you a sec, Donny," I returned.

"What then?"

"It's not exactly how it works," I was still tone deaf to Donny's change of mood.

"Just write it up. Don't have to be anything fancy," Donny did not give up.

"Donny, the Judge did *say* that you get the business, but, you see, there's no *Order* until the Judge *signs it* and *files it.* You can't take the Judge's words to the bank. Yet."

"What do you mean?" Donny was puzzled and disconcerted.

"The order must be written, signed and file-stamped," I retorted, quoting the statute for lack of a better explanation. "Written, signed, file-stamped, then it's valid."

"But the Judge *said* . . ."

"I know. What she *said* actually has no force. Until she *writes* it. And *signs*, and . . ."

"I heard you, *file-stamples.*" Donny's voice betrayed polite misgiving. "We did not win yet is what you are telling me?"

"We did. We won all right, but words have no power until the Judge signs the order."

"What's so wrong about this Judge that her words have no power?"

"Nothing. That's the law for all orders. For all of the judges."

"Fine!" Donny looked like he did not believe me, but did not see a way to make me crack. "Nettle *is* going to write that order?" there was just a touch of panic in his voice.

"Yes. Actually, since we won, I get to write it. The first-draft version, anyway. Boom will give her comments. Nettle will sign."

"Should I worry? Can the Judge take back everything?"

"No. It's a formality. Don't worry a thing," I spat out what he wanted to hear. Usually, I am of the school to never tell a client not to worry, at least not where a judge is involved. But this time, I really did not see a problem.

Donny was worried anyhow, or at least thoroughly annoyed.

"I feel cheated," confided Donny. "You never told me that today was not the end. Now I have to wait for some stupid paper. You should have told me."

"Would that have changed things if I told you?" I countered coldly.

"Does not matter. You should have told me." Donny had dealt with lawyers before, and on occasion was fond of reminding me of the client's right to be informed.

"I'm telling you. I'll write up the order. Judge will sign it, clerk will stamp it, and you will have your business back."

"How long?" Donny was still impatient.

"A couple of weeks, maybe a month. This Judge is not known for swift entry of her orders."

"A moooonth??"

"Think positive. You won."

"Yeah, won what? Some words that mean nothing?" Donny stood up and now, although only three paces separated us physically, a yawning divide seemed to be opening in our relationship.

We walked to the elevator three paces apart and rode

down in awkward silence. Donny could not have looked sadder if I lost the whole thing for him. I felt horrible.

"You know what," he started again, holding the elevator door at the lobby level and letting me slip through, "I am not saying at all that the mix-up with the order is all your fault . . ."

"It is not a mix-up, Donny," I interrupted, "this is how the law works!"

"Sure, sure. I believe you," said Donny, "but anyway, let's hold on that payment to you. At least until you finish with the Order."

"Donny . . ." I started to protest.

"You said yourself," interrupted Donny, "before there's a written order, I have nothing."

I did say that. Sort of. But he still had bills due.

"I need to go," announced Donny, tugging on his tie disconsolately. "You didn't... You should've... I need to go."

He pushed his way through the Plexiglas wings of the handicap exit at the security point without waiting for the sheriff to push-open the remote lock. The wings bent slightly, popped off its joint, and let Donny out into the entrance hall, where he collided with an installation in the middle of the vast marble floor. It was a tiny wreath memorial for fallen police officers, a garland comprised of roses and daisies. It jumped out at Donny with no warning, and the two collided like two ill-fated ships in a desolate ocean. Donny stumbled over the collapsed wreath for the fallen officers and did not once look back.

I was on his heels, wanting to make sure Donny understood: getting a written Order was a *process*. The process starts with an oral rendition by the judge, then the next step is drafting the text of the order, then the judge's signature, and shortly after, the stamp. Every step must be taken, or else you have no valid Order. None of that meant I was in any way failing at my job.

"Look," I wanted to say, "if you were cooking a Thanksgiving dinner, you'd have nothing on your plate until the turkey's roasted. But that does not mean you are doing something wrong if it's still Thanksgiving morning and you already put the turkey in the oven." Cooking the turkey. That was a good metaphor, easy to understand, I thought.

I just needed to catch up with Donny to explain.

The fallen wreath slowed me down. I apologized to the flowers, then said "sorry" to a tipsy bum who was resting in the air conditioned spot between the doors. The bum drifted towards me, thinking there was maybe a dollar for him in this. The commotion attracted the eye of the red-mustached lobby security officer, who sauntered over.

"Why'd you spill the flowers?" inquired the guard, suspecting I was staging a political protest.

"I was putting them back," I explained.

"You better!"

I apologized again, this time to the guard. By the time I popped out of the courthouse, Donny was gone.

That was the last time I ever saw him in person.

IT was the time of year that makes every poet's heart sing and every lawyer question their life choices.

The quick thunderstorm that passed while we were inside the courthouse had lifted the heat. The air outside the courthouse smelled of wild thyme with only just a hint of engine exhaust and of tobacco fumes from the smoking area located right at the far end of the courthouse entrance.

Before I started law school, a weather spell like this would be a clarion call for me to splurge on one last summer dress before the oncoming cold, one last evening to feel the thrilling chill of silk hems swooshing around my knees. And a time to dream big career dreams.

Coming out of the courtroom, though, my knees were camouflaged with the now redundant warmth of gabardine, a pair of knees now too chubby and bluish-white to properly complement any pretty dress anyway. I sniffed the air and felt sorry for myself. The Summer was gone, and I had nothing to show for it. No money and no suntan.

I leaned on the dusty granite column in front of the courthouse and descended into sorrows worthy of Young Werther's, lamenting the departure of my youth. A few paces away, the smokers celebrated life, lifting their faces to release white puffy clouds which drifted up the courthouse walls and cloaked in mystery the inspirational slogans etched in the marble inlays. The Ducklingburg people were proud of their courthouse. The ground level was cast in coarse stone panels, interlaid with polished marble parts, adorned with etchings of wisdom supported by the South Duck elders.

Right at my eye level, a fragment of one quotation almost burnt into my eyes: "... *Sufficient for High Trust* ..." That almost made me cry. My work was not, after all, sufficient for Donny's trust.

"What's wrong, boss?" The shy Boy Friday #1 puffed smoke into my face. Apparently, the kid had followed me out of the lobby and for the last five minutes we were sharing a moment.

"Life is weird, Shy Friday #1," I told him by way of explanation.

"Hoppy," came the correction. "You said once the trial is over, you'd stop calling us both "Kid." Name is Hoppy."

My bout of self-pity was interrupted by the arrival of the last of my troops. The Raccoon was squeezing out of the revolving door, followed by three bankers boxes piled together on an airport two-wheel cart and haphazardly tied crisscross with loops of frazzled stretch cord. The contraption of boxes and wheels jammed the door.

The Raccoon was stuck but not defeated.

"We got paid?!" he inquired optimistically, still stuck in the clenches of the revolving door and wiggling his way out by brute force and pure resolve. The boxes were holding on, but cracking at the lids. The Raccoon was not noticing.

"We will," I said without much trust in my own promise. But Raccoon did not get deterred.

"What a day," he said oblivious to our apparent financial setback, "we showed them! And we still have your bond money!"

The bond money was Hoppy's idea.

After Judge Nettle's first threat to put me in jail, circumspect Hoppy googled "contempt" and "lawyers" and we insisted we start carrying cash to make a bond in case I did get jailed.

"You feel like Chinese?" The Raccoon proposed a solid culinary investment for the now-superfluous bond money.

We decided on a carry-out. I do not like eating in restaurants because you never know who might be eavesdropping from the neighboring table. Hoppy and Raccoon had their own agenda. "Fair enough," agreed Raccoon, "Hoppy can make the restaurant run. Your porch works best to have a drink in peace and quiet, anyway."

The battered bankers boxes stuffed with no longer necessary papers made an excellent improvised table on my patio. Three Christmas ball lights propped up on a linen line gave just enough illumination to tell the pork from the shrimp but not so much that we could get depressed over the dismal state of the flora on the deck.

"So what's the deal with Donny?" wondered Raccoon, helping himself to my sake, straight out of the bottle.

I explained. We would not be paid until there's the signed Order.

"So what's the problem?"

I explained. We lost him. He no longer trusts me.

"Why don't you just push that Order through?" suggested Raccoon. "That would make Donny happy?"

This sounded too simple.

I explained how Donny had lost his faith in me, and how my world was now crushed.

The Raccoon listened, and winced, and gulped more of my sake.

Hoppy nodded and stole my eggroll. Neither of them shared my pain.

"Boss," concluded Hoppy, dropping oily crumbs on the porch, "Just get the darn thing done, and quit whining about it."

IT took me three days to prepare a draft of the Order.

If Donny continued to be disappointed in my services, he had the good sense to keep his mouth shut. Actually, he did not respond to any of my calls.

"Gone to Hilton Head?" suggested Raccoon.

Crafting an Order that would withstand a possible appeal, preserve the Judge's intentions and attract no wrath of the other side does take some effort. Plus, I stealthily distributed to Donny's unsuspecting ex the brunt of various tax burdens from the last year they lived together. In short, my draft was a *chef-d'oeuvre*, a veritable sonnet of a legal document. Of course, the hateful eye of Boom might undermine a few delicate details, but such was life.

At six o'clock, groggy from the day of drafting and looking particularly un-lawyerly, I pushed the button of my fax machine and the alien-sounding connection squealings signaled the arrival of my fax in the enemy's camp. My machine spat out the delivery confirmation, and finding that there's nothing else to do, I turned to bed. There are certainly advantages to practicing out of one's condo, I mused.

An hour later, my fax machine came to life with the urgent screeching of an ambulance. There are also disadvantages to living in one's office, I realized. I knew that the fax from Boom would poison the night, but could not help myself: I had to look.

The fax read succinctly:

We no longer represent Mrs. Beatrice D. Beaver.

This changed everything, and to the better. With Boom gone, I only had Mrs. Beaver herself to deal with. Of course, she'd object to everything and maybe even write to Nettle directly, but she was no real threat. Instead of making wily suggestions about the language of the Order, she would make the typical mistakes of a layperson: she'd rant about "fairness" and fruitlessly try to reargue her case. In any event, Nettle's only concern was an appeal, and, without a lawyer, Mrs. Donny posed almost no danger of appealing. My draft of the Order would sail through untouched.

———

ON my way to the courthouse to leave the Order in Nettle's mailbox for her signature, happy and proud like I just gave birth to a royal heir, I tried dialing Donny's number again.

There were no longer any hurdles for him to pay.

And not a moment too soon. Donny's case had occupied all my time and my little law firm was flat broke. Even the electric and the website provider were threatening to shut me down. A law firm with no lights, website, or email—that would be really hard to explain to any prospective clients.

But my financial distress wouldn't last for long.

"Whew, a narrow escape," I thought.

Entering the courthouse, I left Donny a celebratory voicemail. The Order would be delivered in a matter of seconds, and I expected it'd be signed in a few days. I wanted him to know.

This time, Donny did respond. I had just jumped off the top floor elevator when my phone dinged announcing his text.

"I am informing and instructing you," Donny wrote in a formal tone he'd never used with me before, "to immediately stop any work on my file."

At the foot of the text Donny typed out his full name, including his middle initial and an entirely new post office box address. Under his address, Donny repeated his instructions in even simpler words:

"Stop immediately. Step down. I will not pay for any more work."

You know a man means business when he texts you his middle initial. But when he also adds his full zip code, he must mean war.

I dialed Donny's number. This time, he picked up on the first ring.

"I want you to stop any work," commanded Donny.

"Can you pay today?" I already knew the answer to this question, but I had to hear it.

"I will not pay for any *more* work. I am instructing you. Cease immediately."

"What exactly do you want me to *cease*?"

"Any work."

"Donny," I said calmly, "I already did *all* the work. There is nothing *left*. Except to place the Order in the box. You want me to cease reaching my hand up to the mailbox?" I sounded rather like an angry poodle.

"Cease immediately," he ordered again. "I want the Judge to know you are not my lawyer anymore."

"Why would you want that?!"

"Your name in the Order?" he asked ignoring my remark.

It was. Orders usually list the lawyers. Likely in case somebody needs to go back and punish the guilty.

"I need you to re-type it without your name," he said following an invisible script, "and I need you to announce your *withdrawal*."

"You are firing me? Why?"

"Unsatisfactory performance," kept Donny to his script.

"Look, please do not do that," I got worried for my product. "You are risking to lose the win."

"How's that?" Donny slid off the script momentarily worried.

"It's not really over until the Judge signs it. I told you

that."

"But you said you're confident the Judge will sign off on it."

He got me there. I did say that. I lost my momentum. Donny was back on script:

"You are positioning to manipulate me to get paid. I should have seen it when the Judge told me, warned me."

"Warned you about what?" I exclaimed.

"Your duplicity."

"Donny, you are making a . . ."

"Don't bother, you are fired. Make another step, and I'll file charges."

With that, he hung up. I was not sure what he meant by "filing charges," and I did not want to find out. A young public defender ran by, pulling on his tie with one hand and tucking in his shirt with another. A meeting in Judges' Chambers. Lucky bastard, his client had probably already used his one call and could not call and fire him.

"Rough day?" sympathized the Public Defender.

"Just got fired," I sighed.

"Got your money upfront?" He was untypically practical for a PD attorney.

"You're quick thinking for a public servant," I quipped.

"When's the trial?"

"It's over." I waved the envelope. "I'm here to get the Order to the Judge."

He started laughing.

"This guy does not trust you to walk three steps to shove the letter in the mailbox? He thinks you gonna screw *that* up? Which part—the *walking* or the *shoving* that has him worried in particular?"

"You are right," I agreed, and dialed Donny's number again.

"Don't hang up!" I warned. "Look, the Judge said the order is due tomorrow. If I do not deliver it, I will be disobeying the Judge."

"Get out," said Donny. "I will do it *prowsey* now."

"You what?"

"I'll take it myself." He meant *pro se*, by himself. This time, I hung up on him, not to be emphatic, but because I ran out of things to say other than maybe "oi vey."

"Tough break," observed the public defender, then reminisced about times that he got fired. "This one guy did not trust me to deliver a pizza . . . but I was twelve, and I *did* steal a slice. So no, you still take the prize." He disappeared into the Judges' Chambers area, no doubt to share the anecdote with all the secretaries.

I stuffed my now useless papers back into the bag and dragged myself to the elevator and out of the courthouse.

I was not cut out to be a lawyer, and that was final.

———

AT nine o'clock the next morning, in brisk execution of Donny's wishes to be rid of my services, I stood in Honorable Judge Jane U. Nettle's courtroom.

Judge Nettle started her usual way: "What am I doing

here?"

I wanted to say: "You are a judge in the South Duck State Court, the family law division," or something equally stupid.

I reported, instead: "I would like to withdraw." Nettle lifted in her seat a little and moved closer. Nettle gave me a silent stare and I added by way of explanation: "Client consents," which sounded somewhat better than "I was fired."

"He's not paying?" guessed the Judge.

"No, Your Honor."

The Judge's face rearranged itself into the emoticon for wink-and-smile. She motioned for me to hand up my release papers. It was a laconic affair, titled *Order Allowing Withdrawal of Counsel*. The whole thing fit on one page, even though two thirds of the page were dedicated to the rectangle of the caption, where the names of Donny and his soon-to-be ex-wife were squared off in capital letters and the signature block which listed every possible way to reach my office. This only left about an inch of actual space for the order itself, but there was not too much to say:

Mr. Beaver consents to the withdrawal . . . All notices from now on will be delivered to Mr. Beaver at his P. O. Box address . . .

And that was that. The end of Donny.

A line for the judge's signature. I had typed in today's date, so she did not have to write it in.

Judge Nettle smiled lovingly at the Order, and barked: "Pen?"

On the margins, in her medicinal woman handwriting,

the Judge added in:

No delay will result from entry of this order.

Judge Nettle signed, Tonya-the-clerk crisply pressed the stamp to the paper, and I was abruptly freed from all my lawyerly duties. Donny was left to fend for himself. I had nothing left to do.

"While I am here," I decided to take advantage of the uncharacteristically well-disposed Judge to settle an old score, "does Your Honor recall the Order Prohibiting Sale? Did that ever surface? The Stop-Sale Order?"

"Not your problem, counsel," snapped the Judge, "here you go," she reached down and handed my withdrawal order, signed stamped and ready on the spot—the only Order that ever did get properly entered in Donny's case, as far as I could figure.

"Good luck, counsel," wished Judge Nettle almost warmly, obviously glad to see me go.

———

THE news of my departure reached Wife's former lawyers even before I exited the courthouse.

While I was busy with getting Judge Nettle's blessings, Boom was on the prowl for business exactly five floors under Judge Nettle's courtroom. The criminal floor of South Duck Courthouse held the arraignments—an excellent time to scare up some cash by representing people charged with misdemeanors.

Civil lawyers often underestimate criminals as a source of steady income. Boom did not make that mistake. Other lawyers may have looked down their noses on the likes of the "all guilty" who'd "never pay," but that was a myopic generalization: plenty of alleged criminals pay very well and easily. A lawyer just has to know how to pick them. What you want is a college kid with his first drunk-driving ticket. Or else a teenager charged with petty theft. Or rounded up in a campus fracas. You want the white and the wealthy, if you can get it. You want young first time offenders—ridiculously scared of jail and easy to separate from their parents' cash, especially after they learn that their crimes could carry jail sentences. Of course, the Assistant District Attorney has absolutely no intention of jailing kids who barely stumbled over the line of the Criminal Code. And so, Boom came out a champion every time. The ADA was grateful for a lawyer to help move files off his desk, the clients could not believe their luck at being free again, and Boom got paid a couple of thousand dollars for a few hours of her time. Plus, Boom saw it as a public service: she'd be sure to scare the kids into clean living. Win. Win! WIN!

Upon receiving the news of Beaver file development, Boom dropped her hunt and bolted upstairs.

The courtroom was almost empty. Judge Nettle in full regalia of black starched polyester was still sitting royally on her bench, engrossed in research of homeopathic treatment for hemorrhoids. Secretary Tonya was kneeling on her chair with her back to the courtroom gallery, squeezing the last five hundred pages of the Beaver file into a 300-page capacity filing box. Tonya sported an unusually colored tattoo on a part of her back that should absolutely be covered in court. It was a private time for Tonya and the Judge: Boom was not expected.

"Help you?" mused the Judge, smirking at the lawyer.

"Donny Beaver unrepresented now, I understand?" started Boom on an informal foot, still a little winded.

The Judge made a face like she just heard her favorite pizza place was revealed as a hotbed of e-coli.

"You got out of this case a month ago?" confirmed the Judge.

"Not that long, Judge, not that long. Far less than that. And we are getting rehired, we are in the process of being rehired," lied Boom.

"Come when the *process* is finished," advised Nettle. "You know you can't speak for Mrs. Beaver now."

"Just housekeeping, Judge, just housekeeping," retorted Boom quite undeterred with small matters like handling a case for woman technically not her client. "We need twenty minutes."

"For what?" inquired Judge Nettle gruffly.

"My client's *Motion to Reconsider*. That must be heard without delay."

"I do not see any *Motion to Reconsider*," Tonya butted in, twisting herself back into the chair with the sound of an ink cartridge plopped snugly into a huge printer.

"We are in the process of submitting that, Your Honor. In the process. But my client wishes to proceed without undue delay." That, technically, was also a lie: Mrs. Beaver had sacked Boom first thing after trial, in a big huff. Boom was rightly sure, however, that the news of Mr. Beaver's new *pro se* status would bring Mrs. Beaver around.

There was another hitch. A Motion to Reconsider could not exist until there was an Order.

"There's nothing to reconsider yet," observed the Judge, betraying her solid grasp of post-trial procedure. She was quite right. Boom had to wait until there was something to reconsider. But both the lawyer and the Judge knew that divorce courts did not stand upon ceremony that firmly.

"Even better, Judge," Boom immediately found her footing, "we can have an informal meeting. We'll hammer out the final order. There were some discrepancies."

"Same time on Thursday," caved in Nettle. "Don't forget to serve *him*," she pointed at the Order Allowing Withdrawal: "Mr. Beaver's address here. Serve him."

"Of course!" assured Boom, then bid her good-buys and left without taking Donny's address.

Less than an hour after I was booted as Donny's lawyer, the process of undoing my Summer's work was in full swing.

In a few weeks, it would become irreversible.

A PERFECT PATSY

QUARTER OF SEVEN in the evening is dubbed "the hour of a coward" because no one calling at 6:45 P.M. can honestly expect to go mano-a-mano, like a man.

6:45 P.M. is when the sneaky coward leaves a message so she could turn up in court next morning and tell the Judge what lawyers straight-facedly call "the truth": that her message "went unanswered."

"Your Honor, we cannot reach Mr. Beaver," Boom would sing out. "We even reached out to the ex-lawyer," she'd bellow, "we left a message and, of course, there was no answer!" At that point, Boom would roll her eyes to play up the strife between Donny and his ex-lawyer. Boom would leave out the part about the careful timing of her call and would snidely lay it on even thicker:

"Mr. Beaver was not good enough to leave us his phone number and there's simply no way to reach him." The Judge would nod, and Boom would move in for the kill:

"I move we have the meeting right now, without Mr. Beaver. The man simply did not bother to be found."

As any lawyer will tell you, the easiest way to argue is against an empty chair. Coincidentally, every time Boom had a case against unrepresented folks, these folks had trouble showing up in court. Boom, of course, swore that she did notify the opposition of the hearings. If the judges suspected the foul play, they never said a word about it.

At 6:45 in the evening, Boom's number lit up on my caller ID, and I picked up the phone: "What's up, Boom?" There was a rustle and the line went dead. I did not think much of the misdial and nodded off. Twelve hours later, at 6:45 A.M., Boom's secretary dialed me again—a shrewd calculation on her part. Sometimes a lawyer leaves an office late in the night. And then again, there are those crazy Southern lawyers who like to show up at work at sunrise. But nobody, not in South Duck, would do both. Nobody stays at work till seven in the evening and then turns up again at seven in the morning. Not even workaholic Manhattan lawyers would do that on a normal day. Those poor New York bastards call an eleven PM exit "an early night," but they rarely turn up at the office before 9:00 in the morning.

To catch both 6:45 P.M. and 6:45 A.M. you'd have to be a crazy bum practically living at your office. Which no self-respecting South Duck lawyer would do.

The phone woke me up.

"Hello again, Boom" I said getting suspicious.

"It's Attorney Boom's assistant."

"Yes?"

"We've been trying to reach your client," spat out the assistant venomously.

That was most likely a lie, but I did not dispute it.

"We called you yesterday, but you did not answer."

That was most certainly a lie, but I did not contest that either.

"What can I do for you, now that you have me?" I inquired diplomatically.

"Ms. Boom will be heard on a motion to reconsider today."

"When did Ms. Boom *serve* this motion to reconsider? I certainly do not have a copy. Or when did she even *file* it?"

"I wouldn't know." The secretary was now beyond hostile. "I am just doing you a favor and telling you this. I don't even have to tell you this."

She was right: she did not have to tell *me*. But she did very much have to tell *Donny*. My guess was that Boom's office never reached out to Donny. In essence, they were contriving to hold a meeting with the Judge without inviting Donny.

"When is the hearing?" I reached for the pen and paper.

"It's today."

"What time?"

"I am not sure. After twelve sometime."

Nothing else could be gotten out of the assistant, not

335

even with waterboarding.

"Thanks for looping me in," I signed off and dialed Donny.

Truthfully, I had no business in the middle of this conspiracy, but Donny was defenseless against Boom's tricks, and I could not bear to just stand aside and watch my hard work go down the drain. It was like my baby, my legacy!

The court rules forbade Boom from talking to Judge Nettle without Donny present, but the work-around was easy for Boom: if Donny was notified of the hearing but did not bother to attend, the hearing would go on without him. He would be deemed to have forfeited his right to be heard. Moreover, in the nebulous world of notice by telephone call, it would be Boom's word against Donny's.

Besides, Judge Nettle was not all that particular about notice when the other guy was unrepresented. Her reputation on that point was a red flag from the start, as soon as Donny kicked me off the case.

According to the annals, Judge Nettle even once let a whole lawsuit go on for two years without ever notifying the guy who was being sued.

"The first time this one dude got wise to the fact that he *had* a baby *and* was being sued for child support was when the SWAT team surrounded his condo to arrest him for non-payment. He'd have happily supported the kid, except the spiteful ex decided it was more fun to jail him instead," according to Hoppy, perhaps embellishing his tale with some colorful exaggeration. We were discussing "all things that can go wrong with Donny's case now that we're out of there."

"Boom is never going to be straight up with Donny, and Nettle will cover up," opined Hoppy suspiciously. "There will be SWAT on Donny's lawn too, you'll see."

"You are being dramatic," I said. "No way they'd send SWAT. Probably just an old, beer-bellied sheriff."

But Hoppy was right to worry. I figured Donny could use my help, and dialed him.

Donny picked up on the first ring.

"Look, Donny, you need to be in court today." I said. "They . . ."

"Do not threaten me, I know you are after my money," interrupted Donny.

"No, not me. Boom already concocted some scheme. You best go see. I do not know the time, but I'd show up as soon as you can get there."

"It's not your case," roared Donny, "I told you: *you are fired*. You are trying to suck even more money out of me. I told you: *stop the bleeding*. I am not scared of you."

"Look, just do me a favor and go see what they are up to," I repeated.

"I will," warned Donny, "and I will tell Judge Nettle all about your tricks. Trying to make me pay you the money which the Judge said specifically not to use. The Judge will know all about you. You're getting your wish, I am going to see the Judge. You will not scare me into paying you. Rest assured, you are not getting one penny."

Somehow, that sounded more true than his promise he'd pay "every penny." I wondered if the divorce business was making me a gloom-and-doom pessimist.

——————

As I suspected, Boom's secretary could not be trusted: The Beaver hearing was scheduled for ten o'clock, not "after twelve sometime."

By 11:32, when Donny strolled into the courtroom, the meeting was already breaking up. Boom and Judge Nettle had not opted for the audio recording system to be turned on at the start of the meeting, and so history did not preserve the first hour or so. However, Judge Nettle's secretary did push the "ON" button and rolled the recording as soon as she caught sight of Donny.

The recording, which the enterprising Raccoon got off his friendly young secretary later that same day, started mid-hearing:

". . . Nice of you to join us, Mr. Beaver," remarked the Judge with faux sweetness.

She meant it, too: Donny's arrival was advantageous. Now she would not be blamed for an impermissible *ex parte* hearing, a hearing where only Boom was present. Now that Donny arrived, the Judge was quite determined to assure that the record would prove that Donny participated. The Appellate Division was not too keen on ambush, but if the victim of ambush did not protest, did not ask to reschedule, and said at least two words in his defense, well, then the line got very blurry between an ambush and a plain old agreement between two litigants to hold a hearing without the burdensome formality of service and the required waiting

338

periods. Blurry lines are a trial court judge's best friend on appeal because the appellate courts mostly resolve all blurriness in favor of the judge.

"We were all finished here, but since you do not have a lawyer, I will accommodate you, Mr. Beaver. Anything you want to add to Ms. Boom's motion?" The Judge was all helpfulness.

"I . . . she . . . I never got any papers from her?" Donny was confused.

"Attorney Boom, what do you say to that?" turned Nettle to Boom, with a smile reminiscent of the Cheshire Cat.

"That's right, Your Honor. It was only a *motion in limine*, we did not file anything. There are no papers. It was an oral motion."

"What do you say to that, Mr. Beaver?"

"But Judge, the case is finished! You gave me all my property," protested Donny.

"Judge, you did not sign the final Order yet," Boom was quick with her retort.

"She is right," nodded Judge Nettle. "I have not signed. Nothing is finished."

"I . . . I want a lawyer," reacted Donny with the phrase he knew to be the last resort. "I want my lawyer back."

Judge Nettle stifled a smile, and nodded at Boom to respond.

"Your Honor, there's no need for that, my client would like to resolve things quickly, and besides, you already heard from Mr. Beaver's attorney on that matter precisely."

"That's right!" exclaimed the Judge. She was talking to

Donny now: "Your lawyer wasted a good deal of my time trying to prove that she filed those affidavits before the deadline. I even put her in jail for lying to me about those affidavits..."

"You did? When?" Donny was gullible.

"*Almost* put her in jail," corrected herself Nettle. "I'll be open with you, Mr. Beaver, your attorney got you into a kettle of hot water here. But that is not Attorney Boom's fault. Attorney Boom filed her affidavit . . ." Nettle was preparing to say "on time," but then remembered the score, and wrapped up her spiel: "You want to pick this up when you have an attorney again?"

"I am sorry, Your Honor, but you already said the affidavits were OK?" Donny asked, dumfounded.

"No, I didn't," the Judge bolted upright, suddenly furious. "Don't you dare put words in my mouth. I let you talk and tell your side of the story for three days. I did, out of the goodness of my heart, and I bent over backwards for you, and now I am considering whether to accept your testimony or not. I am considering. Considering. . .."

Donny was going to remind Honorable Nettle that she did not let him talk at all in those three days, but that seemed like a technicality. He insisted, instead:

"But you already *decided*. Everything's divided. My lawyer said you cannot change your mind."

"It's a *motion in limine*" interrupted Boom, and Judge's eyes lit up.

"This is something an attorney should really explain to you," advised Nettle, looking down at Donny with sorrowful eyes. "I cannot be your attorney; I can just tell you that this sort of motion can be reconsidered in the end of the hearing."

Donny stared momentarily, wondering if he heard it right, then mounted the best fight he could: "Judge, you already gave me all my... it's mine."

"You can change it, Judge," corrected Boom helpfully, "motion *in limine* can be reconsidered at any time during the trial."

"It's my . . ." started Donny again.

"It's no longer yours, Mr. Beaver, not necessarily . . ." interrupted Boom with impatient disregard of court decorum.

Donny made a noise that sounded like a death rattle, but that just caused the Judge to back up and repeat:

"In the light of recent . . .

"In the light . . .

"Having considered, I reconsidered. I now rule Husband's affidavits were late.

"All Husband's evidence is excluded. Everything you said."

"You *gave* it to me," Donny was getting belligerent.

"Gave it to you," echoed the Judge, "Now I am reconsidering it. I changed my mind."

RACCOON, Hoppy and I circled around the computer

listening to the recording, more and more horrified with the passing of every second, like scouts scared by the horror story at campfire.

Left to his own devices, Donny found only one thing to say to Judge Nettle:

"But you said that affidavits were OK. You said that Boom was late too!"

That was certainly true, but not Donny's strongest argument.

I jumped up and down, swearing out-loud: "The deadline was on *Friday*, dammit *Friday*, and you know it!" I wished that I would have ignored Donny's threats and gone to court with him anyway. But it was too late.

"I can revisit a ruling on a *motion in limine*," correctly observed the Judge on the recording.

"I already ruled. Affidavits were late. Attorney Boom, will you prepare that order, please?"

Boom had anticipated the easy victory and came prepared:

"Already done, Judge. I have the 'Order on Motion In Limine' here, ready for you. Right here. May I approach? Yes? Thank you. Right here, Judge. If you'll sign right here. We only need to add a notation of Mr. Beaver's presence; I did not think he'd be here."

In her most legible handwriting, Judge Nettle personally scribbled at the end of the Order's first page, then read out loud:

> *Husband participated at the hearing and objected solely on the grounds of prior ruling.*

342

Overruled because motion in limine was re-considered.

The "Order on Motion In Limine" prepared by Boom was short and muddled. "Husband's affidavits were late, and all Husband's evidence is stricken" was pretty much the gist of it.

Booom had protected against an appeal the best she could: it would be harder to appeal a muddy text. Which affidavits were supposedly late? The Order did not say. When were those supposedly late affidavits filed? What was the supposed deadline? The Order did not say that either. Appellate lawyers would be forced to find every affidavit in the file, list every deadline. Because of the word limit in appellate briefs, long lists would pose some daunting hurdles. Not insurmountable, though.

Judge Nettle lifted the pages of the draft order up to her eye level, inhaled and sighed happily, then hastily put the wavy line of her signature on all three copies of the "Order on Motion in Limine."

Tonya quickly stamped the first pages, and the Order in *Beaver v. Beaver* was fully cooked.

Boom had unraveled my whole Summer's topnotch legal work right back to the bobbin. The "Order on Motion in Limine" turned the clock back to the start of litigation, then threw out every persuasive submission that I'd placed into the file. With a clean slate, and Donny now effectively under a gag, the Judge would soon re-divide Donny's property. Judge Nettle had not done that last bit yet, but it did not take a legal genius to predict how it would go.

"We still can win on appeal though?" cried out the Raccoon militantly.

"Screw him," retorted cautious Hoppy. "Not our client."

"We could win though," did not let up Raccoon. "Maybe he'll ask for us?"

If you find yourself in a game of cards where the dealer favors your rivals, you can either do the clever thing and point the accusing finger at the trick in hopes to take down the House—or you can do the wise thing, pack up your chips and bolt as quickly as you can. Raccoon was partial to the clever thing when wise would do just fine.

Hoppy interrupted our musings: "You guys, come listen, he's asking for a lawyer!"

———————

"I think . . . I need a lawyer," stumbled into it Donny.

Boom was quick to disagree: "He fired his lawyer, Judge, this is just another attempt at delay."

But Nettle saw an opportunity.

"You're looking for a new lawyer?"

The Judge spoke warmly, leaning off her bench towards Donny—an intimate conversation of a kindly jurist concerned with the well-being of a litigant in her courtroom. "You need time to look for a new lawyer, Mr. Beaver?"

"Yes, I'm hiring a new lawyer," Donny sensed a trap, but still repeated the answer Judge Nettle fed him.

"You got until Friday," brightened the Judge.

The new "Order on Motion In Limine" paved the way for an entirely different division of the Beaver money. Now at last, it was easy enough for the Judge to take every red cent away from Donny and give it all to his poor, long-suffering wife. The Judge could just go ahead and do it: writing that up in a final Property Division Order would be quick and satisfying. But it would not be legally sturdy. Any decent appellate lawyer could dig up the record which confirmed that Donny had never missed those crucial deadlines, and the whole house of cards might fall on appeal.

The scheduling chicanery worked well in the heated fuss of courtrooms, but was way too on the nose to invite an Appellate Division in for a look.

Besides, Judge Nettle would be a fool to expose her well-working trick of "missed" deadlines. After Donny's case, Judge Nettle got more cautious. In years to follow, the audio recording of her scheduling hearing—the meetings where the deadlines were announced—all but disappeared. The recorder became beset with disasters more horrendous than the fate of Job: long stretches of the recording were indecipherable through sudden spells of coughing, screeching, clicking, rustling, pouring, echoing and even voices that overlapped from some other proceedings. There were blank spots about which the secretary swore that the machine rebelled and refused to record. Or the entire record got mysteriously erased. The mysterious gap in the Nixon tape was bush league play compared to the mishaps that plagued recordings of scheduling proceedings in Judge Nettle's court-room!

Noticing a pattern, for future proceedings before Nettle, I took to hiring live court reporters, but their presence was read as an insult to the integrity of the judicial process itself, and made everybody nervous.

But I anticipate.

In Donny's case, the Judge was already caught on the record. I had the disk, the positive proof of the deadlines.

Judge Nettle knew it.

Boom knew it.

But there was one person who wouldn't have a clue: Donny's new lawyer. The one he said he planned to hire. The brave soul who'd jump into this case just before the end.

The perfect patsy.

LETTERS TO PATSY

MY REPLACEMENT was called Ninette.

Ninette Newby.

A thoroughly Southern gal with almost thirty years of experience in hobnobbing with everybody who was anybody in Ducklingburg. She was most certainly well connected.

The day she filed her *Notice of Appearance* in Judge Nettle's court, announcing that she took on Donny's case, I shot Ninette an exalted email. I wanted her to know that she and Donny had a friend, that I was ready to help. There was quite a bit that she needed to figure out, and in a very big hurry. So I emailed:

Please call me ASAP!

With my pluck and Ninette's connections, Donny

could still be safe again. I just prayed that Ninette would respond to me.

My email to Ninette went out at half past six in the morning. The same day, at nine A.M. sharp, my Google-voice announced authoritatively "Attorney Ninette Newby."

She called! She called!

Praising the patrons of travelers, I pushed the code to accept her call, pressing the buttons so hard that my finger slipped off.

"Hello, Ninette," I started, "Here's what you need to know about the—"

"Shut the f— up, you dumbass bitch," retorted the seasoned Southern sweetie in a high-pitched voice with tremulous cadence. The high pitch was as unexpected as the content of her greeting.

I complied by shutting up, aghast.

". . . Mr. Beaver told me all about you," went on Ninette. "I know who you are. The Bar will deal with what you did."

"Wait!" I interrupted. "Listen to me! The Judge is setting Donny up, let me explain what happened . . ."

"Lying about the Judge," raged Ninette, "that's just who you are, you just proved it again!"

"Look, pay attention," I persisted, "you are about to get slammed. Those affidavits we filed . . ."

"Save that for somebody else, Portia. You missed the deadline. Whatever. We'll make you pay for that."

"Just let me . . . " I stayed on message.

"And don't you foul-mouth Judge Nettle! And better call your malpractice insurance!!"

"Ninette, you . . ."

"Don't call this phone again," she snapped and hung up.

"You called me," I yelped into the phone, but the line was already dead.

―――――――

NINETTE called back in a couple of days.

After a few preliminary unpleasantries, she got to the point about what she needed: "You need to fax over the 'Stop-Sale' Order. Now!"

"Love to, Ninette. Don't have it."

"The Bar will deal with that too," she promised.

"Why do you need it, anyway?"

"You'll hear from the Bar," she hissed and hung up.

The next call did come from the Bar Council.

"There was a complaint, and we do not normally interfere," said a strong, manly voice.

"I appreciate your concern," I lied. "What's the matter exactly?"

"It says here you are refusing to turn over a client's file. If you could deliver it over today? We do not have to start an investigation."

Some States allow lawyers to hold on to the file until the client pays, but the State of South Duck is decidedly not one of them. For a South Duck lawyer, holding the client's file hostage is a gross violation. Lawyers have been sanctioned for dilly-dallying with the file transfer. I felt that I might be in bigtime hot water.

"Here's the thing," I said truthfully, "Mr. Beaver already has copies of everything in his file."

"We don't want to start an investigation, Ms. Porter, but we'll have to if the client states he did not receive the file."

"He has the file already," I repeated.

"Copy the file, Ms. Porter. Deliver it to your client. Have it over today."

"Deliver it twice?"

"You might want to send us a copy too. Else we have to investigate."

The boxes with my copy of Donny's file—depositions, document production requests and exchanges, court filings, legal research, and pages and pages of charts—were still piled on every surface of the war room, spilling out of the boxes in no particularly good order.

I popped my head into the living room where my troops were busy debating something about some clouds and girls: "How many pages in Donny's file?"

"About seven boxes. 5,000 sheets per box. So roughly 35,000 sheets," was quick with his basic math Raccoon.

"It's only 34,873, actually," butted in Hoppy argumentatively.

"How do you know? Never mind that. What's the quickest you can make a copy?"

"24 pages per minute on the Canon, so on two machines.... 12 hours on two machines. But that's not counting the two-sided, and the bound, and the staples. So two days, just to be safe," predicted Raccoon, "What's wrong?"

"Why'd we need to copy the file?" protested Hoppy. That kid never wanted to make copies.

"Donny wants a copy," I explained listlessly.

"So?" still argued Hoppy. "34,870 paper copies will cost you a mint."

"If I'm lucky, 2100 pages per cartridge. At $74 per cartridge, that's $1228," added up Raccoon.

"You have not paid us this week," reminded Hoppy in case it slipped my mind.

"Guys, the Bar says deliver today or else."

"So?" Still did not get the graveness Hoppy. "Why can't we deliver it on a flash drive?"

"You guys scanned it in? All thirty-five thousand pages?"

"34,870," argued Hoppy.

"Hoppy likes the scanner," offered Raccoon.

"Scanner does not steam and fume," shrugged Hoppy.

WE gave Ninette the second copy of the file, just as she asked, but Donny's problem was not of a sort that could be solved with file copies.

Donny's wife, the Spiteful Witch had put the crown jewel on the block *again*. Ninette protested: it was "against the Judge's orders." Boom retorted: "What Order? Show me the Order!"

Predictably, Boom had a bout of selective forgetfulness

that plagues most veteran lawyers when a new lawyer enters a case. Anything that is not nailed down gets forgotten. And, not for want of trying, I had never been able to nail down the signed and sealed "Stop-Sale" Order.

———————

I sat down at my MacBook to write Ninette a note.

"Dear Ninette, we've been had. The Judge lost the blinking 'Stop-Sale' Order."

(deleted)

"Dear Ninette, I've seen Judge Nettle sign that Order."

(deleted)

"Dear Ninette, let's get the Appellate Court involved. I can file a mandamus by tomorrow."

(deleted)

"Dear Ninette, I think that Nettle's secretary Tonya lost that Order."

(deleted)

"Dear Ninette, Donny he should've never fired me and hired you!"

(deleted with a vengeance)

There was simply no good way to write that email.

"Dear Ninette," I finally wrote, *"Please call me. Maybe I can help."*

I slammed the laptop cover, and at that very moment, the lights went out with a click. Duck Power at long last must've caught up with my bill-paying delinquency. There was not much left but to slink off to my bedroom, bury my face in a pillow, and hope for a better morning tomorrow.

THE morning started at 3:30 A.M. with a clutter of appliances which, suddenly re-infused with electric power, all woke up at once. It had only been a neighborhood blackout. The long suffering Duck Power Company did not shut me down, after all.

An excellent start to the new day, a promising start.

And then the morning fell into a precipitous abyss for which I only had myself to blame.

Ninette called, obviously avoiding any paper trail.

"I'd like to trust you," she started without any provocation, "but I can't."

I resisted the urge to ask why not.

But she did not hang up, which was at least a little step forward in our budding friendship. Ninette knew that she needed help: Boom had kicked her butt.

353

Unfortunately, Ninette was apparently laboring under the misapprehension that my only motive was to worm my way into the case and destroy Donny's fortune in an act of revenge for his having stiffed me on my bill.

"Look," I said, striving for a popular example. "Suppose Michelangelo did not get paid for the Sistine Chapel. I see the artist lodging a dispute about the bill, don't you? But do you see him rebuilding the scaffold and climbing back to desecrate Adam's image by adding monstrous red horns and a grotesque twirly mustache?"

"You did what?" she said.

"Why would I destroy my own work, my masterpiece of lawyering?" I said, wishing I would not have gotten entrenched in the fine arts metaphor.

"Who is this fellow Adam?" she was suspicious now.

"Never mind."

"No, you better tell me now. You tell me about Adam or I am telling Donny."

"It's an old painting, I said."

"Donny's?"

I gave up: "I'll email you the link," I said.

And I did. I googled "Adam + Sistine Chapel" and sent her a screen shot. Which turned out to be a mistake.

THE Bar Council called again.

"Hello again," I said.

"There was a complaint, and we do not normally interfere," said the same strong, manly voice.

"I appreciate your continuing concern," I said. "What is it this time?"

"Let me ask you this. Is it true you sent pictures of naked men to an opposing counsel?"

"I apologize," I said. "It was just one naked man. Adam. And Ninette is not an opposing counsel, she is my replacement."

"Unfortunately, we will have to open an investigation."

"Knock yourself out," I said with baseless defiance.

Clearly, I am not cut out to be a lawyer.

OTHER UNDONE THINGS

AT THIS juncture, we briefly interrupt the Beaver v. Beaver saga to consider an understandable question about it. You may be reading Donny's story and thinking:

"That does not apply to me! Our local judges are nothing like Judge Nettle.

"I live in Cook County, and that's far, far away from Ducklingburg, South Duck.

"I doubt that one of our judges could even find Ducklingburg on the map!

"Our courtroom personnel never lose track of any of judicial Orders. Our courts file every Order just hours after the hearing. Any judge that I'd have would likely be both consci-entious and a legal genius.

"Why should I worry about the kinds of things that hap-pened to Donny?"

And all that may be true, but does that mean that you are safe during the delicate time while your Original Lawyer bows out and a New Lawyer takes over your case? Unfortu-nately, no, you are not safe.

There are many tricks your opposition might try during that time. Let's face it, some lawyers are opportunistic vul-tures, ready to swoop down and take advantage of any ap-parent weakness.

But how?

A few of the most common ploys are mentioned below.

The Vanishing Discovery Ploy

THIS PLOY is part of discovery games. "Discovery" is the industry term for the forced exchange of information during a lawsuit.

Here's the libretto of a hypothetical divorce case:

In this particular hypothetical, wife is the so-called "out-spouse" in the marriage, meaning that she was never in charge of the family finances, and does not have all the in-formation and documents. Husband is the "in-spouse," inti-mately connected with all the family finances. (The hypothetical's lesson would be the same if the roles of the spouses were reversed.)

Wife, who has filed for divorce, catches wind of Husband's secret off-shore nest eggs, and makes this request for documents:

> *Produce copies of all bank statements for all accounts held with EFG Bank (Luxembourg)—whether personal, corporate, numbered, custodial, [yada-yada-yada] for the past five years.*

Is Wife entitled to see these bank statements? Of course she is. Is she entitled to see these statements straight away? Of course not. The Rules of Civil Procedure give Husband a couple of months to get his ducks together.

After sixty days or so, Husband responds to Wife's request with this:

> *Husband is in the process of collecting EFG Bank statements. Will produce.*

That is a little victory for Wife. She has not gotten the actual documents yet, but she gotten the Husband to admit that he will share the documents. At least he is not fighting the request. He promises to give the documents.

So what's the danger to Wife if she changes lawyers now? Wife's New Lawyer takes a look at her file and nudges the Husband for those EFG Bank accounts.

In response, Husband unexpectedly sends this answer:

Previously produced.

What?!?

Throwing a conniption, New Lawyer calls Husband's lawyer, but Husband's lawyer is adamant: "Look to your file, we gave all that months ago. Its not there? Not my problem. The guy before you must've lost it."

(If you were expecting divorce lawyers to exemplify the very soul of honesty, think again! Divorce lawyers may fear to engage in *provable* dishonesty, but not all dishonesty is provable.)

All of a sudden, Wife is saddled with the forbidding task of proving a negative: no, she does not have the EFG Bank statements, no they were never produced. It is hard to imagine that a ploy like this actually would work, but you have to remember that litigation almost always involves a tangled heap of papers floating back and forth. During the time between Husband's first answer (will produce) and last answer (previously produced), *some* papers were, indeed, produced in response to other parts of Wife's discovery request. When Wife's lawyer drags in Husband to see the Judge about it, the confusing exchange may go something like this:

Husband's Lawyer: Those bank statements were produced in June, Your Honor! Here's the post office receipt.

Wife's Lawyer: Those were only the Wachovia statements!

Husband's Lawyer: We also sent over statements in July.

Wife's Lawyer: I will have to look in the file about what was produced in July, but it was not the EFG Bank statement.

Judge: Why don't you go back and look in the file, Mr. Wife's Lawyer.

Husband's Lawyer: We already produced thousands of pages, Your Honor. This is harassment! This is abuse! This is a violation! We demand an order to close this discovery already.

Judge: So ordered. Enough's enough. No more discovery. Mr. Wife's Lawyer, go look carefully in your files. And you might want to contact the Wife's Original Lawyer.

The Original Lawyer is not completely immune to being the target of this sort of trick either, but it is really much easier to thus bamboozle a new lawyer who just inherited the file and whose command of the document inventory is easy to challenge.

The Reverse Vanishing Discovery Ploy

SUPPOSE AGAIN that, at some point during the litigation, Wife changes lawyers.

But this time, Wife went to great pains to prepare for the change.

All documents in discovery are exchanged. Wife's previous lawyer delivered all the documents, answered all the questions, tied all loose ends.

There's simply nothing left to get undone.

Nevertheless, as soon as Wife's new lawyer enters the

case, Husband's lawyer springs to action. Inconceivably, months after discovery was finished, Husband's lawyer insists that Wife is delinquent in her discovery obligations, demands documents that had long since been delivered, threatens to ask the court for sanctions, and hauls Wife and her new lawyer before the Judge.

Will Husband's lawyer end up winning in this racket? Maybe, maybe not. One thing for sure, Wife's New Lawyer is now saddled with the difficult task of going back through the file, re-checking the inventory of delivered documents, finding the mail receipts to prove delivery, and so on and so forth. All of this under time pressure and with insufficient time to study the file properly.

Indeed, Husband's lawyer will potentially increase the pressure of the attack by playing several of these or similar ploys at the same time. No doubt you by now get the general idea: the newbie attorney is vulnerable to being hoodwinked. So, switching lawyers—for whatever reason—creates dangerous opportunities for the opposing side to exploit.

MY first time on the receiving end of the reverse vanishing discovery ploy was brutal.

My client was a Wife.

Three days after I took the case, Husband's lawyer demanded "all bank statements, household bills, credit card

361

statements, etcetera, etcetera, for five years prior whether titled in my client's name or in the name of her companies, or
in somebody else's name for her benefit, or yada-yada-yada
. . .." According to Husband's lawyer, these papers were
never delivered and were now four months late, in violation
of the Discovery rules. According to my client, everything
was delivered on time, months ago.

The Judge chose to resolve the dispute by informal conference and summoned us into her chambers the same day.
(That was before the time I made a rule to never ever agree
to anything *informal* where judges are involved.)

Among the many, many boxes I inherited from my predecessor, two were marked "copy of all the June 5 discovery
we delivered to Attorney A-Hole." By the looks of it, there
were about 7,000 pages "delivered to Attorney A-Hole," and
I only had about an hour before the meeting with the Judge.
Time being short, I poured all 7,000 or so pages into a rolling
suitcase, parked illegally on the street by the courthouse and
rushed upstairs. I wheeled all of this into a stuffy room behind the courtroom where the pow-wow was scheduled to
be held just five minutes before curtain.

"Copies of every document delivered," I declared triumphantly, squeezing my loaded suitcase through the doors.

"We never seen any of these papers," objected the opportunistic opponent.

"How do you know these were delivered, Ms. Porter,"
inquired the Judge.

"I read it on a Post-it," I said honestly. "Copy of discovery delivered on June 5."

"Tell you what, Ms. Porter," accommodated the Judge, "She says she's never seen it. You say you read it on a Post-It. Mr. Original Lawyer is gone, so we can't ask him. Tell you what. Just deliver it all again."

"Ms. Porter will have all these papers organized, tagged, labeled and responsive, right?" chimed in the opportunist.

"That too," agreed the Judge.

Wait a minute, what just happened?! The Judge just turned the clock back and ordered me to re-do all the work that my predecessor had already finished doing. Expensive!

The Vanishing Gentlemen's Agreement

DISCOVERY GAMES are not the only games you should fear.

If you already had an agreement with the other side, you are in danger of the disappearing agreements problem.

Not long ago, I represented Mr. Jack Fox of the locally famous Fox & Hen Construction.

Jack was divorcing Jill, his wife of forty years. It was a traditional marriage, and they were getting a traditional divorce.

Jack would pay alimony; he was fine with that. He wanted the Judge to tell him how much, and he wanted to pay what the Judge told him to pay, and feel a man about it.

Also, Jack wanted to buy Jill out of her share of the business assets and wanted the Judge to tell him what was a fair price. It was a quiet, dignified, solemn deal of a divorce. Jack and Jill knew exactly what a divorce should be about, and Jill's lawyer and I went along obediently.

But there was one tricky part which neither Jack nor his estranged wife Jill wanted to expose to the blinding light of justice. Jack and Jill had a side agreement made on a handshake, a Gentlemen's Agreement so to speak.

It was simple:

Jill would pay Jack $648,922.

That's right. After the proceedings in court were finalized, Jill would pay money back to Jack. The reason Jill went along with this plan was that she'd *stolen* the $648,922. And I had caught her.

Everything was moving in a copacetic progression towards a fair resolution when I spoiled everything. I reminded Jack, rather emphatically, that my bills were upwards of $50,000 in the red and over three months overdue and told Jack to pay up or find himself a new lawyer. Jack figured a new lawyer had to be cheaper than fifty thousand dollars, and moved on.

At few days later, Jill and her lawyer developed a memory problem.

"Why should Jill fork over $648,922 for nothing?" they protested. "Jill is not paying. Take it to trial if you want."

Jack's New Lawyer turned to Jack, but could not get much out of his client other than "Jill stole it!" and "No, no trial!"

The counselor figured Jack wasn't telling something; but what?

———————

WHAT Jack did not want anyone to know was that Jill had been stealing from Jack almost since the first day they were married. At first, Jill stole tiny sums. She siphoned from the credit cards and the joint bank accounts. Little transfers, which added up to a few thousand dollars over the first few years of their marriage. When we figured it out in divorce discovery and told Jack, he said not to worry about it. He was just going to let it go. It was not worth the embarrassment.

But then we dug deeper into the bank accounts and learned an uncomfortable truth: Jill had eventually discovered the magnitude and accessibility of Jack's corporate income stream and she grew bolder. Almost three quarter million dollars bolder.

The Raccoon was the one in charge of tracing Jill's thieving.

"Boss, she siphoned some real money."

"How?" I mumbled absentmindedly.

The Raccoon jabbed his finger down, as if he was suggesting we dig for oil, then pointed to the schematics he had constructed and hung on the wall of our war room.

Our Eastern wall was home to charts of corporations, the rectangles connected by sticks to represent the structures of entities which Jack had created, merged, abandoned, dismantled, revived and managed during the marriage. There were quite a few drawings, most of them representing unremarkable corporate structures.

One rectangle stood out, though. It was a subsidiary created by one of Jack's boring real estate holdings.

Jack and his buddies owned three identically structured companies. Each company was home to one tiny apartment complex, one almost empty bank account and a sensible truck. The setup was unremarkable and, for people familiar with tax law, perfectly predictable. Jack was a treasurer in all three of the companies. Jack's buddies took turns being the president.

Because the apartment complexes were in the area called Gooseneck, the companies were unoriginally named Gooseneck 1, Gooseneck 2 and Gooseneck 3.

So far so good.

"But look here!" insisted Raccoon. I looked at the chart. Gooseneck 3 had set up a subsidiary irreverently called EGG Inc. That arrangement was notably asymmetrical. Goosenecks 1 and 2 did not have any EGGS.

But what really made us think was the unusual governance structure. The South Duck Secretary of State website listed Jack as the president and Jill as the treasurer of the EGG. Jack was astonished when we told him: he'd never before heard of such a thing as EGG Inc.

Quick review of the books confirmed that Gooseneck 3

was being robbed blind. Jill moved rental income from the Gooseneck 3, into the EGG, Inc., then quietly to her own private account.

The worst part for unsuspecting Jack was that he was listed as the president of this pirating scheme, and his (forged) signatures of approval were all over the place. If Jack's business partners caught wind of this, they'd either think him a moron or a crook in cahoots with his wife. Either way, others in the South Duck business community would view Jack with suspicion for quite some time.

For obvious reasons, Jack and Jill elected to forgo putting any resolution of this embarrassing swindle in writing. Instead, they shook hands on it. And the handshake deal would have worked, except that Jill was a shameless, incorrigible thief. When Jack switched lawyers, she sensed an opportunity and could not help herself.

"I am not paying," announced Jill. "Let Jack pay it!"

———

THERE are problems in almost every marriage that simply cannot be made public. I am not talking about the innocently amusing problems like erectile dysfunction or a brush with treatable VDs. I am talking about family secrets, the sort of things one wants to settle with the spouse as quietly as possible.

Take legal infractions, for example.

When your divorce lawyer catches your spouse red-handed, committing an actual crime, it is easy to think that you now have leverage in your divorce.

Not so.

Getting proof of your spouse's crimes is only half the battle. Actually using that proof to your advantage in divorce is a forbidding task.

Do you think you can say something like this to your husband or wife: "I will not tell the district attorney that you sell crack *if* you agree to better custody terms"? Think again! That sort of negotiation is prohibited by at least five different laws and regulations.

And it gets worse.

Once you and your crime-committing spouse actually get divorced, you may yet become unwillingly involved in a criminal case. You may find out about charges such as "obstruction of justice," "accessory," and "co-conspirator"! It is a very tricky business.

And if you are in possession of evidence of a crime, it

gets even trickier. Next thing you know, you are surfing the internet looking for your own criminal defense lawyer.

So, spouses sometimes end up resorting to handshake agreements and hoping that the informal accord is not disavowed at a vulnerable future time. It's a tricky business and just about any change in the scenery is a threat to upsetting the balance.

THE Gentlemen's Agreements in divorce litigation are, of course, not always as dramatic as Jack & Jill's. Sometimes there's no crime or legal infraction involved. Sometimes these oral agreements are simply a matter of convenience.

Handshakes are made on all manner of completely trivial stuff.

We shake that the household items are all divided and we won't have a trial on the dishes and the shower curtains. It might be prudent to put that agreement in writing, but many times lawyers don't because it doesn't seem worth the time and expense. Then one of the spouses switches lawyers and all of the sudden the opposition goes bonkers and demands a hearing on who keeps the "good china." That ends up costing lots of time and money, but the especial loss to the new lawyer is that the "china trial" eats up precious time, distracting the still-getting-up-to-speed attorney's attention from some other, more vital aspect of the client's case.

Handshake agreements are often made for small temporary obligations, to avoid a costly hearing.

For example, Husband agrees to pay temporary alimony on a handshake, without any writing. There's a *quid pro quo* though: maybe Husband takes his lawnmower, or the better car, or the newer helicopter.

When Wife switches lawyers—and all of a sudden the promise to pay alimony slips Husband's mind. And, of course, the quid pro quo already in Husband's possession is where it is; try and get it back!

Or there could be something as trivial as a side agreement for time extensions between the two lawyers. Both the Husband's and the Wife's lawyer missed a deadline by a hair, and neither wants to tell his respective client, so they agree to never mention being late.

The Rules of Procedure mostly allow it and, ordinarily, the secret would die with the lawyers.

But if a new lawyer takes over, the previously agreeable opponent all of a sudden forgets all about the handshake extension and starts filing motions for sanctions for the supposedly "late" submission. The lateness of his own side's submission, of course, will never be discovered. Or so he bets.

The point here is this: divorce litigation involves quite a few deals that are held together by handshake alone. Once there's a change of guard, an unscrupulous opponent who is willing to play dirty can find plenty of ways to take advantage.

But even if your case does not have any side agreements,

discovery games, unfinished orders or scoundrel opposing lawyers, you are not out of the woods yet.

If you ever consider changing lawyers, will you be smart enough to first consider the cost of the necessary *file review*.

THE COST OF EDUCATION

"FILE REVIEW" is an industry term. What does it mean? At a minimum, it means that your new lawyer will simply read through your file. Very carefully, you should hope. That makes sense, doesn't it? Your new lawyer must know what's in your file, right?

Otherwise, what would he tell the Judge come next hearing: "Your Honor, let's stop the hearing and look for answers in the file together because your guess about this is as good as mine"?

To be sure, "file review" is much more than plain reading the file. But let's talk about the plain reading first. At first glance, reading may not sound like a particularly expensive proposition. After all, clients always say, all the work is already done. What could possibly be the cost of flipping through the pages?

Let's take a look. According to a recent speed-reading test sponsored by Staples (and embraced by at least one Forbes opinion), an average adult reads fiction at the speed of 300 words per minute. There are speed-readers, of course, and they completed the Staples test faster. But then again, the comprehension part of the Staples test only requires answering two out of three questions correctly to pass it. You want your lawyer to comprehend what's in your file three times out of three, don't you? So let's say we stick with the (possibly too optimistic) rate of 300 words per minute for now. Agreed?

Now take a look at the stack of papers making up your file, an imposing stack that you will carry to your new lawyer and expect him to read and to know cold. Of course, the number of words on a page varies widely depending on how the text is spaced.

Appellate filings are vigorously well-spaced, which means fewer words. Expect about 220 words per page here. But also, appellate file paper requires a particularly intense read. And, hopefully, you are not at the appeal stage yet.

Trial court filings are a little tighter. Expect about 300 words per page—which incidentally is what an average American supposedly reads in a minute.

Transcripts of hearings and depositions are usually about 250 words to a page, but look out for what's called "condensed transcripts." It's the way they are printed—tiny text, four pages printed on one sheet. That's how most lawyers order and read transcripts, at about 1,000 words to a page.

Bank statements have hardly *any* words, but sometimes I find myself staring at the same page for a long time, don't you?

And then there are *financial documents*: loan agreements, corporate charters, leases, sale documents. Those are all in small print at a gazillion words to a page and take long, excruciating passages of time to read.

Letters between lawyers average 150 words to a page, but most of them are just petty name-calling and can be skimmed rapidly.

Emails between you and your spouse are the biggest time-sucking vortex. The word count here averages 500 words per page. *Texts* between you and your spouses are sparser on the word count, but often take a long time to read because of the idiosyncratic abbreviations and allusions. Plus, it is sometimes hard to tell who is who. (And, just in case you didn't already know it: yes, your smartphone texts and your emails are commonly part of discovery in divorce cases.)

To sum up, assuming your lawyer reads at a pace of 300 words per minute, one hour of the lawyer's time will cover:

Appellate filings	82 pages
Trial court filings	60 pages

Transcripts (full)	72 pages
Transcripts (con-densed)	18 pages
Letters	120 pages
E-mails	36 pages

So what does that mean for you? That gives you a quick-and-dirty way to figure your absolute minimum cost to switch lawyers.

Let's consider an especially low-cost situation. Suppose your file stacks 150 pages, and consists entirely of the trial court filings. No depositions, emails, or other time-sucking papers.

If that's the case, it will take your new lawyer two and a half hours to read the stack. At an average industry rate of $300 an hour, that's $750 you will spend before your new lawyer knows your file from Adam.

And don't forget: condensed transcripts, emails, financial documents are even more expensive to read.

But that is not all. We were only figuring the cost for an uncritical read. But your new lawyer cannot just *read* the file and leave it at that. If the lawyer is putting his name as your representative, that requires careful, critical reading. Is the research in the file correct? Did the law change since the research was done? Is the affidavit of the star witness accurate and unassailable? Are all the witnesses still available? Will they cooperate with the new lawyer? None of these things can be taken on faith. And all of it takes lawyer's time and, consequently, your money.

And even that is not all. If you had hearings in court, your New Lawyer either has to obtain the audio record and listen to it or pay a court reporter to transcribe it and only then read the resulting transcript. That, of course, would add to your expenses dramatically.

Having added up all these numbers, do you understand why ditching the Original Lawyer and moving to a New Lawyer will usually not save on the bill?

If you weighed all the pros and cons and you ever *do* decide to switch lawyers, consider calling your Original Lawyer and asking for help in bringing the New Lawyer up to speed.

Clients usually resist this because they figure that the Original Lawyer will refuse to help. Nevertheless, it is actually worth a try. Even if you stiffed your Original Lawyer, he still has a reputation on the line. He put sweat and soul into your case, and is likely to go out of his way to protect the integrity of the work. Besides, it does not hurt to ask. Even if he says no, what do you have to lose?

THE PRICE OF IGNORANCE

IT IS EASY to explain the need for full file review: you want your lawyer to know all the facts and to use them to your full advantage. The last thing your lawyer wants is to lose on a point that, unbeknownst to him, already *has* a winning answer in the file. You want the lawyer to know every page of your file, so he has a comeback for any attack.

Still, I know you are wondering: do people really pay thousands of dollars just to have their file read—with no visible yield? And if you have a skeptical bend, you may even be wondering: how do you know that the New Lawyer will read your file instead of just *charging* for full read but doing a light skim instead? It is not like you'll be giving your New Lawyer a comprehension quiz.

The first time I quoted the cost of the *file review* to a client, I got a reaction similar to speed-emoting through every successive stage of grief.

The client started by informing me impolitely and firmly that I was mistaken: reading every page of her file was not necessary, in her view. The information was there for reference, she explained. And furthermore, her previous lawyer never charged her just to read the file. I countered with: "That's because he charged you to write it." But that got me nowhere.

Then she got angry and insisted I was only out for her money, just like all of my creed. Still angry, she fired me, even though I had not been hired yet.

Next she returned and bargained wanting to know: *Could I read quicker?* (I could not read quicker, not if I hoped to understand what I was readings.) *Could I charge less* (I could charge less, but I would not.) *Could I only read the most important parts?* (I could, if only I could establish without first reading the file which parts were important. If I blindly threw out some parts of the file without reading, I'd probably end up ignoring a critical part of her original lawyer's work.)

Finally, she fled my office, her shoulders slumped and face graven with dismal depression.

This string of denial-anger-despair is a fairly typical reaction. Indeed, if the previous chapter tempted you to angrily hurl this book across the room, do not feel bad. You are not alone. The cost of educating a New Lawyer about every aspect of your Original Lawyer's work is, more often than not, borderline prohibitive. Nevertheless, it is the truth universally acknowledged that the unbearable cost of education is only rivaled by the unpredictable price of ignorance.

So what happens if, instead of spending hours and thousands of dollars on studying your file, your New Lawyer agrees to skim the "important parts" and forges on, just hoping for the best? Sometimes, you get lucky. Most of the time, you get figuratively nailed to the wall in the ensuing litigation. It is impossible to predict the price of ignorance.

For sure, we never could have predicted the abysmal end in Donny's case. And, that said, we return to his tale.

————————

THE first thing to go to the dogs was Donny's darling Warehouse.

When Donny spotted the Mercedes SUV in cardinal red metallic parked conspicuously by the warehouse entrance, he did a double take: Mercedes-Benz cars were his business rival's brand. Donny slammed his unpretentious Land Cruiser into reverse so hard that it got accidently knocked into four-wheel. Stealthily, he backed up into position to make out the intruder's plates. Sure enough: "FATCAT5". The rival-mobile! What was *he* doing on Donny's land?! Trembling with anger, Donny pulled out his cell, rubbed the glass and snapped three pictures of the intruder's tail. Then he invoked Ninette.

"Get that prick off my land!" boomed Donny into the phone. "Pull up the 'Stop-Sale' Order!

He has no business on my property, it's contempt. Immediately!"

"I'll get the Judge right quick," squeaked back Ninette, "I got Her Honor on speed dial."

Ninette did not exaggerate about having Nettle on speed dial: Ninette *was* tuned in.

Three hours later, Judge Nettle's chambers was enlivened by a brawl.

Left waiting on a bench outside the courtroom door, Donny sat bolt upright, getting paler with fury by the minute.

Donny had, he fumed, the Warehouse sale stopped the very first thing, months ago. It should be no trouble shooing off the bold intruder, Donny assured himself, as he watched his protector Ninette sail past him into chambers, her confident smile lingering in the tense air. But something was not right, Donny's businessman's gut told him. His gut was never wrong. Ten minutes later, Ninette flew out of chambers, hissing into her phone. She waved at him, a forced, fake wooden-doll wave. He overheard the words "file" and "grievance" and "no Order." Minutes later, Ninette swooshed back into the chambers, and Donny thought he noticed her left eye-shadow smudged.

"But there is the 'Stop-Sale' Order," he tried to calm himself. What fool would go against an Order?!"

BEHIND the chambers doors, Ninette was getting crushed by the "fools" who went against the supposed Order.

"Show me the Order!" Boom challenged her.

"You are saying there is a Stop-Sale Order?

Show.

Us.

The.

Order!!!"

Ninette took a step back and shook her head in rapid jerks, like a bear shaking off an attack by hunting dogs. The chambers confrontation was her idea, but it was not going at all as planned, not according to her script at all.

Ordinarily, calling an opponent into the Judge's chambers—as Ninette had aggressively done—is the prelim to what's expected to be a knockout punch. Imagine getting a summons to the Judge out of the blue! There's the element of surprise, aided by suspicion that the Judge is already on the side of the caller. And there's the emergency that makes anybody stupid. Ninette was sure she'd knock the opposition silly before the brawl even started. But Boom emerged unscathed. Instead, Boom had her own surprise: The Warehouse was sold three days ago!

"What?!" gasped Ninette, seeing black clouds in place of smiley-faces. "Sold? How? To who?!"

Boom was just getting warmed up. Boom was authorized, she informed the Judge, to act on behalf of the new legal owner. Who preferred to stay anonymous.

"Who?!" exhaled Ninette. "We have a 'Stop-Sale' Order in place!"

But Boom knew better: "She is lying, Your Honor. If you gave that Order, Your Honor, why doesn't Attorney Newby show it to us?"

If this were a *physical* fistfight, Ninette would at this point have had her back against the ropes, sliding down on her ass.

"I," she gasped, wishing that some kind soul would come and squirt cold water in her mouth, "I—I need to locate the Order. Recess, please?"

Judge Nettle nodded "yes" for the recess, and Ninette ran out in a panicky frenzy.

That's when Donny saw Ninette run past him, hissing threats into her phone. Back at her office, Ninette's beleaguered secretary led a desperate search in the file, a search which led to the only possible conclusion: the existence of the "Stop-Sale" Order was no more than an unprovable part of the courthouse's oral folklore.

Ninette ran back into the chambers, ready to throw in the towel, to negotiate the least humiliating surrender terms possible.

———

To be sure, the "Stop-Sale *Order*" was technically a misnomer. A more accurate legal description for what had early happened with the Warehouse sale matter was a "Stop-Sale *Rendition*." *Rendition* is what you get when a Judge says some words, but puts nothing on paper, like an oral declaration.

As you by now understand, an "Order" must be tangible—a piece of paper with the Judge's signature, which the clerk can stamp. An "Order" is a document to brandish in defense of one's rights, something to slap on the desk of a wayward realtor and, thereby, halt any sale.

Despite my best efforts, despite my clear win, and despite everybody's repeated assurances, there was never any signed and sealed document to brandish.

No matter how hard I pushed, Judge Nettle never did produce a usable Order.

Sure, there was an email from the Judge assuring (falsely) that the "Stop-Sale" Order was "in the mail."

There was also an email from the Judge's secretary assuring (also falsely) that the Order had been "presented to the counsel."

But, when it came right down to it, there was no signed Order to be found. And one cannot take an email to the bank, even if it comes from the Judge herself.

Back when I was Donny's lawyer, I could have pressed on. I could have squeezed the Judge. I could have complained to the South Duck Court of Appeals—leveled a *mandamus petition*, notified the judges higher than Judge Nettle that the Order was promised but not entered. Complained that Nettle and her minion Tanya were refusing to do their jobs properly. That would have created a commotion and probably would have forced Nettle's hand. That would have scared the proper "Stop-Sale" Order out of whatever mysterious cubbyhole into which it had disappeared.

But, back then, I had chosen not to do all that.

I reasoned that leveling a mandamus petition would infuriate Nettle. She'd detest Donny even more. And what was there to gain? It's not like Boom was chomping at the bit to start the sale.

Judge Nettle was skilled in ruling her roost by oral wishes, and Boom had heard the Judge's wishes loud and clear. She got the same emails from the Judge that I did: "the Order's in the mail." What was Boom to do: dispute the Judge's veracity?!

And so I did nothing. I sailed on, secure in the knowledge that, deep at the bottom of his correspondence file, we had an email from the Judge herself that (falsely) proved the Stop-Sale Order existed. I knew the email was a lie, that the Emperor was naked. But in a pinch I'd be able to dig it up and brandish it.

An attorney defending Donny's interests would have to know both that the all-important email existed and where to look for it.

Regrettably, my replacement Ninette never dug into the correspondence file. Donny would have never authorized the funds for her to properly read the file. Nor, in any event, was there enough time to dig that deep. Instead, Donny should have requested my help and Ninette should have accepted it.

BACK in chambers, Ninette found Boom alone, leaning on the glass above the abyss of the street.

"Her Honor had to go," murmured Boom softly.

The brawl that Ninette had triggered was finished abruptly, like a disconnected phone call. Ninette was relieved.

The two lawyers stood alone, side by side, watching traffic under their feet, talking in normal voices.

"Judge would want us to settle, you know," proposed Boom.

"They always do," muttered Ninette. "Judges all love settlements."

"Judicial economy," nodded Boom.

"My Man would not go for it," shook her head Ninette.

"Work on his expectations," smiled Boom, then added softly: "He should forget that Warehouse. What's sold is sold. Settle it."

"What are you offering?"

"My Woman keeps seventy percent of assets. No alimony. How about it?"

"That what the Judge wants?" pondered Ninette.

"Judge wants this over," returned Boom.

"I'll take it to my Man."

The two shook hands and exited walking in step. Boom beaming quietly, Ninette considerably deflated but resolute to, literally, make the best of a bad deal.

***

IN times of defeat, South Duck lawyers looked for comfort to the words of the Code. Ninette marched up to the impatient Donny, and declared with reproach: "Donny, the 'Stop-Sale' Order was never entered, you were lied to." Before her client could protest, she added haughtily: "It would be *unethical* for me to say that the Order exists."

"Call Portia!" groaned Donny.

"Already did," assured Ninette somewhat inaccurately.

"We appeal!" threatened Donny.

That did not sit well with Ninette, who was strictly a trial lawyer. She had never filed an appeal, and was not liking the direction her client was taking.

"Perhaps we should think of settlement," Ninette urged softly. "To put all behind. Move on. Start over. For your family."

JUDGES like to appear impervious to criticism, even seemingly inviting it. In public, judges like to joke that "the judge's work is done when both parties hate the Order."

"If both sides are pissed, fairness must have prevailed," judges urge with an owlish smile. An empowering and noble sentiment, for sure. But, when divorce judges speak frankly, they admit that the judge's work is actually not done until those infuriated litigants are effectively cut off from pressing an appeal. When every avenue to an appeal is blocked, that's when the judge's work *is* done. In any event, that's when the judge's job is *safe*.

Of all the weapons available to the servants of justice, nothing is as sure at killing an appeal as forcing parties to settle. Whatever the circumstances, settlements can never be successfully appealed. They are not orders. What would you be appealing: your own gullibility? What would you say: I was possessed when I signed my agreement?

That's why the first and the last thing you'll hear from every judge in every trial is "have you considered a settlement?"

"**WHY** do I need to settle if I won already," disagreed Donny. "Judge Nettle gave me all my property."

"That was before," objected Ninette.

"Make Nettle go back to that," demanded Donny. "Or else let's go to trial."

"The Judge asked us to settle," implored Ninette. "Honestly, Donny, I cannot recommend going to trial."

"No!" protested Donny. "If trial is bad, we appeal!"

IN a one-stall bathroom at the end of the judges' hall, Judge Nettle consulted her distorted reflection in the paint-speckled mirror:

"If there's an appeal??"

Nettle's last ruling hinged on the ostensibly missed deadlines for the affidavits. She crossed her arms and hugged her shoulders, rocking back and forth.

Any fool could listen to the scheduling conference and prove it to the judges upstairs that Donny's affidavits were on time. Jumping Jehoshaphat! You did not even need to be an appellate lawyer to argue that point, Nettle thought.

Nettle shut her eyes and swallowed. An appeal would be bad. Last year, the Judges of the Court of Appeals took three whole paragraphs just to scold her ... . She took a shallow breath and slowly let the air out. The air smelled like dust and chlorine.

That bathroom was unpopular because its only stall was out of order more often than it worked. That was fine by the Judge: it saved the effort of checking for unwanted company. She murmured to herself:

"What do I do if he appeals?"

The mirror was in no hurry to reassure, and so the Judge Nettle answered her own question:

"No appeals for the Beavers," pronounced Judge Nettle out-loud, her voice cracking. She was not persuading herself, not really. But her shrink had told her she had to at least "give it a try."

"Give it a try," she assured herself. Straightening her back, she jerked her head up, the dark glasses moved further up into the hair, and Her Honorable Nettle marched out of the bathroom. The door behind her slammed and fluttered the white sign with vivid red letters signing "Out of Order."

"GATHER back the Beaver parties," Her Honor barked unnecessary orders at her secretary: everybody was still waiting outside. "Ya'll here already? Be seated."

The lawyers jumped, the soon-to-be ex-Husband and ex-Wife started climbing clumsily to their feet, all a bit like dazed drunkards.

"Sit, sit," commanded the Judge, from her throne.

The room complied and four pairs of eyes had her in their attentive gaze.

"Mr. Beaver," the Judge started gravely, "the Court allowed you an opportunity and time to look for a new counsel. You have a very competent counsel now, that is an excellent choice."

Donny sat up straighter, unsure of the protocol. The Judge talking to him directly, over his lawyer's head. That felt odd.

"Has your lawyer talked to you about the possibility of settlement?" went on the Judge.

"*Can she talk to me like that?*" wondered Donny.

He threw a look askance at Ninette, but Ninette was staring at the Judge with the fawning admiration of the old dog welcoming home her long absent master.

Ninette was nodding in affirmation.

"Yes," exhaled Donny. "We talked about settlement."

"Would you like more time to discuss that option?" warmed up the Judge.

"No, Your Honor, I believe you ruled already. Your Honor. I already won."

Boom sprung on her feet: "That ruling has been superseded by my motion *in limine*," she started an incantation, but Nettle did not seem to hear her:

"In that case," pronounced the Judge in a solemn crescendo, "I am ready to rule now."

The tearing of writing papers echoed over the lawyers' tables: each word of the Judge's ruling is precious.

Her face sour, Judge Nettle commenced.

Donny heard her list the date of his marriage, his addresses, his ex-wife's address, the names of his companies and those inane last century phrases ending with "whereas" and "therefore" that have no meaning to anybody, not even the lawyers who say them.

Nettle's voice was loud and choppy, and even though she looked straight at Donny, she sounded as though reading off a paper she herself could not comprehend.

"... and whereas the motion *in limine* had been granted and all Husband's pleadings stricken off the record, the Court concludes that ninety-five percent of marital assets is to be distributed to Wife and Wife's alimony entitlement is to be set for hearings at ..."

"What?" leapt Donny on his feet, interrupting. "Judge, no alimony!! We have a pre-nup-tial agreement! She didn't even ask for alimony!"

"Prenup is stricken with his other pleadings," howled Boom victoriously.

Donny's Ninette interjected with "Your Honor, may

I—" and the courtroom abruptly turned into an unseemly verbal brawl.

"The affidavits were on time, ask Portia," implored Donny, but Ninette hissed in his ear. He did not make it out exactly, but heard "not in the file," and "unethical."

At that moment, Donny experienced a feeling often described by near-death victims, an out-of body view of the scene. Donny could not feel his face, but he saw his own silhouette, shocked into stony stillness by the unimaginable twist of justice Nettle-style.

He saw Boom throw her hands up in the air, in victory.

He saw his own lawyer leaning towards him, as though she rushed unnecessarily to break Donny's fall—but Donny was not falling, he was stuck, as if dead, to his chair.

Donny's eyes turned to the Judge, waiting for the gavel to break the cacophony, but there was no gavel. The Judge's eyes were closed and Donny could have sworn he saw a tiny momentary smile slyly run off the Honorable face.

Still letting the lawyers scream, Judge Nettle turned her entire body towards Boom and Donny's wife, and, in response, Boom scaled down her tirade from yelp to a mutter, and shrugged her shoulders. The Judge's own shoulders moved up as Boom's went down, as though the Judge and the Wife's lawyer were two parts of the same mechanical toy. There was a sense of perfect harmony between the two, like two actors in the same old pantomime on a long-running show.

At that moment, Donny's lawyer finally reached him, and, touching his hand, whispered urgently: "I can ask for recess if you wanted to settle."

Donny did not feel his body nod, but he must have. Ninette was on her feet, covering the courtroom in her shrill voice: "We'd like a recess, Judge."

Judge Nettle smiled and got up on her feet. Heavily, happily, she lumbered down from her throne and disappeared behind the chambers door.

The Beaver case was settled two hours later.

AS are all settlements, it was a compromise, on terms not as bad for Donny as Nettle's latest ruling, but nowhere near as good as Nettle's original ruling.

In exchange, Donny's Wife avoided the possibility of an appeal that might restore Judge Nettle's original ruling.

And Judge Nettle? Because the parties settled by mutual consent, her screw-ups in hearing and deciding the case were protected from review by the Appellate Court. Win-win!

Before the sun set that day, word of the Beaver case's settlement had, much to the amusement of most, percolated through the Ducklingburg legal community. At 6:30, Judge Nettle was back in her condo, warming up one of her usual frozen dinners in the microwave oven. Pouring herself a hefty slug of Jim Beam Single Barrel "sipping whiskey" bourbon, Nettle mused to herself smugly about the delightful turn of events earlier that day.

"If I do say so, m'self, the way I got the Beaver case

wrapped up was a purty play! That carpetbagger lawyer from Noo Yawk, whatsersname? Yeah, mebbe Marcia Potter, or somethin' like. Whatever. That haughty, stuck-up lil' piece of work that acts like her poop don't smell. Anyways, I sure did fix her wagon, pitched out all she won like garbage.

"And fixed her slimy client's wagon too. Got what he deserved, cheatin' on two women. Wronged his precious lil' wife by fornicating like an alley cat and then stiffed Miss Smartypants lawyer on the bill for a shit-load of fancy-schmancy lawyering hours. Well, 'what goes around, comes around.' Except for me. Settlement covers up that judging mess I made, worked it so's the appeals court will never get wind of a bit of it."

Selected Bibliography & Sources

Books and Periodicals

Dewey, Frank L. *Thomas Jefferson, Lawyer*. University of Virginia Press, 1986.

Gillers, Stephan. "Lowering the Bar: How Lawyer Discipline in New York Fails to Protect the Public." 17 New York University Journal of Legislation and Public Policy, no. 2 (September, 2014).

Goldman, Michael. "Discipline of McLendon and Discipline of Peterson: Adding Chaos to Confusion in Washington Legal Ethics." 29 Note. Gonz L. Rev. (1993/94): 193-

203.

Levin, Leslie C. "The Emperor's Clothes and Other Tales About the Standards for Imposing Lawyer Discipline Sanctions." American University Law Review 48 no.1 (October, 1998): 1-83.

Lisagor, Nancy and Frank Lipsius. *A Law Unto Itself: The untold story of the Law Firm Sullivan and Cromwell.* William Morrow and Company, Inc., 1988.

Neil Martha. "Top Partner Billing Rates at BigLaw Firms Approach $1,500 per Hour." ABA Journal (February 8, 2016, accessed February 14, 2016); available from http://www.abajournal.com/news/article/top_partner_billing_rates_at_biglaw_firms_nudge_1500_per_hour/?utm_source=maestro&utm_medium=email&utm_campaign=weekly_email

Nelson, Brett. "Do You Read Fast Enough To Be Successful?" Forbes (June 4, 2012, accessed January30, 2016); available from http://www.forbes.com/sites/brettnelson/2012/06/04/do-you-read-fast-enough-to-be-successful/

Woods, Michele J. "The Adoption of the ABA Standards for Imposing Lawyer Sanctions by the Alaska Supreme Court: In re Buckalew." 6 Alaska L. Rev. 6365 (1989).

Case Law

Bartlett v. Christhilf, 14 A. 518, 520 (Md 1888).

Farber v. Dale, 392 S.E.2d 224, 227 (W.Va. 1990).

Morgan Pottinger Attorneys, P.S.C v. Botts 348 S.W.3d 599 (Ky. 2011)

N.C. State Bar v. Small, 750 S.E.2d 917 (N.C. Ct. App. 2013

    N.C. State Bar v. Talford, 356 N.C. 626 (N.C. 2003).

    Stone v. Rosen, 348 So.2d 387, 389 (Fla. Dist.Ct.App. 1977)

State Bars & American Bar Association Information

The State Bar of California. 2014 Statement of Expenditures of Mandatory Membership Fees and Independent Auditor's Report, prepared by Moss Adams LLP, Certified Public Accountants—Business Consultants. (Year Ended December 31, 2014, accessed 30 January 2016); available from http://www.cal-bar.ca.gov/LinkClick.aspx?fileticket=rxJG72KWGKY%3d&tabid=224&mid=1534

The State Bar of California. Financial Statement and Independent Auditor's Report (Years ended December 31, 2011 and 2010 at 39, accessed 30 January 2016, available from http://www.calbar.ca.gov/portals/0/documents/reports/Financial-Statement-and-Independent-Auditors-Report-for-the-Years-Ended-December312011and2010.pdf

The State Bar of North Carolina website. Assessment of Administrative Fees and Actual Costs. (accessed 5 February 2016, available from http://www.ncbar.gov/discipline/admin_fees_costs.pdf)

Special Comm. on Evaluation of Disciplinary Enforcement, American Bar Ass'n, Problems and Recommendation in Disciplinary Enforcement 1 (1970).

Miscellaneous

Staples e-reader interactive test (accessed 30 January, 2016) available from http://www.staples.com/sbd/cre/marketing/technology-research-centers/ereaders/speed-reader/

Acknowledgments

I owe my sense of *how the law should work* to the faculty of The University of Virginia Law School. If not for the clear map that my professors had provided, I would be long lost in the Alice-in-Wonderland world of divorce law.

Professor Charlie J. Goetz explained the "cost of risk," that everything in life and law is "as compared to what," and that there's always a good reason for liquidated damages. I took every class with "3D Goetz" until there was no more to take. Professor Julia Mahoney taught all of us in her Property class to ask "whom is this law supposed to help," and to follow up with, "well, does it?!" She also gave us the wisdom to "follow the money," even when the system spokesmen pretended that there was no money in the mix. Dean Paul Mahoney had saved my behind once, even though I doubt he remembers it, or even who I am.

I owe my sense of *how the law should be practiced properly* to the partners and grunts of Sullivan & Cromwell. They gave me the courage to insist on proper practices and proper client service no matter where I went on in my work—even in the trenches of divorce courts.

The University of Chicago Professor Martha Nussbaum introduced me to *the glamour of the law,* which makes more sense if you actually met the professor. In person. So what if the glamour is reflected?

To the lawyers and judges of Ducklingburg, South Duck I owe the sad revelation that there are places where law is practiced with little sense, propriety or glamour—and my determination to write a book to do something about that.

Guru Yakov Yazlovitsky imparted critical managerial wisdom that helped my little firm survive.

Finally, without Professors Michael Bowman and Richard Hellie, nothing would be possible at all. My only regret is that I was too slow to write this book for Professor Hellie to read and mock it. But I know he would have said he dodged a bullet.

82800411R00250